PRENTICE HALL

Teacher's **SCIENCE EXPLORER** Edition

Earth's Changing Surface

Prentice Hall

Needham, Massachusetts
Upper Saddle River, New Jersey
Glenview, Illinois

ISBN 0-13-054079-X
2 3 4 5 6 7 8 9 10   05 04 03 02 01

Chart your own course.

15 motivational hardcover books make it easy for you to create your own curriculum; meet local, state, and national guidelines; and teach your favorite topics in depth.

Prepare your students with rich, motivating content...

Science Explorer is crafted for today's middle grades student, with accessible content and in-depth coverage of all the important concepts.

...and a wide variety of inquiry activities.

Motivational student- and teacher-tested activities reinforce key concepts and allow students to explore science concepts for themselves.

Check your compass regularly.

Science Explorer gives you more ways to regularly check student performance than any other program available.

Utilize a variety of tools.

Integrated science sections in every chapter and Interdisciplinary Explorations in every book allow you to make in-depth connections to other sciences and disciplines. Plus, you will find a wealth of additional tools to set your students on a successful course.

Chart the course you want with 15 motivating books that easily match your curriculum.

Each book in the series contains:

- Integrated Science sections in every chapter
- Interdisciplinary Explorations for team teaching at the end of each book
- Comprehensive skills practice and application—assuring that you meet the National Science Education Standards and your local and state standards

EXPLORATION TOOLS: BASIC PROCESS SKILLS

Observing

Measuring

Calculating

Classifying

Predicting

Inferring

Graphing

Creating data tables

Communicating

LIFE SCIENCE TITLES

From Bacteria to Plants
1 Living Things
2 Viruses and Bacteria
3 Protists and Fungi
4 Introduction to Plants
5 Seed Plants

Animals
1 Sponges, Cnidarians, and Worms
2 Mollusks, Arthropods, and Echinoderms
3 Fishes, Amphibians, and Reptiles
4 Birds and Mammals
5 Animal Behavior

Cells and Heredity
1 Cell Structure and Function
2 Cell Processes and Energy
3 Genetics: The Science of Heredity
4 Modern Genetics
5 Changes Over Time

Human Biology and Health
1 Healthy Body Systems
2 Bones, Muscles, and Skin
3 Food and Digestion
4 Circulation
5 Respiration and Excretion
6 Fighting Disease
7 The Nervous System
8 The Endocrine System and Reproduction

Environmental Science
1 Populations and Communities
2 Ecosystems and Biomes
3 Living Resources
4 Land and Soil Resources
5 Air and Water Resources
6 Energy Resources

 Integrated Science sections in every chapter

Posing questions

Forming operational definitions

Developing hypotheses

Controlling variables

Interpreting data

Interpreting graphs

Making models

Drawing conclusions

Designing experiments

EARTH SCIENCE TITLES 🔵

Inside Earth
1 Plate Tectonics
2 Earthquakes
3 Volcanoes
4 Minerals
5 Rocks

Earth's Changing Surface
1 Mapping Earth's Surface
2 Weathering and Soil Formation
3 Erosion and Deposition
4 A Trip Through Geologic Time

Earth's Waters
1 Earth: The Water Planet
2 Fresh Water
3 Freshwater Resources
4 Ocean Motions
5 Ocean Zones

Weather and Climate
1 The Atmosphere
2 Weather Factors
3 Weather Patterns
4 Climate and Climate Change

Astronomy
1 Earth, Moon, and Sun
2 The Solar System
3 Stars, Galaxies, and the Universe

PHYSICAL SCIENCE TITLES 🔵

Chemical Building Blocks
1 An Introduction to Matter
2 Changes in Matter
3 Elements and the Periodic Table
4 Carbon Chemistry

Chemical Interactions
1 Chemical Reactions
2 Atoms and Bonding
3 Acids, Bases, and Solutions
4 Exploring Materials

Motion, Forces, and Energy
1 Motion
2 Forces
3 Forces in Fluids
4 Work and Machines
5 Energy and Power
6 Thermal Energy and Heat

Electricity and Magnetism
1 Magnetism and Electromagnetism
2 Electric Charges and Current
3 Electricity and Magnetism at Work
4 Electronics

Sound and Light
1 Characteristics of Waves
2 Sound
3 The Electromagnetic Spectrum
4 Light

 Integrated Science sections in every chapter

Turn your students into science explorers with a variety of inquiry activities.

Motivational student- and teacher-tested activities reinforce key concepts and allow students to explore science concepts for themselves. More than 350 activities are provided for each book in the Student Edition, Teacher's Edition, Teaching Resources, Integrated Science Lab Manual, Inquiry Skills Activity Book, Interactive Student Tutorial CD-ROM, and *Science Explorer* Web Site.

STUDENT EDITION ACTIVITIES

Time

Long-term

Chapter Project
Opportunities for long-term inquiry—
start of each chapter

1 Class Period

Real-World Lab
Everyday application of science concepts—
one per chapter

Skills Lab
In-depth practice of an inquiry skill—
one per chapter

10–25 Minutes

Sharpen Your Skills
Practice of a specific inquiry skill—
two per chapter

Discover
Exploration and inquiry before reading—
start of every lesson

Try This
Reinforcement of key concepts
— two per chapter

Directed   Guided   Open-ended

Inquiry

Check your compass regularly with integrated assessment tools.

Prepare for state exams with traditional and performance-based assessment.

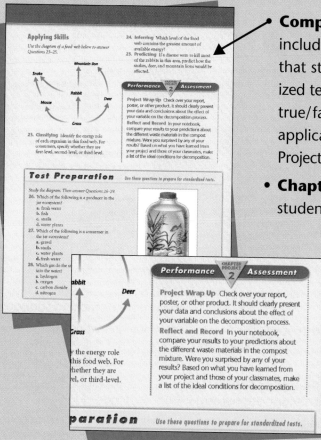

- **Comprehensive Chapter Reviews** include a wide range of question types that students will encounter on standardized tests. Types include multiple choice, enhanced true/false, concept mastery, visual thinking, skill application, and critical thinking. Also includes Chapter Project "Wrap Up."

- **Chapter Projects** contain rubrics that allow you to easily assess student progress.

- **Section Reviews** provide "Check your Progress" opportunities for the Chapter Project, as well as review questions for the section.

Additional *Science Explorer* assessment resources:
- **Computer Test Bank with CD-ROM**
- **Resource Pro® with Planning Express® CD-ROM**
- **Standardized Test Practice Book**
- **Interactive Student Tutorial CD-ROM**
- **On-line review activities** at www.phschool.com
  See pages T8 & T9 for complete product descriptions.

Self-assessment opportunities help students keep themselves on course.

- **Caption Questions** throughout the text assess critical thinking skills.

- **Checkpoint Questions** give students an immediate content check as new concepts are presented.

- **Interactive Student Tutorial CD-ROM** provides students with electronic self-tests, review activities, and Exploration activities.

- **www.phschool.com** provides additional support and on-line test prep.

Utilize a wide variety of tools.

Comprehensive print components

Easy-to-manage, book-specific teaching resources

15 Teaching Resource Packages, each containing a Student Edition, Teacher's Edition, Teaching Resources with Color Transparencies, Interactive Student Tutorial CD-ROM, Guided Study Workbook, Guided Reading Audio CD, and correlation to the National Science Education Standards.

15 Teacher's Editions with a three-step lesson plan–Engage/Explore, Facilitate and Assess–that is ideal for reaching all students. Chapter planning charts make it easy to find resources, as well as to plan for block scheduling and team teaching.

15 Teaching Resource Books with Color Transparencies offer complete teacher support organized by chapter to make it easy for you to find what you need–when you need it.

15 Guided Reading Audio CD's and Audiotapes provide section summaries for students who need additional support. Available in English and Spanish.

15 Guided Study Workbooks containing blackline master worksheets for assessing, understanding, and developing study skills. Teacher's Edition available for each workbook.

Integrated Science Lab Manual SE & TE—74 in-depth labs covering the entire curriculum, with complete teaching support.

Inquiry Skills Activity Book—additional activities that introduce basic and advanced inquiry skills and reinforce skills on an as-needed basis.

Program Planning Guide—course outlines, block scheduling pacing charts, correlations, and more.

Reading in the Content Area with Literature Connections—provides students with additional strategies for successful reading.

Standardized Test Preparation Book—provides students with hints, tips, strategies, and practice to help them prepare for state and local exams.

How to Assess Student Work—professional articles and example activities that help you design assessments, use rubrics effectively, and develop a portfolio assessment program.

Student-Centered Science Activities—five regional activity books, for the Northeast, Southeast, Midwest, Southwest, and West.

How to Manage Instruction in the Block—comprehensive collection of block scheduling resources, from managing classroom routines to checklists for monitoring and assessing small group learning.

Teacher's ELL Handbook—provides multiple strategies for reaching English language learners. Select appropriate activities to meet the needs of individual students.

Program-wide technology resources

Interactive Student Tutorial CD-ROMs—
provide students with self-tests, helpful hints, and Exploration activities. Tests are scored instantly and contain a detailed explanation of all answers.

Probeware Lab Manual—
provides detailed instructions for using probeware to perform selected labs. Blackline masters of labs are included.

Resource Pro® CD-ROM—
electronic version of the Teaching Resources for all 15 books—ideal for creating integrated science lessons. Contains Planning Express software and Computer Test Bank. Organized by chapter to save you time.

Science Explorer Web Site—
activities and teaching resources for every chapter at: www.phschool.com

Science Explorer Videotapes and Videodiscs
—explore and visualize concepts through spectacular short documentaries containing computer animations. Videotapes also available in Spanish.

Lab Activity Videotapes—
provide step-by-step instruction with students performing activities from every chapter. Promote and teach proper lab techniques, inquiry skills, and safety procedures.

iText—
An interactive text version of the Student Edition at www.phschool.com containing animations, simulations, and videos to enhance student understanding and retention of concepts.

Interactive Physics—
explore physics concepts with computer simulations that encourage what-if questions.

Computer Test Bank Book with CD-ROM—
comprehensive collection of assessment resources containing Computer Test Bank Software with Dial-A-Test; provides you with unparalleled flexibility in creating tests.

ADDITIONAL RESOURCES

Materials Kits—
Prentice Hall and Science Kit, Inc. have collaborated to develop a Consumable Kit and Nonconsumable Kit for each book. Ordering software makes it easy to customize!

Interdisciplinary Explorations—
designed to help you connect science topics to social studies, math, language arts, and students' daily lives.

Options for Pacing *Earth's Changing Surface*

The Pacing Chart below suggests one way to schedule your instructional time. The *Science Explorer* program offers many other aids to help you plan your instructional time, whether regular class periods or **block scheduling.** Refer to the Chapter Planning Guide before each chapter to view all program resources with suggested times for Student Edition activities.

Pacing Chart

	Days	Blocks		Days	Blocks
Nature of Science: Mammals of the Jurassic Period	1	$\frac{1}{2}$	**4** Glaciers	1–2	$\frac{1}{2}$–1
			5 Waves	1–2	$\frac{1}{2}$–1
Chapter 1 Mapping Earth's Surface			**6** Wind	1–2	$\frac{1}{2}$–1
Chapter 1 Project Getting on the Map	Ongoing	Ongoing	Chapter 3 Review and Assessment	1	$\frac{1}{2}$
1 Exploring Earth's Surface	2–3	1–1$\frac{1}{2}$	**Chapter 4 A Trip Through Geologic Time**		
2 Models of Earth	2–3	1–1$\frac{1}{2}$	Chapter 4 Project A Journey Back in Time	Ongoing	Ongoing
3 Integrating Technology: Maps in the Computer Age	1–2	$\frac{1}{2}$–1	**1** Fossils	2–3	1–1$\frac{1}{2}$
			2 Finding the Relative Age of Rocks	2–3	1–1$\frac{1}{2}$
4 Topographic Maps	2–3	1–1$\frac{1}{2}$	**3** Integrating Chemistry: Radioactive Dating	1–2	$\frac{1}{2}$–1
Chapter 1 Review and Assessment	1	$\frac{1}{2}$			
Chapter 2 Weathering and Soil Formation			**4** The Geologic Time Scale	2–3	1–1$\frac{1}{2}$
			5 Earth's History	3–4	1$\frac{1}{2}$–2
Chapter 2 Project Soil for Seeds	Ongoing	Ongoing	Chapter 4 Review and Assessment	1	$\frac{1}{2}$
1 Rocks and Weathering	4–5	2–2$\frac{1}{2}$	Interdisciplinary Exploration: The Gift of the Nile	2–3	1–2
2 Soil Formation and Composition	3–4	1$\frac{1}{2}$–2			
3 Integrating Environmental Science: Soil Conservation	2	1			
Chapter 2 Review and Assessment	1	$\frac{1}{2}$			
Chapter 3 Erosion and Deposition					
Chapter 3 Project Changes in the Land	Ongoing	Ongoing			
1 Changing Earth's Surface	2–3	1–1$\frac{1}{2}$			
2 Water Erosion	4–5	2–2$\frac{1}{2}$			
3 Integrating Physics: The Force of Moving Water	1–2	$\frac{1}{2}$–1			

RESOURCE PRO®

The Resource Pro® CD-ROM is the ultimate scheduling and lesson planning tool. Resource Pro® allows you to preview all the resources in the *Science Explorer* program, organize your chosen materials, and print out any teaching resource. You can follow the suggested lessons or create your own, using resources from anywhere in the program.

Thematic Overview of *Earth's Changing Surface*

The chart below lists the major themes of *Earth's Changing Surface*. For each theme, the chart supplies a big idea, or concept statement, describing how a particular theme is taught in a chapter.

	Chapter 1	Chapter 2	Chapter 3	Chapter 4
Patterns of Change	Satellite images and computer mapping can be used to analyze environmental change.	Rock exposed on Earth's surface is subject to mechanical and chemical weathering. Over time, weathered rock develops into soil.	Erosion and deposition by mass movement, running water, glaciers, waves, and wind each change Earth's surface in a different way.	A variety of processes can form fossils from the remains of organisms. The fossil record shows that organisms have evolved from simple to complex and that mass extinctions have occurred several times in Earth's history.
Scale and Structure	Earth's land surface is made up of different types of landforms, such as plains, mountains, and plateaus. Maps and globes are made to scale to represent topography and other features of Earth's surface.	Soil is a mixture of weathered rock particles, dissolved minerals, humus, air, and water. As soil forms, its texture changes and it develops characteristic layers called soil horizons.	The different types of erosion and deposition create a variety of landforms.	Using the law of superposition, geologists can interpret the relative age of sedimentary rock layers. Scientists developed the Geologic Time Scale based on the relative ages of rock layers.
Unity and Diversity	Earth near the surface is divided into four spheres: the lithosphere, atmosphere, hydrosphere, and biosphere.	Soil types vary across Earth's surface depending on many factors, including local bedrock, climate, and vegetation.		Using index fossils, geologists can correlate rock layers found at different locations on Earth's surface.
Systems and Interactions		Some farming and ranching methods can cause damage to, or loss of, soil. Soil conservation practices can help to prevent soil loss. Climate and type of rock are factors that affect the rate of soil formation. Living organisms in soil affect the soil's texture, composition, and fertility.	Weathering, erosion, and deposition act together in a cycle that wears down and builds up Earth's surface. A river's slope, volume of flow, and streambed shape all affect the river's speed and how it erodes and deposits sediment.	Geologists can learn about Earth's history by studying rock layers in relation to unconformities, faults, extrusions, and intrusions.
Evolution				Evidence from the fossil record shows that different kinds of organisms have evolved over long periods of time.
Energy			Gravity is the force that causes mass movement and the downhill flow of rivers and glaciers. The kinetic energy of moving water does the work of water erosion. Waves form when winds transmit their energy to water.	Radioactive decay of certain elements can be used to determine the absolute age of rocks and fossils.
Modeling	Students make a topographic map based on a landform model. Students produce a map of a small area in their neighborhood.		Students build models showing a landform before and after erosion. Using a stream table, students model erosion and deposition by running water.	Students model the scale of geologic time using reams of paper. Students create a time line of Earth's history showing the development of life during each geologic period.

Inquiry Skills Chart

The Prentice Hall *Science Explorer* program provides comprehensive teaching, practice, and assessment of science skills, with an emphasis on the process skills necessary for inquiry. The chart lists the skills covered in the program and cites the page numbers where each skill is covered.

Basic Process SKILLS				
	Student Text: Projects and Labs	Student Text: Activities	Student Text: Caption and Review Questions	Teacher's Edition: Extensions
Observing	25, 56, 82–83	19, 57, 69, 98, 108, 114, 147	37, 77, 97, 136	91, 116, 152
Inferring	25, 56	40, 45, 85, 89, 106, 112, 147	27, 37, 109, 112, 122, 143	109, 111, 152
Predicting	46–47, 64–65, 82–83	26, 44, 51, 72, 119	15, 45, 60, 63, 69, 73, 91, 97, 100, 103, 131	78, 152
Classifying			63	17, 114, 153
Making Models	12–13, 34, 64–65, 82–83, 104–105, 126–127	29, 123		20, 108, 124, 153
Communicating	104–105	48, 59, 84, 86, 115, 145, 149	36, 62, 102, 142	132, 153
Measuring	12–13, 70–71, 126–127		24, 143	154–155
Calculating	126–127	30, 95, 121, 151	37, 120	53, 124
Creating Data Tables	46–47, 70–71			133, 135, 162
Graphing	70–71		103	133, 163
Advanced Process SKILLS				
Posing Questions	56	94, 128	63	137, 156
Developing Hypotheses	70–71	66, 87	63, 96, 103	156
Designing Experiments	38–39, 46–47, 70–71, 82–83		63	42, 90, 157
Controlling Variables	38–39, 46–47			157
Forming Operational Definitions		14, 49		157

Advanced Process SKILLS (continued)

	Student Text: Projects and Labs	Student Text: Activities	Student Text: Caption and Review Questions	Teacher's Edition: Extensions
Interpreting Data	118	31, 136	143	157
Drawing Conclusions	25, 118	54, 74		27, 157

Critical Thinking SKILLS

Comparing and Contrasting			18, 37, 81, 99	51, 73, 81, 110, 116, 130, 138, 158
Applying Concepts			37, 103, 114, 117, 122, 143	158
Interpreting Diagrams, Graphs Photographs, and Maps			15, 23, 33, 37, 50, 55, 75, 80, 117, 124, 125	24, 158
Relating Cause and Effect			55, 63, 67, 68, 69, 88, 93, 95, 103, 139, 143	121, 131, 136, 159
Making Generalizations			28, 140	159
Making Judgments			63, 103, 143	159
Problem Solving			37, 60, 103, 143	159

Information Organizing SKILLS

Concept Maps			36, 62, 142	160
Compare/ Contrast Tables				17, 45, 93, 112, 141, 160
Venn Diagrams				16, 161
Flowcharts			102	27, 59, 77, 107, 161
Cycle Diagrams				161

The *Science Explorer* program provides additional teaching, reinforcement, and assessment of skills in the Inquiry Skills Activities Book and the Integrated Science Laboratory Manual.

Throughout the *Science Explorer* program, every effort has been made to keep the materials and equipment *affordable, reusable,* and *easily accessible.*

The *Science Explorer* program offers an abundance of activity options so you can pick and choose those activities that suit your needs. To help you order supplies at the beginning of the year, the Master Materials List cross-references the materials by activity. If you prefer to create your list electronically, you can use the Materials List CD-ROM.

There are two kits available for each book of the *Science Explorer* program: a Consumable Kit and a Nonconsumable Kit. These kits are produced by **Science Kit and Boreal Laboratories,** the leader in providing science kits to schools. Prentice Hall and Science Kit collaborated throughout the development of *Science Explorer* to ensure that the equipment and supplies in the kits precisely match the requirements of the program activities.

The kits provide an economical and convenient way to get all of the materials needed to teach each book. For each book, Science Kit also offers the opportunity to buy equipment and safety items individually. For additional information about ordering materials to accompany *Science Explorer,* please call:

1-800-848-9500

or access the *Science Explorer* Internet site at: **www.phschool.com**

Master Materials List

Consumable Materials

*	Description	Quantity per class	Textbook Section(s)	*	Description	Quantity per class	Textbook Section(s)
C	Alka Seltzer Tablets, Pkg/24	1	2-1 (DIS)	SS	Newspaper, Sheet	5	3-2 (TT)
SS	Cardboard	45	1-4 (DIS)	SS	Noodle, Round, Hollow	5	4-2 (TT)
C	Clay, Modeling (Cream) lb (water-resistant)	5	1-4 (Lab) 2-3 (DIS) 4-1 (TT)	SS	Orange	5	1-2 (DIS)
				SS	Paper Towel Roll (120 sheets)	1	2-1 (Lab) 3-4 (DIS)
C	Clay, Modeling (four colors) lb (Red, Blue, Green, Yellow)	5	4-2 (DIS) 4-3 (DIS)	SS	Paper, Ream	5	4-4 (Lab)
C	Cornmeal, 454 g	1	3-6 (DIS)	SS	Paper, Sheet	50	1-1 (DIS) 1-3 (DIS) 1-4 (DIS) 1-4 (Lab) 2-3 (DIS) 3-1 (Lab) 4-5 (TT)
C	Cup, Plastic Clear, 10 oz graduated, oz & cc graduations	5	3-3 (DIS)				
C	Cup, Plastic Clear, Cocktail, 9 oz	10	2-1 (DIS) 3-4 (DIS)				
C	Cup, Styrofoam, 6 oz	5	3-2 (Lab)	SS	Paper, Tracing, 9 × 12", Pad/50	1	1-2 (Lab)
C	Detergent, Household, 14.7 oz (dish detergent)	1	3-2 (Lab)	C C	Pebbles/Gravel, 1 kg (2-1/2 Cups)	2	2-3 (DIS) 3-3 (DIS)
C	Food Coloring, Blue, 30 mL,	1	1-4 (Lab) 3-2 (Lab)	SS	Pencil	5	1-3 (DIS) 1-4 (DIS) 3-1 (Lab)
C	Graph Paper, Metric Coordinates, pkg/100, 1 cm grid	1	2-2 (Lab)				
SS	Map, U. S., with Latitude, Longitude, and State Borders	5	1-2 (Lab)	SS	Pencils, Colored, Pkg/12	5	1-2 (Lab) 1-3 (DIS)
SS	Marker, Black, Permanent	5	1-2 (DIS)	C	Rock, Limestone Chips, 4 oz Bag (Approx. 270 Chips)	3	2-1 (Lab)
C	Marking Pencil, Black Wax	5	1-4 (Lab) 2-1 (Lab)				

KEY: **DIS**: Discover; **SYS**: Sharpen Your Skills; **TT**: Try This; **Lab**: Lab
* Items designated **C** are in the Consumable Kit, **NC** are in the Nonconsumable Kit, and **SS** are School Supplied.

Master Materials List

Consumable Materials (cont.)

*	Description	Quantity per class	Textbook Section(s)	*	Description	Quantity per class	Textbook Section(s)
SS	Sand Collected from a Beach, Sample	2	3-5 (DIS)	C	Steel Wool Pads, Pkg/6	1	2-1 (TT)
C	Sand, Fine, 2.5 kg (7-1/2 Cups)	2	3-1 (Lab) 3-3 (DIS) 3-4 (DIS)	C	Sticks, Craft, Pkg/50	1	2-3 (DIS)
				C	Stirrer Sticks Pkg/50	1	3-2 (Lab)
				C	Straws, Plastic (Wrapped) Pkg/50	1	3-6 (DIS)
C	Sand, Quartz, Coarse, lb	1	3-3 (DIS)	C	String, Cotton, 200 ft	1	2-2 (TT)
SS	Sandwich	5	4-2 (TT)	C	Sugar Cubes, 1 lb (Pkg/96)	1	4-1 (TT)
C	Soap, Ivory, Bar	5	3-2 (DIS) 3-4 (DIS)	C	Tape, Adding Machine Roll, 2-1/4" Width (100 ft. length)	1	4-4 (DIS)
C	Soil, Clay, 500 g (2-1/2 Cups)	1	3-3 (DIS)	SS SS	Tape, Masking, 3/4" × 60 yd	1	2-1 (Lab) 3-1 (Lab)
C	Soil, Diatomaceous Earth, lb	3	3-2 (Lab)	C C	Toothpicks, Flat, Box/750	1	2-2 (DIS) 2-2 (Lab)
C	Soil, Loam, 2.5 kg (12-1/2 Cups)	2	2-2 (DIS) 2-2 (Lab) 2-3 (DIS) 3-2 (TT) 3-3 (DIS)	C	Vinegar, 500 mL	3	2-1 (Lab)
				SS	Worksheet with 2,000 Asterisks	5	4-4 (Lab)

Nonconsumable Materials

*	Description	Quantity per class	Textbook Section(s)	*	Description	Quantity per class	Textbook Section(s)
NC	Bowl, Plastic, Small, 20 oz	5	4-1 (TT) 4-2 (DIS)	NC	Fossil, Fern Imprint	5	4-1 (DIS)
SS	Bucket	5	3-2 (Lab)	NC	Jar, Plastic, 16 oz, 89 mm diameter	20	2-1 (TT) 2-1 (Lab) 2-3 (DIS) 3-3 (DIS)
SS	Clock or Watch	1	3-2 (Lab)				
NC	Cloth, Cotton, White, 18" × 22"	1	2-1 (Lab)				
NC	Compass, Pocket, 40 mm	5	1-1 (DIS)	NC	Knife, Plastic	5	1-2 (DIS) 4-2 (DIS) 4-3 (DIS)
NC	Container, Plastic Clear w/C-Thru Lid, 11-3/4" × 6" × 3-1/4"	5	1-4 (Lab)				
NC	Cylinder, PP, Graduated, 100 mL	5	2-1 (DIS) 2-1 (Lab) 3-2 (Lab)	NC	Lid, Metal, 89 mm, Screw Type	20	2-1 (TT)
				NC	Magnifying Glass, 3x, 6x	5	2-2 (DIS) 3-2 (Lab) 3-5 (DIS) 4-1 (DIS)
NC	Dish, Plastic Petri, Top & Btm, 100mm	5	2-2 (Lab) 3-2 (TT)	NC	Marbles, 5/8", Pkg/20	1	3-1 (DIS)
NC	Dropper, Plastic	5	2-2 (Lab) 3-2 (TT)	NC	Meter Stick, Half (50 cm in length)	5	2-2 (TT) 3-2 (TT)

KEY: **DIS**: Discover; **SYS**: Sharpen Your Skills; **TT**: Try This; **Lab**: Lab
* Items designated **C** are in the Consumable Kit, **NC** are in the Nonconsumable Kit, and **SS** are School Supplied.

Nonconsumable Materials (cont.)

*	Description	Quantity per class	Textbook Section(s)	*	Description	Quantity per class	Textbook Section(s)
NC	Pan, Aluminum Foil, 13" × 10" × 2"	5	3-1 (Lab) 3-2 (Lab) 3-6 (DIS)	SS	Trowel	5	2-2 (TT)
NC	Pan, Aluminum Foil, 22.5 cm Diam	5	2-3 (DIS)	NC	Tube, Cardboard, 7.5 × 4 cm OD	5	3-1 (Lab)
NC	Paper Clips, Box/100	1	1-2 (Lab) 2-3 (DIS)	NC	Wire, Bare Copper, 20 Gauge, 4 oz.	1	3-2 (Lab)
SS	Ruler, Plastic, 12"/30 cm	5	1-3 (DIS) 1-4 (Lab) 3-1 (Lab) 4-3 (DIS) 4-4 (DIS) 4-4 (Lab)	NC	Wood, Block, 1" (Cube)	5	3-1 (DIS)
				NC	Wood, Board, 1" × 4" × 8"	10	3-1 (DIS) 3-2 (Lab)

Equipment

NC	Sandpaper, Medium, 9 × 11" Sheet	5	3-1 (DIS)	*	Description	Quantity per class	Textbook Section(s)
SS	Scissors	5	1-4 (DIS) 3-2 (Lab)	SS	Apron, Vinyl	30	3-2 (Lab)
SS	Skewer, Wooden Barbecue	5	3-1 (Lab)	SS	Balance, Triple Beam	5	2-1 (Lab)
NC	Spoons, Plastic, Pkg/24	1	2-2 (Lab) 3-1 (Lab) 3-2 (Lab) 3-5 (DIS) 4-1 (TT)	SS	Globe, Political	5	1-2 (TT)
				SS	Goggles, Chemical Splash— Class Set	1	2-1 (DIS) 2-1 (Lab) 2-2 (Lab) 2-3 (DIS) 3-1 (Lab) 3-2 (TT) 3-2 (Lab) 3-3 (DIS) 3-6 (DIS)
NC	Spray Bottle, 16 oz	5	3-2 (Lab)	SS	Stereomicroscope	5	2-2 (Lab)
NC	Stirring Rod, Glass, 5 × 150 mm	5	2-1 (DIS)	SS	Stopwatch	5	2-1 (DIS)

KEY: **DIS**: Discover; **SYS**: Sharpen Your Skills; **TT**: Try This; **Lab**: Lab
* Items designated **C** are in the Consumable Kit, **NC** are in the Nonconsumable Kit, and **SS** are School Supplied.

PRENTICE HALL
SCIENCE EXPLORER

Earth's Changing Surface

Book-Specific Resources

Student Edition
Annotated Teacher's Edition
Teaching Resources with Color Transparencies
Consumable and Nonconsumable Materials Kits
Guided Reading Audio CDs
Guided Reading Audiotapes
Guided Reading and Study Workbook
Guided Reading and Study Workbook, Teacher's Edition
Lab Activity Videotapes
Science Explorer Videotapes
Science Explorer Web Site at **www.phschool.com**

Program-Wide Resources

Computer Test Bank Book with CD-ROM
How to Assess Student Work
How to Manage Instruction in the Block
Inquiry Skills Activity Book
Integrated Science Laboratory Manual
Integrated Science Laboratory Manual, Teacher's Edition
Interactive Student Tutorial CD-ROM
Prentice Hall Interdisciplinary Explorations
Probeware Lab Manual
Product Testing Activities by Consumer Reports™
Program Planning Guide
Reading in the Content Area with Literature Connections
Resource Pro® CD-ROM (Teaching Resources on CD-ROM)
Science Explorer Videodiscs
Standardized Test Preparation Book
Student-Centered Science Activity Books
Teacher's ELL Handbook: Strategies for English Language Learners

Spanish Resources

Spanish Student Edition
Spanish Guided Reading Audio CDs with Section Summaries
Spanish Guided Reading Audiotapes with Section Summaries
Spanish Science Explorer Videotapes

Science Explorer Student Editions

From Bacteria to Plants

Animals

Cells and Heredity

Human Biology and Health

Environmental Science

Inside Earth

Earth's Changing Surface

Earth's Waters

Weather and Climate

Astronomy

Chemical Building Blocks

Chemical Interactions

Motion, Forces, and Energy

Electricity and Magnetism

Sound and Light

Acknowledgments

Excerpt from *Dust Storm Disaster* on page 59 by Woody Guthrie. Copyright © 1960 (Renewed) by Ludlow Music, Inc. c/o The Richmond Organization. All rights reserved. Used by permission.

Excerpt from *The Hymn to Hapy* on page 145 by Miriam Lichtheim. Copyright ©1973-1980 Regents of the University of California.

Cover: One of the many red sandstone arches in Arches National Park, Utah

ISBN 0-13-054078-1
2 3 4 5 6 7 8 9 10 05 04 03 02 01

Teacher's Edition ISBN 0-13-054079-X

Program Authors

Michael J. Padilla, Ph.D.
Professor
Department of Science Education
University of Georgia
Athens, Georgia

Michael Padilla is a leader in middle school science education. He has served as an editor and elected officer for the National Science Teachers Association. He has been principal investigator of several National Science Foundation and Eisenhower grants and served as a writer of the National Science Education Standards.

As lead author of *Science Explorer,* Mike has inspired the team in developing a program that meets the needs of middle grades students, promotes science inquiry, and is aligned with the National Science Education Standards.

Ioannis Miaoulis, Ph.D.
Dean of Engineering
College of Engineering
Tufts University
Medford, Massachusetts

Martha Cyr, Ph.D.
Director, Engineering
  Educational Outreach
College of Engineering
Tufts University
Medford, Massachusetts

Science Explorer was created in collaboration with the College of Engineering at Tufts University. Tufts has an extensive engineering outreach program that uses engineering design and construction to excite and motivate students and teachers in science and technology education.

Faculty from Tufts University participated in the development of *Science Explorer* chapter projects, reviewed the student books for content accuracy, and helped coordinate field testing.

CHAPTER PROJECT

Book Author

Joseph D. Exline, Ed.D.
Former Director of Science
Virginia Department of Education

Contributing Writers

Rose-Marie Botting
Science Teacher
Broward County
  School District
Fort Lauderdale, Florida

Colleen Campos
Science Teacher
Laredo Middle School
Aurora, Colorado

Holly Estes
Science Teacher
Hale Middle School
Stow, Massachusetts

Edward Evans
Former Science
  Teacher
Hilton Central School
Hilton, New York

Sharon Stroud
Science Teacher
Widefield High School
Colorado Springs,
  Colorado

Reading Consultant

Bonnie B. Armbruster, Ph.D.
Department of Curriculum
  and Instruction
University of Illinois
Champaign, Illinois

Interdisciplinary Consultant

Heidi Hayes Jacobs, Ed.D.
Teacher's College
Columbia University
New York, New York

Safety Consultants

W. H. Breazeale, Ph.D.
Department of Chemistry
College of Charleston
Charleston, South Carolina

Ruth Hathaway, Ph.D.
Hathaway Consulting
Cape Girardeau, Missouri

G ◆ 3

Tufts University Program Reviewers

Behrouz Abedian, Ph.D.
Department of Mechanical
Engineering

Wayne Chudyk, Ph.D.
Department of Civil and
Environmental Engineering

Eliana De Bernardez-Clark, Ph.D.
Department of Chemical Engineering

Anne Marie Desmarais, Ph.D.
Department of Civil and
Environmental Engineering

David L. Kaplan, Ph.D.
Department of Chemical Engineering

Paul Kelley, Ph.D.
Department of Electro-Optics

George S. Mumford, Ph.D.
Professor of Astronomy, Emeritus

Jan A. Pechenik, Ph.D.
Department of Biology

Livia Racz, Ph.D.
Department of Mechanical Engineering

Robert Rifkin, M.D.
School of Medicine

Jack Ridge, Ph.D.
Department of Geology

Chris Swan, Ph.D.
Department of Civil and
Environmental Engineering

Peter Y. Wong, Ph.D.
Department of Mechanical Engineering

Content Reviewers

Jack W. Beal, Ph.D.
Department of Physics
Fairfield University
Fairfield, Connecticut

W. Russell Blake, Ph.D.
Planetarium Director
Plymouth Community
Intermediate School
Plymouth, Massachusetts

Howard E. Buhse, Jr., Ph.D.
Department of Biological Sciences
University of Illinois
Chicago, Illinois

Dawn Smith Burgess, Ph.D.
Department of Geophysics
Stanford University
Stanford, California

A. Malcolm Campbell, Ph.D.
Assistant Professor
Davidson College
Davidson, North Carolina

Elizabeth A. De Stasio, Ph.D.
Associate Professor of Biology
Lawrence University
Appleton, Wisconsin

John M. Fowler, Ph.D.
Former Director of Special Projects
National Science Teacher's Association
Arlington, Virginia

Jonathan Gitlin, M.D.
School of Medicine
Washington University
St. Louis, Missouri

Dawn Graff-Haight, Ph.D., CHES
Department of Health, Human
Performance, and Athletics
Linfield College
McMinnville, Oregon

Deborah L. Gumucio, Ph.D.
Associate Professor
Department of Anatomy and Cell Biology
University of Michigan
Ann Arbor, Michigan

William S. Harwood, Ph.D.
Dean of University Division and Associate
Professor of Education
Indiana University
Bloomington, Indiana

Cyndy Henzel, Ph.D.
Department of Geography
and Regional Development
University of Arizona
Tucson, Arizona

Greg Hutton
Science and Health
Curriculum Coordinator
School Board of Sarasota County
Sarasota, Florida

Susan K. Jacobson, Ph.D.
Department of Wildlife Ecology
and Conservation
University of Florida
Gainesville, Florida

Judy Jernstedt, Ph.D.
Department of Agronomy and Range Science
University of California, Davis
Davis, California

John L. Kermond, Ph.D.
Office of Global Programs
National Oceanographic and
Atmospheric Administration
Silver Spring, Maryland

David E. LaHart, Ph.D.
Institute of Science and Public Affairs
Florida State University
Tallahassee, Florida

Joe Leverich, Ph.D.
Department of Biology
St. Louis University
St. Louis, Missouri

Dennis K. Lieu, Ph.D.
Department of Mechanical Engineering
University of California
Berkeley, California

Cynthia J. Moore, Ph.D.
Science Outreach Coordinator
Washington University
St. Louis, Missouri

Joseph M. Moran, Ph.D.
Department of Earth Science
University of Wisconsin–Green Bay
Green Bay, Wisconsin

Joseph Stukey, Ph.D.
Department of Biology
Hope College
Holland, Michigan

Seetha Subramanian
Lexington Community College
University of Kentucky
Lexington, Kentucky

Carl L. Thurman, Ph.D.
Department of Biology
University of Northern Iowa
Cedar Falls, Iowa

Edward D. Walton, Ph.D.
Department of Chemistry
California State Polytechnic University
Pomona, California

Robert S. Young, Ph.D.
Department of Geosciences and
Natural Resource Management
Western Carolina University
Cullowhee, North Carolina

Edward J. Zalisko, Ph.D.
Department of Biology
Blackburn College
Carlinville, Illinois

Teacher Reviewers

Stephanie Anderson
Sierra Vista Junior
    High School
Canyon Country, California

John W. Anson
Mesa Intermediate School
Palmdale, California

Pamela Arline
Lake Taylor Middle School
Norfolk, Virginia

Lynn Beason
College Station Jr. High School
College Station, Texas

Richard Bothmer
Hollis School District
Hollis, New Hampshire

Jeffrey C. Callister
Newburgh Free Academy
Newburgh, New York

Judy D'Albert
Harvard Day School
Corona Del Mar, California

Betty Scott Dean
Guilford County Schools
McLeansville, North Carolina

Sarah C. Duff
Baltimore City Public Schools
Baltimore, Maryland

Melody Law Ewey
Holmes Junior High School
Davis, California

Sherry L. Fisher
Lake Zurich Middle
    School North
Lake Zurich, Illinois

Melissa Gibbons
Fort Worth ISD
Fort Worth, Texas

Debra J. Goodding
Kraemer Middle School
Placentia, California

Jack Grande
Weber Middle School
Port Washington, New York

Steve Hills
Riverside Middle School
Grand Rapids, Michigan

Carol Ann Lionello
Kraemer Middle School
Placentia, California

Jaime A. Morales
Henry T. Gage Middle School
Huntington Park, California

Patsy Partin
Cameron Middle School
Nashville, Tennessee

Deedra H. Robinson
Newport News Public Schools
Newport News, Virginia

Bonnie Scott
Clack Middle School
Abilene, Texas

Charles M. Sears
Belzer Middle School
Indianapolis, Indiana

Barbara M. Strange
Ferndale Middle School
High Point, North Carolina

Jackie Louise Ulfig
Ford Middle School
Allen, Texas

Kathy Usina
Belzer Middle School
Indianapolis, Indiana

Heidi M. von Oetinger
L'Anse Creuse Public School
Harrison Township, Michigan

Pam Watson
Hill Country Middle School
Austin, Texas

Activity Field Testers

Nicki Bibbo
Russell Street School
Littleton, Massachusetts

Connie Boone
Fletcher Middle School
Jacksonville Beach, Florida

Rose-Marie Botting
Broward County
    School District
Fort Lauderdale, Florida

Colleen Campos
Laredo Middle School
Aurora, Colorado

Elizabeth Chait
W. L. Chenery Middle School
Belmont, Massachusetts

Holly Estes
Hale Middle School
Stow, Massachusetts

Laura Hapgood
Plymouth Community
    Intermediate School
Plymouth, Massachusetts

Sandra M. Harris
Winman Junior High School
Warwick, Rhode Island

Jason Ho
Walter Reed Middle School
Los Angeles, California

Joanne Jackson
Winman Junior High School
Warwick, Rhode Island

Mary F. Lavin
Plymouth Community
    Intermediate School
Plymouth, Massachusetts

James MacNeil, Ph.D.
Concord Public Schools
Concord, Massachusetts

Lauren Magruder
St. Michael's Country
    Day School
Newport, Rhode Island

Jeanne Maurand
Glen Urquhart School
Beverly Farms, Massachusetts

Warren Phillips
Plymouth Community
    Intermediate School
Plymouth, Massachusetts

Carol Pirtle
Hale Middle School
Stow, Massachusetts

Kathleen M. Poe
Kirby-Smith Middle School
Jacksonville, Florida

Cynthia B. Pope
Ruffner Middle School
Norfolk, Virginia

Anne Scammell
Geneva Middle School
Geneva, New York

Karen Riley Sievers
Callanan Middle School
Des Moines, Iowa

David M. Smith
Howard A. Eyer Middle School
Macungie, Pennsylvania

Derek Strohschneider
Plymouth Community
    Intermediate School
Plymouth, Massachusetts

Sallie Teames
Rosemont Middle School
Fort Worth, Texas

Gene Vitale
Parkland Middle School
McHenry, Illinois

Zenovia Young
Meyer Levin Junior
    High School (IS 285)
Brooklyn, New York

PRENTICE HALL
SCIENCE EXPLORER

Contents

Earth's Changing Surface

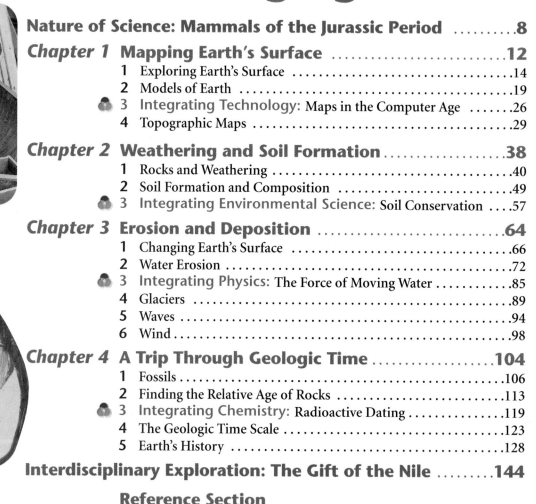

Activities

Inquiry Activities

CHAPTER PROJECT

Opportunities for long-term inquiry

DISCOVER

Exploration and inquiry before reading

Sharpen your Skills

Practice of specific science inquiry skills

TRY THIS

Reinforcement of key concepts

Skills Lab

In-depth practice of inquiry skills

Real-World Lab

Everyday application of science concepts

Interdisciplinary Activities

Math Toolbox

Science and History

Science and Society

Connection

Mammal Fossils of the Jurassic Period

Focus on Paleontology

This four-page feature introduces the process of scientific inquiry in an interview with a young scientist, Kelli Trujillo, a graduate student in vertebrate paleontology. Using Ms. Trujillo's search for mammal fossils, the interview focuses on the collection and analysis of data as a key element of scientific inquiry.

Students will learn how scientists use fossils to learn about Earth's history in Chapter 4 of this book. However, they do not need any previous knowledge of that chapter's content to understand this feature.

Scientific Inquiry

◆ Before students read the article, ask them what they know about dinosaurs. Ask: **How do you think scientists have learned about dinosaurs, even though they have been extinct for millions of years?** *(Some students might know that scientists have learned about dinosaurs from fossils.)* Then have students look at the pictures in the article. Ask: **What kinds of tools does Kelli Trujillo use to find and study fossils of mammals that lived during the time of dinosaurs?** *(A screen box, rock hammer, and microscope are shown. Students might also infer that she uses shovels, picks, and chisels.)*

◆ Invite a student to read aloud the caption on page 8. If students do not know what it means to be a graduate student, explain that graduate students have graduated from college and are continuing their education to earn a higher degree, either a master's degree or a doctorate. Graduate students take some courses and work on research projects of their own under the guidance of a professor.

Mammals of the JURASSIC PERIOD

Kelli Trujillo, 31, is a graduate student in vertebrate paleontology at the University of Wyoming. During the summer, she splits her time between several fossil digs. Kelli is a musician as well as an outdoor enthusiast. She plays guitar, flute, and piano.

Spending half your summer alone in a tiny trailer in a deserted part of Wyoming may not sound like fun. But for Kelli Trujillo, a graduate student in paleontology (pay lee un TAHL uh jee), it's a dream come true. As a paleontologist, she studies the remains of ancient living things.

Kelli Trujillo is working near Como Bluff, Wyoming, one of the most famous dinosaur graveyards in the United States. But she is not searching for dinosaur bones. Kelli is looking for the remains of mammals that lived during the late Jurassic Period, about 150 million years ago.

During the Jurassic Period, southeast Wyoming was flat and dotted with lakes and streams. The Rocky Mountains had not yet formed. Small animals lived in the shadows of the dinosaurs. Among these small animals were some of the earliest mammals: mouselike and shrewlike creatures. Very little is known about these mammals. Their bones are tiny, so finding them is difficult. "If I find a mammal tooth, that's a big deal, because those discoveries are still really rare," says Kelli.

Apatosaurus **and small mammals lived in the same period.**

Background

Paleontology is the study of ancient plants and animals based on the fossil remains of organisms. Paleontology is a branch of historical geology, the study of the history of Earth. Paleontologists search for and identify fossil organisms and make inferences about the environments in which these organisms lived. This research enables scientists to trace the evolution of organisms.

Paleontology is divided into three distinct disciplines, invertebrate paleontology, vertebrate paleontology, and paleobotany. Invertebrate paleontologists study fossils of animals without backbones, including coral animals and mollusks. Vertebrate paleobiologists, like Kelli Trujillo, focus on fossils of animals with backbones, including mammals and dinosaurs. Paleobotanists study the fossils of plants.

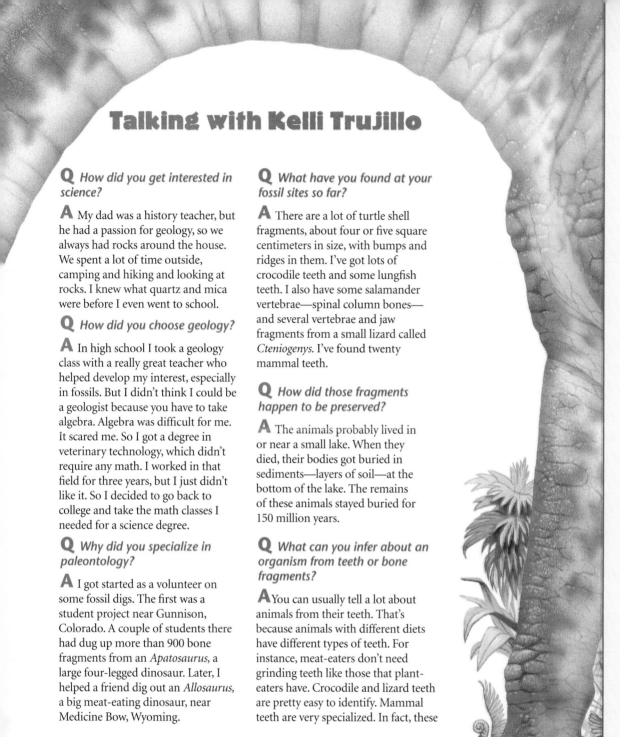

Talking with Kelli Trujillo

Q *How did you get interested in science?*

A My dad was a history teacher, but he had a passion for geology, so we always had rocks around the house. We spent a lot of time outside, camping and hiking and looking at rocks. I knew what quartz and mica were before I even went to school.

Q *How did you choose geology?*

A In high school I took a geology class with a really great teacher who helped develop my interest, especially in fossils. But I didn't think I could be a geologist because you have to take algebra. Algebra was difficult for me. It scared me. So I got a degree in veterinary technology, which didn't require any math. I worked in that field for three years, but I just didn't like it. So I decided to go back to college and take the math classes I needed for a science degree.

Q *Why did you specialize in paleontology?*

A I got started as a volunteer on some fossil digs. The first was a student project near Gunnison, Colorado. A couple of students there had dug up more than 900 bone fragments from an *Apatosaurus,* a large four-legged dinosaur. Later, I helped a friend dig out an *Allosaurus,* a big meat-eating dinosaur, near Medicine Bow, Wyoming.

Q *What have you found at your fossil sites so far?*

A There are a lot of turtle shell fragments, about four or five square centimeters in size, with bumps and ridges in them. I've got lots of crocodile teeth and some lungfish teeth. I also have some salamander vertebrae—spinal column bones— and several vertebrae and jaw fragments from a small lizard called *Cteniogenys.* I've found twenty mammal teeth.

Q *How did those fragments happen to be preserved?*

A The animals probably lived in or near a small lake. When they died, their bodies got buried in sediments—layers of soil—at the bottom of the lake. The remains of these animals stayed buried for 150 million years.

Q *What can you infer about an organism from teeth or bone fragments?*

A You can usually tell a lot about animals from their teeth. That's because animals with different diets have different types of teeth. For instance, meat-eaters don't need grinding teeth like those that plant-eaters have. Crocodile and lizard teeth are pretty easy to identify. Mammal teeth are very specialized. In fact, these

G ◆ 9

- After students have read the feature, encourage them to tell what they know about mammals. Ask: **What makes mammals different from other kinds of animals?** *(Mammals maintain a constant body temperature, have hair, and feed their young milk produced in mammary glands.)* Explain that the first mammals appeared during the time of the dinosaurs, and they probably looked like a shrew, a very small mouselike animal with a pointed nose. They were probably nocturnal and ate mostly insects. Ask: **How do you think we know this about the first mammals?** *(From the fossil evidence uncovered and analyzed by paleontologists)*

- Point out that Kelli has found many different kinds of fossils at her site. Then ask: **Why is it important for Kelli to classify the fossils she finds?** *(She is interested in studying mammals from the Jurassic Period and she wants to examine only fossils of mammals, not fossils of other animals.)* **What process do you think Kelly follows when she classifies the fossils that she finds?** *(She must examine each fossil and identify its characteristics, then she can identify the group of animals to which each fossil belongs, based on its characteristics.)* **How do you think Kelli knows which characteristics classify a fossil into a particular animal group?** *(Kelli knows how to classify fossils based on what she has learned in school and at various digs, as well as from information in reference books and from her advisor.)*

Background

When paleontologists find fossils, they carefully record the exact location of the fossil, the kind of rock in which it was found, and other fossils found nearby. This data gives clues to the fossil's age and its classification, as well as to how the organism lived and interacted with other organisms and its environment.

Paleontologists use the physical features of fossils to classify them. Usually they compare the features of the found fossil to those of fossils that are already identified. Often they compare the features of fossils to those of living organisms using the principle that similar structures have similar functions in extinct organisms and in living organisms. Many fossils cannot be classified until a similar, more complete fossilized organism is found.

◆ Point out that the steps in the scientific process described in this interview include the collection and analysis of data. Ask: **What kind of data does Kelli collect?** *(Sedimentary rock that contains fossils)* **How does Kelli collect data in the field?** *(She uses tools— brooms, picks, shovels, rock hammers, chisels, and screen boxes—to search for mammal fragments in rock.)* Point out that one of the most important tools Kelli uses that isn't mentioned is a logbook and a pencil. Emphasize the importance of recording every piece of information during the process of collecting data. Specific details are easily forgotten later when it's time to analyze the data.

◆ Emphasize that Kelli didn't start to look for mammal fragments haphazardly. Ask: **How did Kelly know where to collect data?** *(She is working at a site already known to contain large numbers of dinosaurs.)* Point out that Kelli inferred that mammal remains are located at her site because the mammals she is studying lived at the same time as the dinosaurs already found there. **How has her inference been proven to be correct?** *(She has found twenty mammal teeth at her site.)*

◆ After Kelli collects data in the field, she brings it into the lab for analysis. Ask: **What tool does Kelli use to analyze data?** *(a microscope)* Point out that if Kelli disregarded even the smallest rock, she might miss the mammal skull or bone that she is looking for.

◆ Tell students that Kelli analyzes data by observing the features of the fossils and comparing those features to the features of fossils already identified. Then she can classify them as coming from turtles, lungfish, salamanders, lizards, or mammals. Ask: **How can Kelli conclude that she has found a mammal tooth?** *(Based on its size and shape she can identify the tooth as mammalian.)*

▲ Kelli looks for mammal fragments at this site in Wyoming (above). Kelli and a co-worker examine a fossil from the Jurassic Period (right).

◄ Kelli worked at some of the mammal and dinosaur sites located on this map.

KEY Dinosaur sites ■   Cities ●

specialized teeth are one of the things that separate mammals from other animals.

With bones, it really depends. If you have the entire bone, you can usually make a good guess about what type of animal it came from. But often you just find unidentifiable fragments.

Q *How does the rock where the fossil is found provide clues to the age of the fossil?*

A It's difficult to get an absolute age on sedimentary rocks. Often we just go by the rule that younger rocks are on top of older rocks. If we're really lucky, there will be a volcanic ash layer in the rocks, or certain crystals or iron minerals that we know how to date. In Wyoming, I'm working in a layer of rocks known as the Morrison Formation, which has been dated to the late Jurassic Period.

Q *How do scientists know where to dig for fossils?*

A Usually you see something on the surface, some scraps of bone sticking out from the rock. Bone has a different shape and texture and is often a different color. So if you know what you're looking for, a bone catches your eye.

Q *What tools do you use?*

A One of my most useful tools is a broom. I use it to clean the rocks so I can see their surfaces clearly. When you're digging out big bones, you use everything from picks and shovels to power tools like jackhammers and air drills. For small or delicate pieces, you need hand tools, like rock hammers and chisels, and a screen box. A screen box is basically a wooden box with a screen bottom. You put a couple of handfuls of rock in it and put the box

Background

Reptiles with mammalian characteristics began to evolve during the Pennsylvanian Period, about 80 million years before the Jurassic Period. One mammalian characteristic of these reptiles was the difference in structure and function between the front teeth and the back teeth. The front teeth caught and killed prey while the back teeth crushed or chewed food. In contrast, reptiles' mouths have uniform teeth.

The first fossils of mammals occur in rock dating to the Jurassic Period. These mammals, which Kelli Trujillo is studying, were very small animals resembling present-day shrews. Their diet probably consisted chiefly of insects. Paleontologists think these early mammals were also nocturnal.

Dinosaur and Mammal Teeth

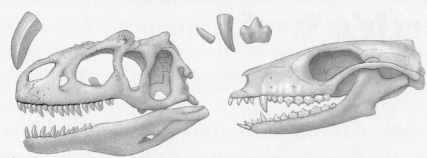

The strong jaws and long pointed teeth of *Allosaurus* (above) worked like a saw to tear apart smaller dinosaurs. *Allosaurus* was a large, meat-eating dinosaur of the Jurassic Period.

Mammal teeth are different from dinosaur teeth. The teeth of Jurassic mammals (above) are specialized for different functions. The combination of canines, incisors, and molars allowed the mammal to tear, shred, and grind.

← Actual size of early mammal tooth

Actual size of *Allosaurus* tooth

in a big trough of water. You let the water wash the rock off the fossil. If you have the right kind of rock, it will wash away. But some rock never dissolves, and you're just out of luck.

Q *How do you recover the small mammal fossils?*

A I collect a couple of bags of rocks and bring them back to the lab. Then I wash them in the screen box, dry what's left, and search through it. The fossils are very small—some of them fit on the head of a pin! So you have to look at everything under a microscope, grain by grain, to see if you've got any fossils mixed in with the rock. It takes an awful lot of patience.

Q *What do you hope to find?*

A Usually teeth are all that's left of early mammals, but I'm hopeful this site will yield skulls and other bones, like arms or legs or vertebrae. I was

pretty excited when I found those twenty mammal teeth.

Q *Do you ever get discouraged or lonely out in the field?*

A When I'm out working at the site, the time goes so fast I don't even think about it. Being outside all day is wonderful. The bugs and wind aren't so good, but I'm in the middle of nowhere, and it's absolutely beautiful.

In her lab, Kelli uses her microscope to examine tiny mammal teeth.

In Your Journal

Kelli Trujillo's work as a paleontologist involves a number of different steps. At each step, from searching a site for fossils to drawing conclusions in the lab, Kelli uses a wide range of skills. Make a two column list. In one column list the steps Kelli follows. In the second column describe the skills Kelli uses at each step.

G ◆ 11

- Have students compare the size and shape of mammal teeth with those of a dinosaur by examining the illustration. Ask: **What inferences can you make about the diet of each animal based on the shape of its teeth?** (*The dinosaur is a meat-eater because it has teeth that work like a saw to tear apart flesh. The mammal has teeth of different shapes that perform different functions, allowing the animal to tear, shred, and grind.*) Explain that paleontologists make inferences like these when they analyze the fossils that they find.

In Your Journal Students should identify the following steps in Kelli Trujillo's work: searching the site for fossils, recovering fossils, classifying fossils, and drawing conclusions about the fossils. As Kelli searches for and recovers fossils, she is observing the site to gather and record data about where the fossils were found. Once she recovers the fossils, she classifies them based on her observations of their structure and physical features. She makes inferences and draws conclusions about the fossilized animal based on the fossil's physical features.

Introducing Earth's Changing Surface

Have students look through the table of contents to find parts of the book that relate most closely with this feature. (*Chapter 4, A Trip Through Geologic Time, particularly Section 1*) Ask: **What other topics in geology will you be learning about in this book?** (*How Earth's surface is explored and mapped; how weathering, erosion, and deposition change Earth's surface; and how scientists learn about Earth's history.*)

CHAPTER 1 Mapping Earth's Surface

Sections	Time	Student Edition Activities		Other Activities
CHAPTER PROJECT 1 **Getting on the Map** p. G13	Ongoing (2 weeks)	Check Your Progress, p. G18 Check Your Progress, p. G24 Check Your Progress, p. G33 Project Wrap Up, p. G37		
1 Exploring Earth's Surface pp. G14–18 ◆ 1.1.1 List the factors that determine the topography of Earth's surface. ◆ 1.1.2 Name and describe the main types of landforms. ◆ 1.1.3 Identify the four "spheres" that make up Earth's surface.	2–3 periods/ 1–1½ blocks	**Discover** What Is the Land Like Around Your School?, p. G14		**TE** Building Inquiry Skills: Organizing Information, p. G16 **TE** Exploring Landforms, p. G17 **TE** Building Inquiry Skills: Classifying, p. G17
2 Models of Earth pp. G19–25 ◆ 1.2.1 Explain how maps and globes represent Earth's surface and state what a map projection is. ◆ 1.2.2 Identify the equator and prime meridian and state how latitude and longitude are used to locate points on Earth's surface.	2–3 periods/ 1–1½ blocks	**Discover** How Can You Flatten the Curved Earth?, p. G19 **Try This** Where in the World?, p. G22 **Real-World Lab: You and History** A Borderline Case, p. G25		**TE** Building Inquiry Skills: Comparing and Contrasting, p. G20 **TE** Using the Visuals: Figure 7, p. G20 **TE** Building Inquiry Skills: Making Models, p. G20 **TE** Inquiry Challenge, p. G21, G24 **TE** Cultural Diversity, p. G22 **TE** Including All Students, p. G23 **TE** Demonstration, p. G23
3 *INTEGRATING TECHNOLOGY* **Maps in the Computer Age** pp. G26–28 ◆ 1.3.1 Describe how satellites and computers are used in mapmaking.	1–2 periods/ ½–1 block	**Discover** Can You Make a Pixel Picture?, p. G26 **Science at Home**, p. G28		**TE** Building Inquiry Skills: Drawing Conclusions, p. G27
4 Topographic Maps pp. G29–34 ◆ 1.4.1 Describe a topographic map. ◆ 1.4.2 Explain how elevation, relief, and slope are shown on topographic maps. ◆ 1.4.3 Identify the Global Positioning System.	2–3 periods/ 1–1½ blocks	**Discover** Can a Map Show Relief?, p. G29 **Sharpen Your Skills** Interpreting Data, p. G31 **Skills Lab: Making Models** A Map in a Pan, p. G34		**TE** Building Inquiry Skills: Making Models, p. G32 **ISLM** G-1, "Using a Topographic Map"
Study Guide/Assessment pp. G35–37	1 period/ ½ block			**ISAB** Provides teaching and review of all inquiry skills

 For Standard or Block Schedule The Resource Pro® CD-ROM gives you maximum flexibility for planning your instruction for any type of schedule. Resource Pro® contains Planning Express®, an advanced scheduling program, as well as the entire contents of the Teaching Resources and the Computer Test Bank.

Key: SE Student Edition
PLM Probeware Lab Manual
ISAB Inquiry Skills Activity Book

CHAPTER PLANNING GUIDE

Program Resources	Assessment Strategies	Media and Technology
TR Chapter 1 Project Teacher Notes, pp. G6–7 **TR** Chapter 1 Project Overview and Worksheets, pp. G8–11	**TE** Check Your Progress, pp. G18, G24, G33 **TE** Performance Assessment: Chapter 1 Project Wrap Up, p. G37 **TE** Chapter 1 Project Scoring Rubric, p.G12	Science Explorer Internet Site Audio CDs and Audiotapes, English-Spanish Section Summaries
TR 1-1 Lesson Plan, p. G13 **TR** 1-1 Section Summary, p. G14 **TR** 1-1 Review and Reinforce, p. G15 **TR** 1-1 Enrich, p. G16 **SES** Book F, *Inside Earth,* Chapter 1 **SES** Book H, *Earth's Waters,* Chapter 1 **SES** Book I, *Weather and Climate,* Chapter 1	**SE** Section 1 Review, p. G18 **TE** Ongoing Assessment, pp. G15, G17 **TE** Performance Assessment, p. G18	Exploring Earth Science Videodisc, Unit 1 Side 1, "Flying Over America" Transparencies 1, "Landform Regions of the United States"; 2, "Exploring Landforms"
TR 1-2 Lesson Plan, p. G17 **TR** 1-2 Section Summary, p. G18 **TR** 1-2 Review and Reinforce, p. G19 **TR** 1-2 Enrich, p. G20 **TR** Real-World Lab blackline masters, pp. G29–31	**SE** Section 2 Review, p. G24 **SE** Analyze and Conclude, p. G25 **TE** Ongoing Assessment, pp. G21, G23 **TE** Performance Assessment, p. G24	Exploring Earth Science Videodisc, Unit 2 Side 2, "Let's Map" Lab Activity Videotape, *Earth's Changing Surface,* 1 Transparency 3, "Determining Latitude and Longitude"
TR 1-3 Lesson Plan, p. G21 **TR** 1-3 Section Summary, p. G22 **TR** 1-3 Review and Reinforce, p. G23 **TR** 1-3 Enrich, p. G24 **SES** Book J, *Astronomy,* Chapter 1	**SE** Section 3 Review, p. G28 **TE** Ongoing Assessment, p. G27 **TE** Performance Assessment, p. G28	Audio CDs and Audiotapes, English-Spanish Summary 1-3 Interactive Student Tutorial CD-ROM, G-1
TR 1-4 Lesson Plan, p. G25 **TR** 1-4 Section Summary, p. G26 **TR** 1-4 Review and Reinforce, p. G27 **TR** 1-4 Enrich, p. G28 **TR** Skills Lab blackline masters, pp. G32–33	**SE** Section 4 Review, p. G33 **SE** Analyze and Conclude, p. G34 **TE** Ongoing Assessment, p. G31 **TE** Performance Assessment, p. G33	Lab Activity Videotape, *Earth's Changing Surface,* 2 Transparency 4, "Exploring Topographic Maps"
GSW Provides worksheets to promote student comprehension of content **RCA** Provides strategies to improve science reading skills **ELL** Provides multiple strategies for English language learners	**SE** Study Guide/Assessment, pp. G35–37 **TR** Performance Assessment, pp. G138–140 **TR** Chapter 1 Test, pp. G141–144 **CTB** *Earth's Changing Surface,* Chapter 1 Test **STP** Provides standardized test practice	Interactive Student Tutorial CD-ROM, G-1 Computer Test Bank, *Earth's Changing Surface,* Chapter 1 Test

TE Teacher's Edition
RCA Reading in the Content Area
GSW Guided Study Workbook

TR Teaching Resources
ISLM Integrated Science Laboratory Manual
ELL Teacher's ELL Handbook

CTB Computerized Test Bank
STP Standardized Test Preparation Book
SES Science Explorer Series Text

Meeting the National Science Education Standards and AAAS Benchmarks

National Science Education Standards	Benchmarks for Science Literacy	Unifying Themes
Science As Inquiry (Content Standard A) ◆ **Use appropriate tools and techniques to gather, analyze, and interpret data** Students create a scale map of a small area. *(Chapter Project)* ◆ **Develop descriptions, explanations, predictions, and models using evidence** Students study maps to infer which state borders were determined by lines of latitude and longitude. Students make a topographic map of a model landform. *(Real-World Lab; Skills Lab)* **Science and Technology** (Content Standard E) ◆ **Understandings about science and technology** Maps and globes are drawn to scale and use symbols to represent topography and other features on Earth's surface. Satellites and computers have revolutionized mapmaking. Topographic maps provide highly accurate information on the elevation, relief, and slope of the ground surface. *(Sections 2, 3, 4; Skills Lab)* **History and Nature of Science** (Content Standard G) ◆ **History of science** Centuries ago, people invented instruments and techniques to show Earth's surface accurately. *(Section 2; Science & History)*	**1B Scientific Inquiry** Students study maps to infer which state borders were determined by lines of latitude and longitude. *(Real-World Lab)* **1C The Scientific Enterprise** Centuries ago, people invented instruments and techniques to show Earth's surface accurately. Powerful computers use satellite data to make maps quickly and accurately. *(Science & History; Section 3)* **3A Technology and Science** Maps and globes are drawn to scale and use symbols to represent topography and other features on Earth's surface. Satellites and computers have revolutionized mapmaking. Topographic maps provide highly accurate information on the elevation, relief, and slope of the ground surface. *(Sections 2, 3, 4)* **4B The Earth** Topography is determined by elevation, relief, and landforms. *(Section 1)* **8E Information Processing** With computers, mapmakers have new ways of storing and displaying map data. *(Section 3)* **12B Computation and Estimation** Students create a scale map of a small area and make a topographic map of a model landform. *(Chapter Project; Skills Lab)*	◆ **Modeling** Students create a scale map of a small area. Maps and globes are drawn to scale and use symbols to represent topography and other features on Earth's surface. Topographic maps provide highly accurate information on the elevation, relief, and slope of the ground surface. Students make a topographic map of a model landform. *(Chapter Project; Sections 2, 4; Skills Lab)* ◆ **Scale and Structure** The three main types of landforms are plains, mountains, and plateaus. *(Section 1)* ◆ **Systems and Interactions** You can use lines of latitude and longitude to find locations anywhere on Earth. As technology develops, mapmaking becomes more precise. Students infer which state borders were determined by lines of latitude and longitude. Powerful computers use satellite data to make maps quickly and accurately. Mapmakers use contour lines to represent elevation, relief, and slope on topographic maps. *(Sections 2, 3, 4; Science & History; Real-World Lab)* ◆ **Unity and Diversity** Scientists divide Earth into the lithosphere, hydrosphere, atmosphere, and biosphere. A map is a model of all or part of Earth's surface as seen from above, while a globe is a sphere that represents Earth's entire surface. *(Sections 1, 2)*

Take It to the Net

 Interactive text at www.phschool.com

Science Explorer comes alive with iText.

- **Complete student text** is accessible from any computer with a browser.
- **Animations, simulations, and videos** enhance student understanding and retention of concepts.
- **Self-tests and online study tools** assess student understanding.
- **Teacher management tools** help you make the most of this valuable resource.

STAY CURRENT with **SCIENCE NEWS**®

Find out the latest research and information about Earth's surface at: **www.phschool.com**

Go to **www.phschool.com** and click on the Science icon. Then click on Science Explorer under PH@school.

ACTIVITY	Time (minutes)	Materials Quantities for one work group	Skills
Section 1			
Discover, p. 14	10	**Consumable** piece of unlined paper **Nonconsumable** magnetic compass	Forming Operational Definitions
Section 2			
Discover, p. 19	15	**Consumable** orange or grapefruit **Nonconsumable** globe, felt-tip pen, plastic knife	Observing
Try This, p. 22	10	**Nonconsumable** globe	Observing
Real-World Lab, p. 25	30	**Consumable** tracing paper **Nonconsumable** United States map with latitude, longitude, and state borders; colored pencils or crayons; paper clips	Observing, Inferring, Drawing Conclusions
Section 3			
Discover, p. 26	15	**Consumable** unlined paper **Nonconsumable** metric ruler, colored pencils	Predicting
Science at Home, p. 28	Home	**Consumable** news magazines, newspapers	Communicating
Section 4			
Discover, p. 29	20	**Consumable** 8 pieces of cardboard of increasing dimensions, unlined paper **Nonconsumable** scissors, metric ruler	Making Models
Sharpen Your Skills, p. 31	10	No special materials are required.	Interpreting Data
Skills Lab, p. 34	40	**Consumable** clear, hard sheet of plastic, sheet of unlined white paper, water, modeling clay, food coloring **Nonconsumable** deep-sided pan, marking pencil, metric ruler, scissors, large beaker or pitcher	Measuring, Making Models, Comparing and Contrasting

A list of all materials required for the Student Edition activities can be found beginning on page T15. You can obtain information about ordering materials by calling 1-800-848-9500 or by accessing the Science Explorer Internet site at: **www.phschool.com**

Most students probably have used some sort of map at one time or another, or at least seen adults use road maps. Although students may see the utility of maps, they are likely to not understand how much work goes into the production of a good map.

Purpose In the Chapter 1 Project, students will make a map of a small square or rectangular site of their choosing. This map will be made to scale, which will necessitate measuring the boundaries of the site as well as the location of features of the site. Students will include in this map as many natural and human-made features as possible, using symbols and a map key. In addition, they will use contour lines to show the topography of the site. (The contour lines will be approximate and relative since students are not likely to know the exact elevation of the areas they select to map.) By creating this map, students will gain a better understanding of a small piece of Earth's surface, as well as an appreciation of how maps represent that surface.

Skills Focus Students will be able to
◆ observe and record the natural and human-made features of a neighborhood site;
◆ measure the boundaries and other relationships at the site;
◆ calculate scale relationships using their measurements;
◆ make a model of the site in the form of a map.

Project Time Line The entire project will require about two weeks. Depending on how much time students spend working on the project, a day or two may be required for each of the following phases.
◆ Select a square or rectangular site in the neighborhood to map.
◆ Measure the boundaries of the site, as well as distances between features of the site.
◆ Make a rough sketch of the site, including in the sketch as many details as possible.
◆ Devise a scale to use on the map and

CHAPTER
1
Mapping Earth's Surface

WEB ACTIVITY   www.phschool.com

SECTION 1
Exploring Earth's Surface

Discover **What Is the Land Like Around Your School?**

SECTION 2
Models of Earth

Discover **How Can You Flatten the Curved Earth?**
Try This **Where in the World?**
Real-World Lab **A Borderline Case**

SECTION 3
Integrating Technology
Maps in the Computer Age

Discover **Can You Make a Pixel Picture?**

brainstorm a list of symbols to represent map features.
◆ Create a map of the site, including a map scale, a key, features, and contour lines.
◆ Present the map to the class.

For more detailed information on planning and supervising this chapter project, see Chapter 1 Project Teacher Notes, pages 6–7 in Teaching Resources.

Suggested Shortcuts
◆ You may wish to divide the class into pairs or small groups to carry out the project. The

task of measuring may proceed more smoothly if two or more students work together. Also, since students will be working outside of school and away from their homes, you may want students to work together for security.
◆ You can make this project shorter and less involved by designating small areas of the school's grounds for students to map, either individually or in small groups. This can be accomplished in two days, one for measuring and one for creating the map.

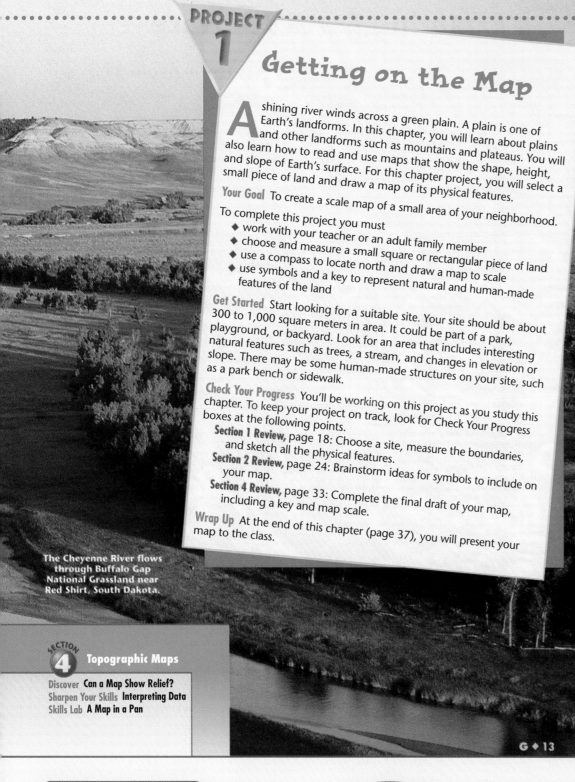

PROJECT 1

Getting on the Map

A shining river winds across a green plain. A plain is one of Earth's landforms. In this chapter, you will learn about plains and other landforms such as mountains and plateaus. You will also learn how to read and use maps that show the shape, height, and slope of Earth's surface. For this chapter project, you will select a small piece of land and draw a map of its physical features.

Your Goal To create a scale map of a small area of your neighborhood.

To complete this project you must
◆ work with your teacher or an adult family member
◆ choose and measure a small square or rectangular piece of land
◆ use a compass to locate north and draw a map to scale
◆ use symbols and a key to represent natural and human-made features of the land

Get Started Start looking for a suitable site. Your site should be about 300 to 1,000 square meters in area. It could be part of a park, playground, or backyard. Look for an area that includes interesting natural features such as trees, a stream, and changes in elevation or slope. There may be some human-made structures on your site, such as a park bench or sidewalk.

Check Your Progress You'll be working on this project as you study this chapter. To keep your project on track, look for Check Your Progress boxes at the following points.

Section 1 Review, page 18: Choose a site, measure the boundaries, and sketch all the physical features.
Section 2 Review, page 24: Brainstorm ideas for symbols to include on your map.
Section 4 Review, page 33: Complete the final draft of your map, including a key and map scale.

Wrap Up At the end of this chapter (page 37), you will present your map to the class.

The Cheyenne River flows through Buffalo Gap National Grassland near Red Shirt, South Dakota.

SECTION 4 **Topographic Maps**

Discover **Can a Map Show Relief?**
Sharpen Your Skills **Interpreting Data**
Skills Lab **A Map in a Pan**

G ◆ 13

Program Resources

◆ **Teaching Resources** Chapter 1 Project Teacher Notes, pp. 6–7; Chapter 1 Project Overview and Worksheets, pp. 8–11; Chapter 1 Project Scoring Rubric, p. 12

Media and Technology

 Audio CDs and **Audiotapes**
English-Spanish Section Summaries

WEB ACTIVITY www.phschool.com

You will find an Internet activity, chapter self-tests for students, and links to other chapter topics at this site.

Launching the Project Describe for students an area of a well-known local park or other area that everyone is likely to have visited many times. Ask: **If you were to make a map of this area, how would you start?** *(Answers will vary. A typical answer might suggest making a sketch of the area, including all the objects that can be seen.)* Emphasize to students that they are not making an artistic landscape painting. Rather, they want to make a map that conveys exactly what is in the park to someone who has never been there before. Ask: **Is there any way to show exactly how far away the various features of the area are from one another?** *(Some students may suggest that they could make measurements and include them on the map.)* Explain that in the course of the Chapter 1 Project as well as in the chapter's sections, they will learn skills that mapmakers use to make an effective representation of an area on a map. To help students get started, pass out Chapter 1 Project Overview and Worksheets, pages 8–11 in Teaching Resources. You may also wish to pass out the Chapter 1 Project Scoring Rubric, page 12, at this time so students know exactly what is expected of them.

Possible Materials Students will need only a few materials to complete the project. For measuring, a tape measure would be useful, though students can measure a section of rope or string with a ruler, as described in Chapter 1 Project Worksheet 2, page 11 in Teaching Resources. To create the map, they will need paper, a ruler, and colored pencils.

Performance Assessment

Use the Chapter 1 Project Scoring Rubric to assess students' work. Students will be assessed on
◆ how accurately they measure the mapped site and make their map to scale;
◆ how many natural and human-made features they map and how effectively they have used symbols;
◆ how accurately they show the shape of the land at the mapped site;
◆ how effectively they present the map to the class.

Objectives

After completing the lesson, students will be able to

♦ list the factors that determine the topography of Earth's surface;
♦ name and describe the main types of landforms;
♦ identify the four "spheres" that make up Earth's surface.

Key Terms topography, elevation, relief, landform, landform region, plain, mountain, mountain range, plateau, lithosphere, atmosphere, hydrosphere, biosphere

1 Engage/Explore

Activating Prior Knowledge

Ask students: **When you think of what the land is like in of our part of the state, what comes to mind?** (*Answers will vary. Encourage students to disagree with one another until the class comes to some consensus.*) Then have students describe a place where they've lived or visited that is different from where they live now.

········ DISCOVER ·········

Skills Focus forming operational definitions
Materials *piece of unlined paper, magnetic compass*
Time 10 minutes
Tips If a compass is unavailable for students to use, point out which way is north of the school. Give students some idea of how far away 1 km is by referring to a local landmark.
Expected Outcome In choosing words to identify local areas, students will construct a simple map of the area's topography.
Think It Over Answers will vary. Students should develop some generalization of the area's topography based on the type of landforms, slopes, and so on.

SECTION 1 Exploring Earth's Surface

DISCOVER ··························· ACTIVITY···

What Is the Land Like Around Your School?

1. On a piece of paper, draw a small square to represent your school.

2. Choose a word that describes the type of land near your school, such as flat, hilly, or rolling. Write the word next to the square.

3. Use a magnetic compass to determine the direction of north. Assume that north is at the top of your piece of paper.

4. If you travel due north 1 kilometer from your school, what type of land do you find? Choose a word to describe the land in this area. Write that word to the north of the square.

5. Repeat Step 4 for areas located 1 kilometer east, south, and west of your school.

Think It Over
Forming Operational Definitions What phrase could you use to describe the land in your area?

GUIDE FOR READING

♦ What determines the topography of Earth's surface?

♦ What are the main types of landforms?

♦ What are the four "spheres" that make up Earth's surface?

Reading Tip Before you read, preview *Exploring Landforms* on page 17. Make a list of questions you have about landforms.

I n 1804, an expedition set out from St. Louis to explore the land between the Mississippi River and the Pacific Ocean. The United States had just purchased a part of this vast territory, called Louisiana, from France. Before the Louisiana Purchase, the United States stretched from the Atlantic coast westward to the Mississippi River. Few United States citizens had traveled west of the Mississippi. None had ever traveled over land all the way to the Pacific.

Led by Meriwether Lewis and William Clark, the expedition traveled up the Missouri River, crossed the Rocky Mountains, followed the Columbia River to the Pacific Ocean—and then returned. The purpose of the expedition was to map America's interior and discover resources.

Topography

On the journey to the Pacific, the Lewis and Clark expedition traveled more than 5,000 kilometers across the continent of North America. As they traveled, Lewis and Clark observed many changes in topography. **Topography** is the shape of the land. An area's topography may be flat, sloping, hilly, or mountainous.

Figure 1 While traveling down the Columbia River, the Lewis and Clark expedition meets the Chinook people.

READING STRATEGIES

Reading Tip Encourage students to write at least one question for each of the terms described in the feature. An example might be, "How are coastal plains different from interior plains?" In addition, students might write a question such as, "What kinds of landforms are there besides plains, mountains, and plateaus?"

Media and Technology

 Transparencies "Landform Regions of the United States," Transparency 1

The topography of an area is determined by the area's elevation, relief, and landforms. The desktop where you do homework probably has piles of books, papers, and other objects of different sizes and shapes. Your desktop has both elevation and relief!

Elevation The height above sea level of a point on Earth's surface is its **elevation**. When Lewis and Clark started in St. Louis, they were about 140 meters above sea level. By the time they reached Lemhi Pass in the Rocky Mountains, they were more than 2,200 meters above sea level.

Relief The difference in elevation between the highest and lowest parts of an area is its **relief**. As the Lewis and Clark expedition entered the Rocky Mountains, the relief of the land changed from flat or rolling land with low relief to huge mountains with high relief.

Landforms If you followed the route of the Lewis and Clark expedition, you would see many different landforms. A **landform** is a feature of topography formed by the processes that shape Earth's surface. All landforms have elevation and relief. A large area of land where the topography is similar is called a **landform region**. Figure 3 shows the landform regions of the United States not including Alaska or Hawaii.

☑️ *Checkpoint* *What is the difference between elevation and relief?*

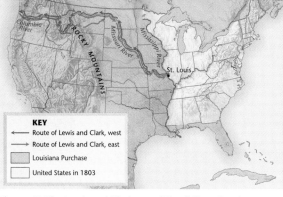

Figure 2 The Lewis and Clark expedition followed major rivers, except when crossing the Rocky Mountains.

KEY
← Route of Lewis and Clark, west
→ Route of Lewis and Clark, east
Louisiana Purchase
United States in 1803

Figure 3 The United States has many different landform regions. *Interpreting Maps In what regions are Charleston, Topeka, Santa Fe, and Walla Walla located?*

Landform Regions of the United States

COASTAL RANGE
CASCADE RANGE
COLUMBIA PLATEAU
Walla Walla
SNAKE RIVER PLATEAU
SIERRA NEVADA
COASTAL RANGE
GREAT BASIN
COLORADO PLATEAU
Santa Fe
ROCKY MOUNTAINS
GREAT PLAINS
SUPERIOR UPLANDS
ADIRONDACK MOUNTAINS
Topeka
CENTRAL LOWLANDS
OZARK PLATEAU
OUACHITA MOUNTAINS
APPALACHIAN PLATEAU
APPALACHIAN MOUNTAINS
PIEDMONT PLATEAU
ATLANTIC COASTAL PLAIN
Charleston
ATLANTIC OCEAN
GULF COASTAL PLAIN
Gulf of Mexico
PACIFIC OCEAN
Columbia River
Missouri River
Mississippi River
Colorado River
Rio Grande
Ohio River

KEY
Coastal plains
Interior plains or lowlands
Mountains
Plateaus or highlands
Plains and mountains

G ◆ 15

Program Resources
◆ **Teaching Resources** 1-1 Lesson Plan, p. 13; 1-1 Section Summary, p. 14
◆ **Guided Study Workbook** Section 1-1

Answers to Self-Assessment

Caption Question

Figure 3 Charleston, Atlantic Coastal Plain; Topeka, Great Plains; Santa Fe, Rocky Mountains; Walla Walla, Columbia Plateau.

☑️ *Checkpoint*

Elevation is the height above sea level of a point on Earth's surface; relief is the difference in elevation between the highest and lowest parts of an area.

2 *Facilitate*

Topography

Including All Students

Encourage students who need additional challenges to prepare a short presentation to the class about the Lewis and Clark expedition. Students can use reference materials to find out who sent them, how long their expedition lasted, and some of what they saw on their journey. Students may be able to find copies of maps made on this expedition. **learning modality: verbal**

Addressing Naive Conceptions

Many students may have difficulty with the difference between height and elevation. Explain that the height of a cliff, for instance, may be 15 m relative to the ground at the bottom of the cliff. The elevation at the top of the cliff, though, may be 1,500 m, because elevation is height above sea level. Ask: **What is your height above ground as you sit in this classroom?** *(Students might respond with 1 to several meters, depending on the floor they are on.)* **What is your elevation?** *(Students should respond that it is the elevation of the area in which they live.)* Encourage student volunteers to find out the elevation of their area. **learning modality: logical/mathematical**

Using the Visuals: Figure 3

Ask students: **What landform region do you live in?** *(Students should respond with the region on the map that corresponds to their area.)* **What other landform regions shown here have you lived in?** *(Most classes will contain students who have lived in other areas.)* Encourage students who have lived elsewhere to compare and contrast those regions with the local one. **learning modality: visual**

Ongoing Assessment

Writing Have students explain in their own words how elevation and relief help determine an area's topography.

G ◆ 15

Types of Landforms

Using the Visuals: Figure 4

Ask students: **If you were to visit the Great Plains, how much difference in relief would you expect to see?** *(There is little difference in relief, since a plain has low relief.)* **What do you think the elevation of the area is?** *(The elevation of an interior plain is higher than that of a coastal plain but not as high as a mountainous region.)* **learning modality: verbal**

Building Inquiry Skills: Organizing Information

Have students make a Venn diagram that shows **ACTIVITY** the relationships among a mountain, a mountain range, a mountain system, and a mountain belt. *(The diagram should be four increasingly large circles, each successive circle fully encompassing the previous one.)* Then ask: **In what mountain system are the Bitterroot Mountains?** *(Rocky Mountains)* **Challenge students to find out what mountain belt the Rockies are part of.** *(The Rockies are part of the Circum-Pacific mountain belt.)* **learning modality: logical/mathematical**

Including All Students

To help students who have difficulty with written English, write the term *plateau* on the board and call on a student to pronounce the word clearly. Explain that it derives from a French word meaning "flat." Then show students a picture of the Grand Canyon. Have them turn back to the map in Figure 3 and point out that the Grand Canyon is within the Colorado Plateau. Ask: **If a plateau is flat, with low relief, how can the Grand Canyon be part of the Colorado Plateau?** *(A landform region is an area where topography is similar, but that does not mean it is all the same. Streams and rivers may cut a plateau's surface, which is the case with the Grand Canyon.)* **limited English proficiency**

Figure 4 The Great Plains of western North America include a vast area of flat or rolling land. The Great Plains are interior plains. *Predicting What do you think would be some differences between interior plains and coastal plains?*

Types of Landforms

Landforms can vary greatly in size and shape—from level plains extending as far as the eye can see, to low, rounded hills that you could climb on foot, to jagged mountains that would take you days to walk around. **There are three main types of landforms: plains, mountains, and plateaus.**

Plains A **plain** is a landform made up of flat or gently rolling land with low relief. A plain that lies along a seacoast is called a coastal plain. In North America, a coastal plain wraps like an apron around the continent's eastern and southeastern shores. Coastal plains have both low elevation and low relief.

A plain that lies away from the coast is called an interior plain. Although interior plains have low relief, their elevation can vary. The broad interior plain of North America is called the Great Plains.

The Great Plains extend from Texas north into Canada. From their eastern border in the states of North and South Dakota, Nebraska, Kansas, Oklahoma, and Texas, the Great Plains stretch west to the Rocky Mountains. At the time of the Lewis and Clark expedition, the Great Plains were a vast grassland.

Figure 5 The Bitterroot Mountains in Idaho are part of the Rocky Mountains system.

Mountains A **mountain** is a landform with high elevation and high relief. Mountains usually occur as part of a mountain range. A **mountain range** is a group of mountains that are closely related in shape, structure, and age. After crossing the Great Plains, the Lewis and Clark expedition crossed a rugged mountain range in Idaho called the Bitterroot Mountains.

The different mountain ranges in a region make up a mountain system. The Bitterroot Mountains are one mountain range in the mountain system known as the Rocky Mountains.

Mountain ranges and mountain systems in a long, connected chain form a larger unit called a mountain belt. The Rocky Mountains are part of a great mountain belt that stretches down the western sides of North America and South America.

Background

Facts and Figures The total area of Earth's surface is about 500 million km², of which about 140 million km²—29 percent—is land area. The average depth of Earth's oceans is 3.8 kilometers. The average elevation of Earth's land surface is 840 m.

Some geographers include hills as a separate type of landform. Hills are less rugged than mountains, with less steep slopes and flatter tops. Interior plains may include extensive areas of hills. And such plains may have much greater elevation than coastal plains, which are often at or near sea level. The High Plains of Colorado rise above 1,500 m. A plateau—sometimes called a tableland—is essentially a high plain that lies above nearby plains.

Plateaus A landform that has high elevation and a more or less level surface is called a **plateau**. A plateau is rarely perfectly smooth on top. Streams and rivers may cut into the plateau's surface. The Columbia Plateau in Washington State is an example. The Columbia River, which the Lewis and Clark expedition followed, slices through this plateau. The many layers of rock that make up the Columbia Plateau are about 1,500 meters thick.

 Checkpoint *What types of landforms have low relief?*

EXPLORING Landforms

Mountains, plains, and plateaus are just a few of the many landforms that make up the topography of Earth's surface.

Mountains
A mountain's base usually covers an area of at least several square kilometers, but its peak may rise to a point. Mountains often have steeply sloping sides.

Plains
Plains may occur along a continent's edges or in the interior.

Plateaus
The top of a plateau forms a level surface.

Media and Technology

 Transparencies "Exploring Landforms," Transparency 2

Exploring Earth Science Videodisc
Unit 1, Side 1, "Flying Over America"
Chapter 7

Answers to Self-Assessment

Caption Question

Figure 4 Interior plains are generally at a higher elevation as well as drier than coastal plains.

Checkpoint
Plains and plateaus have low relief.

EXPLORING
Landforms

Materials *modeling compound, board*
Time 20 minutes

Call on students to read the annotations for each of the three main types of landforms. Ask other students to identify the elevation and relief of each type of landform. Then divide the class into small groups, and have each group make a clay model of their own design that includes each of the three main landforms.
learning modality: kinesthetic

Addressing Naive Conceptions

Students may believe that classifying landforms is as straightforward as classifying birds or rocks. Point out that Earth's land has an almost infinite variety of landforms. Although there are obvious mountains and plains, there are also transitional areas. Ask: **How would you classify an area between mountains and plains?** *(Most will classify it as foothills.)* Emphasize that classification into three main types of landforms is only a starting point in understanding Earth's surface.
learning modality: verbal

Building Inquiry Skills: Classifying

Materials *raised relief maps*
Time 15 minutes

Raised relief maps, molded in vinyl, are available through science supply catalogs or via the Internet. Some are small-scale maps of the U.S. or the world. Others are regional maps at a scale of 1 : 250,000 based on USGS topographic data. Raised relief maps are excellent tools to use with sight-impaired students. Divide the class into small groups, and assign each group a map. Then challenge group members to collaborate on written descriptions of the landforms and landform regions each map contains. **cooperative learning**

Ongoing Assessment

Skills Check Have students each make a compare/contrast table entitled Main Types of Landforms. They should include elevation, relief, and a description for each landform.

Earth's Four Spheres

Including All Students

Write the names of Earth's four spheres on the board. Then, to help students who have trouble with written English, invite all students to play a game of call and response: one student names anything on Earth, and the next student classifies it in one or more of the four spheres. Write the responses underneath the appropriate headings. **learning modality: verbal**

3 Assess

Section 1 Review Answers

1. Elevation, relief, and landforms
2. Plains, mountains, and plateaus
3. A mountain belt is larger than a mountain system.
4. A cloud in the atmosphere; a mountain in the lithosphere; a lake in the hydrosphere; and a tree in the biosphere
5. They are similar in that both have a high elevation; they are different in that plateaus have low relief while mountains have high relief.

Check Your Progress
CHAPTER PROJECT 1

Check that each student or group has chosen a prospective site and has asked for permission where necessary. Inquire about initial measurements, and review students' first sketches of the area.

Performance Assessment

Writing Have students imagine that they are visiting the United States for the first time and have traveled through every region of the country. Have them write a letter to home describing the landform regions they've seen.

Earth's Four Spheres

Lewis and Clark's two-year journey took them across western North America. Along the way, they observed the land, water, air, and living things. Together, these four things make up everything that is on and around planet Earth. **Scientists divide Earth into four spheres: the lithosphere, hydrosphere, atmosphere, and biosphere.** In this book, you will learn mainly about the lithosphere and how it is affected by each of the other spheres.

Earth's solid, rocky outer layer is called the **lithosphere** (LITH uh sfeer). The lithosphere is made up of the continents as well as smaller landmasses called islands. The lithosphere extends under the entire ocean floor. The surface of the lithosphere varies from smooth plains to wrinkled hills and valleys to jagged mountain peaks.

The outermost sphere is the **atmosphere** (AT muh sfeer), the mixture of gases that surrounds the planet. By far the most abundant gases are nitrogen and oxygen, but the atmosphere also contains water vapor, carbon dioxide, and other gases. When water vapor condenses, it forms the droplets that make up clouds.

Earth's oceans, lakes, rivers, and ice form the **hydrosphere** (HY druh sfeer). Most of the hydrosphere consists of the salt water in the oceans, but fresh water is also part of the hydrosphere. Oceans cover more than two thirds of Earth.

All living things—whether in the air, in the oceans, or on and beneath the land surface—make up the **biosphere** (BY uh sfeer). The biosphere extends into each of the other spheres.

Figure 6 A view from space shows all four of Earth's spheres—the atmosphere, hydrosphere, biosphere, and lithosphere. *Observing What evidence of each of the spheres can you see in the photograph?*

Section 1 Review

1. What three factors determine the topography of a region?
2. What are the most common types of landforms?
3. Which is larger, a mountain belt or a mountain system?
4. In which of Earth's spheres would you find a cloud? A mountain? A lake? A tree?
5. **Thinking Critically Comparing and Contrasting** How are mountains and plateaus similar? How are they different?

Check Your Progress
CHAPTER PROJECT 1

Choose a site that is as square or rectangular as possible. **CAUTION:** *Make sure to obtain permission from the property owner before you begin.* To start mapping your site, mark the four corners with stakes, stones, or other markers. Measure the boundaries and record the distances on a rough sketch. Your sketch should show your site's topography, plus natural and human-made features. Include a north arrow on your sketch. How can you determine which direction is north?

Answers to Self-Assessment

Caption Question

Figure 6 The photograph shows green continents of the lithosphere and biosphere, oceans of the hydrosphere, and clouds of the atmosphere.

Program Resources

Science Explorer Series *Inside Earth,* Chapter 1, explains more about the lithosphere; *Weather and Climate,* Chapter 1, explains more about the atmosphere; *Earth's Waters,* Chapter 1, explains more about the hydrosphere.

◆ **Teaching Resources** 1-1 Review and Reinforce, p. 15; 1-1 Enrich, p. 16

DISCOVER • ACTIVITY • • • •

How Can You Flatten the Curved Earth?

1. Using a felt-tip pen, make a rough sketch of the outlines of the continents on the surface of an orange or grapefruit.

2. ✂ Using a plastic knife, carefully peel the orange. If possible, keep the peel in one large piece so that the continents remain intact.

3. Try to lay the pieces of orange peel flat on a table.

Think It Over

Observing What happens to the continents when you try to flatten the pieces? What adjustments would you need to make to the shapes of the continents to get them to match their shape and position on a sphere?

You want to invite relatives from out of town to a sports event at your school. You could use words to explain how to find the school: Take the third exit off the highway, turn left at the first traffic light, and so on. But verbal directions can be hard to follow. Instead, you might sketch a map of the best route to your school. Maps use a picture instead of words to tell where things are.

Maps and Globes

Maps and globes show the shape, size, and position of Earth's surface features. A **map** is a model on a flat surface of all or part of Earth's surface as seen from above. A **globe** is a sphere that represents Earth's entire surface. A globe correctly shows the relative size and shape of landmasses and bodies of water, much as if you were viewing Earth from space.

Maps and globes are drawn to scale and use symbols to represent topography and other features on Earth's surface. A map's **scale** relates distance on a map to a distance on Earth's surface. Scale is often given as a ratio. For example, one unit on the map equals 25,000 units on the ground. So one centimeter on the map represents 0.25 kilometers. This scale, "one to twenty-five thousand," would be written "1 : 25,000." Figure 7 shows three ways of giving a map's scale.

GUIDE FOR READING

◆ How do maps and globes represent Earth's surface?

◆ How are latitude and longitude used to locate points on Earth's surface?

Reading Tip Before you read, rewrite the headings in the section as *how, why,* or *what* questions. As you read, look for answers to these questions.

Figure 7 Here are three ways to show scale on a map.

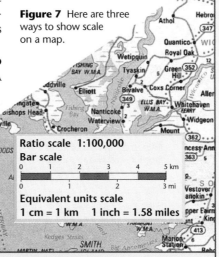

Ratio scale 1:100,000

Bar scale

Equivalent units scale
1 cm = 1 km   1 inch = 1.58 miles

READING STRATEGIES

Reading Tip Students should rewrite the headings in such questions as, "What are maps and globes?" "What is an Earth reference system?" "How are points on Earth's surface located?" "What are map projections?" Encourage students to write an answer to each question as they read through the section, and then use their questions and answers for review of section concepts.

Program Resources

◆ **Teaching Resources** 1-2 Lesson Plan, p. 17; 1-2 Section Summary, p. 18
◆ **Guided Study Workbook** Section 1-2

SECTION
2 Models of Earth

Objectives

After completing the lesson, students will be able to

◆ explain how maps and globes represent Earth's surface and state what a map projection is;

◆ identify the equator and prime meridian and state how latitude and longitude are used to locate points on Earth's surface.

Key Terms   map, globe, scale, symbols, key, equator, hemisphere, prime meridian, degree, latitude, longitude, map projection

1 Engage/Explore

Activating Prior Knowledge

Display a road map of your state, and point out two major cities. Use a ruler to measure the distance between those cities. Then ask: **Is there any relationship between this distance on the map and the real distance in kilometers between these cities?** *(Students may express the concept of proportionality in some way.)* Explain that in this section they will learn how such maps are made to a scale that provides a proportional representation.

• • • • • • • • **DISCOVER** • • • • • • • •

Skills Focus observing
Materials *globe, felt-tip pen, orange or grapefruit, plastic knife*
Time 15 minutes
Tips Have a globe available for students to refer to. Make sure the felt-tip pens are dark enough to make strong lines on the fruit peel. Point out that the continents need only to be roughly sketched.
Expected Outcome In flattening the pieces of peel on the flat surface, the pieces will tear, disconnecting the outlines of the continents.
Think It Over The outlines change as the peel tears. Some may suggest reconnecting the lines, but that would distort the shape of the continents. There is no perfect way to represent the curved space on a flat surface.

2 Facilitate

Maps and Globes

Building Inquiry Skills: Comparing and Contrasting

Materials *globe, pictures of Earth from space*

Time 10 minutes

On a table in a central location, place a globe and photographs of Earth taken from space. (You can find such photos in many books about Earth at a public library as well as in pamphlets published by NASA.) Invite students to examine the photos and compare them to a representation of Earth—a globe. Then call on students to explain similarities and differences. *(Students may mention the covering of clouds in the photographs that is missing from the globe. Landforms may be more exaggerated on the globe.)* **learning modality: visual**

Using the Visuals: Figure 7

Materials *metric ruler, standard ruler*

Time 10 minutes

Have students use their rulers to measure the bar scale on the figure to determine what 1 cm and 1 in represent on the map. *(1 cm = 1 km; 1 in. = 1.58 mi)* Then challenge students to determine the distance in kilometers and miles that the bottom edge of the map represents. *(The bottom edge is about 16 cm and thus represents 16 km; it is also about $6\frac{1}{4}$ in. and thus represents 9.9 mi.)* **learning modality: logical/mathematical**

Building Inquiry Skills: Making Models

Materials *graph paper*

Time 15 minutes

Before class, measure the basic dimensions of the classroom with a tape measure. Provide these measurements to students, and then challenge each student to make a map of the classroom on a piece of graph paper. Students should devise a scale, create a key, and include as many objects as possible in the map. A simple scale might be 3 squares equals 1 m. **learning modality: logical/mathematical**

Mapmakers use pictures called **symbols** to stand for features on Earth's surface. A symbol can represent a physical feature, such as a river, lake, mountain, or plain. A symbol also can stand for a human-made feature, such as a highway, a city, or an airport. A map's **key,** or legend, is a list of all the symbols used on the map with an explanation of their meaning.

Maps also include a compass rose or north arrow. The compass rose helps the map user to relate directions on the map to directions on Earth's surface. North usually is located at the top of the map.

☑ *Checkpoint* *Where can you find the meaning of the symbols on a map?*

Maps and Technology

Centuries ago, people invented instruments for determining compass direction, latitude, and longitude. Mapmakers developed techniques to show Earth's surface accurately.

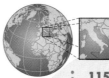

1154 Sicily

The Arab mapmaker Al-Idrisi made several world maps for King Roger of Sicily. Idrisi's maps marked a great advance over other maps of that time. They showed the Arabs' grasp of scientific mapmaking and geography. But unlike modern maps, these maps placed south at the top!

| 1100 | 1200 | 1300 | 1400 |

AROUND 1100 China

Because the needle of a magnetic compass points north, ships at sea could tell direction even when the sun and stars were not visible. Arabs and Europeans adopted this Chinese invention by the 1200s.

AROUND 1300 Spain

Lines representing wind directions criss-crossed a type of map called a portolan chart. These charts also showed coastlines and harbors. A sea captain would use a portolan chart and a compass when sailing from one harbor to another in the Mediterranean Sea.

Background

History of Science The oldest map discovered so far is a clay tablet from about 2300 B.C. The map shows a settlement in a river valley in ancient Babylonia (in present-day Iraq). Ancient Egyptians and ancient Greeks used maps extensively. Ptolemy, a Greek geographer, was the most famous mapmaker of ancient times. Ptolemy's mapmaking ideas had great influence for more than a thousand years.

European voyages of discovery in the 1500s required maps that could show a spherical world on a flat surface. Mercator's solution was to imagine a hollow cylinder around Earth, touching it at the equator. A light at the center of Earth would then "project" the lines of latitude and longitude onto the cylinder. If the cylinder were then unwrapped and laid flat, the result would be the Mercator projection.

An Earth Reference System

When you play chess or checkers, the grid of squares helps you to keep track of where each piece should be. To find a point on Earth's surface, you need a reference system like the grid of squares on a checkerboard. Of course, Earth itself does not have grid lines, but most maps and globes show a grid. The grid is based on two imaginary lines: the equator and the prime meridian.

The Equator Halfway between the North and South poles, the **equator** forms an imaginary line that circles Earth. The equator divides Earth into the Northern and Southern hemispheres. A **hemisphere** (HEH mih sfeer) is one half of the sphere that makes up Earth's surface.

In Your Journal

Choose one period on the time line to learn more about. Use the library to find information about maps in that time. Who used maps? Why were they important? Share what you learn in the form of a letter written by a traveler or explorer who is using a map of that period.

1595 England

To find latitude, sailors used a variety of instruments, including the backstaff. The navigator sighted along the backstaff's straight edge to measure the angle of the sun or North star above the horizon. Later improvements led to modern instruments for navigation.

1684 France

On land, mapmakers developed new ways of measuring land areas accurately. Philippe de La Hire's map of France proved that the country was actually smaller than people had thought. The king of France said that he lost more land because of this map than he would have lost through losing a war.

1500	1600	1700	1800

1569 Belgium

Flemish mapmaker Gerardus Mercator invented the first modern map projection, which bears his name. Mercator and his son, Rumold, also made an atlas and maps of the world such as the one shown below.

1763 England

John Harrison, a carpenter and mechanic, won a prize from the British navy for building a highly accurate clock called a chronometer. Harrison's invention made finding longitudes quicker and easier. With exact longitudes, mapmakers could greatly improve the accuracy of their maps.

Chapter 1   **G ◆ 21**

Answers to Self-Assessment

☑ *Checkpoint*

The meaning of the symbols on a map can be found in the map's key.

G ◆ 21

Locating Points on Earth's Surface

Using the Visuals: Figure 9

Draw a grid on the board to represent the intersections of several streets near the school. Label the streets, and then pose questions to students about stores or other buildings at or near prominent intersections. Direct students' attention to the map showing latitude and longitude. Ask: **What city is near the intersection of 45° N latitude and 15° E longitude?** *(Rome)* Explain that the imaginary grid on a map is as helpful in locating places as the grid of streets is.
learning modality: visual

Materials *globe*
Time 10 minutes
Tips In using the globe, students should find the approximate coordinates or the major city closest to the coordinates.
Expected Outcome The cities are, in order: Guayaquil, Ecuador; Lisbon, Portugal; Osaka, Japan; Buenos Aires, Argentina; Edinburgh, Great Britain; Singapore, Singapore. The word spelled by the cities' first letters is GLOBES.
Extend Challenge students to determine the latitude and longitude for the ten largest cities in the world. (The first step is to find the world's largest cities in an almanac. Then, an atlas can be used to find the coordinates of each.) **learning modality: visual**

Cultural Diversity

Materials *atlas*
Time 15 minutes

Encourage students from diverse parts of the world to use an atlas to find the latitude and longitude of the capital city of the country where they or their parents originated. Write these points on the board. Then invite student volunteers to make a world map for a bulletin board that displays all the points on the list.
learning modality: logical/mathematical

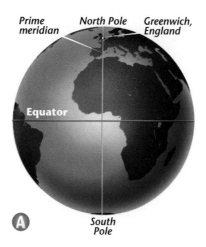

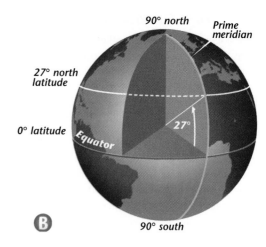

Figure 8 **A.** The equator and the prime meridian divide Earth's surface into hemispheres.
B. Latitude measures distances north or south of the equator.
C. Longitude measures distances east or west of the prime meridian.
D. Cairo, Egypt, is located where the latitude line 30° N crosses the longitude line 31° E.

Where in the World?
Using a globe, determine what city is found at each of the following points:

2° S 79° W
38° N 9° W
34° N 135° E
34° S 58° W
55° N 3° W
1° N 103° E

What word is spelled by the first letters of these city names?

The Prime Meridian Another imaginary line, called the **prime meridian,** makes a half circle from the North Pole to the South Pole. The prime meridian passes through Greenwich, England. Places east of the prime meridian are in the Eastern Hemisphere. Places west of the prime meridian are in the Western Hemisphere.

Measurements on a Sphere To measure distances around a circle, scientists use units called degrees. A **degree** (°) is $\frac{1}{360}$ of the way around a full circle. As you can see in Figure 8, each degree is a measure of the angle formed by lines drawn from the center of Earth to points on the surface. If you started at the prime meridian and traveled west along the equator, you would travel through 360 degrees before returning to your starting point. If you started at the equator and traveled to one of the poles, you would travel 90 degrees—one quarter of the distance in a full circle.

✓ *Checkpoint* *In what two hemispheres is the United States located?*

Locating Points on Earth's Surface

Using the equator and prime meridian, mapmakers have constructed a grid made up of lines of latitude and longitude. **You can use lines of latitude and longitude to find locations anywhere on Earth.**

Latitude The equator is the starting line for measuring **latitude,** or distance in degrees north or south of the equator. Between the equator and both poles are evenly spaced lines called lines of latitude. All lines of latitude are parallel to the equator. Latitude is measured from the equator, which is at 0°. The latitude of each pole is 90° north or 90° south.

Background

History of Science In the 1800s, many countries had their own prime meridians. This caused confusion in both mapping and in determining a standard time. In 1884, a conference of nations agreed that the prime meridian should extend through Greenwich, England. This decision was based both on the great reputation of the Royal Observatory at Greenwich and on Great Britain's importance in that era as a world power. This agreement also established Greenwich Mean Time (GMT) as the standard for international time. Time zones were derived from GMT, which covers 7.5° on either side of the prime meridian. Each time zone covers about 15° (360° ÷ 24 hours). Each day begins at the 180° longitude line, called the International Date Line.

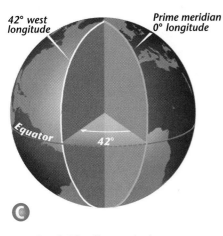

42° west longitude

Prime meridian 0° longitude

Equator

42°

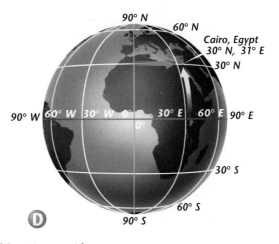

90° N

60° N

Cairo, Egypt 30° N, 31° E

30° N

90° W 60° W 30° W 0° 30° E 60° E 90° E

0°

30° S

60° S

90° S

D

Longitude The distance in degrees east or west of the prime meridian is called **longitude.** There are 360 lines of longitude that run from north to south, meeting at the poles. Each line represents one degree of longitude. The prime meridian, which is the starting line for measuring longitude, is at 0°. Each longitude line crosses the latitude lines, including the equator, at a right angle.

As Figure 9 shows, the longitude lines in each hemisphere are numbered up to 180 degrees. This is one half the total number of degrees in a circle. At 180 degrees east or 180 degrees west lies a single longitude line directly opposite the prime meridian.

Figure 9 Every point on Earth's surface has a particular latitude and longitude. *Interpreting Maps What are the latitude and longitude of New Orleans? Of Sydney?*

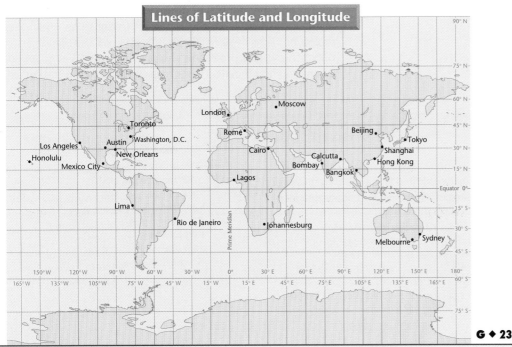

Lines of Latitude and Longitude

90° N

Moscow

London

75° N

Toronto

Los Angeles Austin Washington, D.C. Rome Beijing 60° N

Honolulu New Orleans Cairo Tokyo 45° N

Mexico City Calcutta Shanghai 30° N

Bombay Hong Kong

Bangkok 15° N

Lagos

Equator 0°

Lima

15° S

Rio de Janeiro Johannesburg

30° S

Melbourne Sydney

45° S

150° W 120° W 90° W 60° W 30° W 0° 30° E 60° E 90° E 120° E 150° E 180°

165° W 135° W 105° W 75° W 45° W 15° W 15° E 45° E 75° E 105° E 135° E 165° E 60° S

75° S

G ◆ 23

Answers to Self-Assessment

Caption Question

Figure 9 New Orleans is at 30° N 90° W; Sydney is at about 34° S 150° E.

☑ *Checkpoint*

The United States is in both the Northern Hemisphere and the Western Hemisphere.

Materials *atlas, encyclopedia*

Time 1 day for research; 20 minutes to prepare a report

Form pairs of students with different learning abilities, and have each pair choose a map in an atlas, encyclopedia, or some other reference book. Encourage students to select a map that shows an interesting part of the world or includes symbols that explain something about the area. Students should make a photocopy of the map and write a description of what the map shows, what its scale is, and what symbols are in its key. Invite several pairs to present their maps to the class. **cooperative learning**

Map Projections

Demonstration

Materials *globe, construction paper*

Time 10 minutes

To show how a Mercator projection distorts areas near the poles, set up a globe so that its poles are perpendicular to the floor. Then form a cylinder around the globe with construction paper, with the paper touching the globe only at the equator. Invite a student volunteer to draw a line on the outside of the paper that corresponds to the equator. Then invite another volunteer to draw similar lines that correspond to 70° N and 70° S. A third volunteer can trace the outline of one or two continents. Unwrap the cylinder and have students compare the lines on the flat paper with those on the globe. **learning modality: visual**

Ongoing Assessment

Drawing Have students make a simple labeled drawing of Earth that shows the equator, the prime meridian, the names of the hemispheres, two lines of latitude, and two lines of longitude.

G ◆ 23

Map Projections, continued

Inquiry Challenge

Time 15 minutes

ACTIVITY

Challenge groups to create a map projection that incorporates the best features of a Mercator projection and an equal-area projection. Once groups have made their maps, have them evaluate these maps against the Robinson projection in Figure 10, on page 58 in Chapter 2, which is just such a compromise. **learning modality: logical/mathematical**

3 Assess

Section 2 Review Answers

1. A map's scale relates the distance on the map to a distance on Earth's surface.
2. Latitude measures the distance in degrees north and south of the equator; longitude measures the distance in degrees east and west of the prime meridian.
3. The advantage of an equal-area projection is that it correctly shows the relative sizes of Earth's landmasses. The disadvantage is that the shapes of landmasses near the edges of the map appear stretched and curved.
4. Flying due east from New Orleans at 90° W you would travel 210 degrees to Shanghai at 120° E: 90 degrees to the prime meridian and 120 degrees more to Shanghai. Flying west you would travel 150 degrees: 90 degrees to 180° longitude and 60 degrees more to Shanghai.

> **Check Your Progress** **CHAPTER PROJECT 1**
>
> Help students who are having trouble making a scale for their maps. Encourage them to return to the site for more measurements if they measured only the boundaries. Provide samples of different kinds of maps.

Performance Assessment

Skills Check Assign a city to every student, and challenge them to use a map to describe everything they can about that city, including latitude and longitude and the hemispheres it is in.

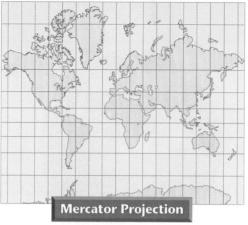

Mercator Projection   **Equal-Area Projection**

Figure 10 On a Mercator projection (left), lines of longitude are parallel, so shapes near the poles are distorted. An equal-area projection (right) shows areas correctly, but distorts some shapes around its edges. *Comparing and Contrasting Why does Greenland appear larger on the Mercator projection than on the equal-area projection?*

Map Projections

To show Earth's curved surface on a flat map, mapmakers use map projections. A **map projection** is a framework of lines that helps to show landmasses on a flat surface.

On a Mercator projection, the lines of latitude and longitude all appear as straight, parallel lines that form a rectangle. On a Mercator projection, the size and shape of landmasses near the equator are distorted only a little. But as you go toward the poles, size and shape become more and more distorted. The reason for this distortion is that the lines of longitude do not come together at the poles as they do on a globe. As you can see in Figure 10, this projection also changes the relative sizes of landmasses.

To solve the problem of distortion on Mercator projections, mapmakers developed equal-area projections. An equal-area projection correctly shows the relative sizes of Earth's landmasses. But an equal-area projection also has distortion. The shapes of landmasses near the edges of the map appear stretched and curved.

Section 2 Review

1. What information does a map's scale provide?
2. What do latitude and longitude each measure?
3. What are the advantages and disadvantages of an equal-area projection?
4. **Thinking Critically** **Measuring** Look at the map in Figure 9. If you fly due east from New Orleans, through how many degrees of longitude must you travel to reach Shanghai? If you flew west from New Orleans, how many degrees of longitude would you pass before reaching Shanghai? Explain.

> **Check Your Progress** **CHAPTER PROJECT 1**
>
> Choose an appropriate scale for your map. Make a list of the types of natural and human-made features for which you will need symbols. Examine the samples of maps in the chapter and those provided by your teacher. Brainstorm ideas for symbols to include. If possible, return to your site and add more detail to your map.

Answers to Self-Assessment

Caption Question

Figure 10 The Mercator projection distorts size and shape of landmasses near the poles, while the equal-area projection correctly shows the relative sizes of Earth's landmasses.

Program Resources

◆ **Teaching Resources** 1-2 Review and Reinforce, p. 19; 1-2 Enrich, p. 20

A Borderline Case

You may have wondered how people first decided where to locate the borders between states.

Problem

Which was more important in locating state borders: lines of latitude and longitude or physical features?

Skills Focus

drawing conclusions, observing, inferring

Materials

United States map with latitude, longitude, and state borders

tracing paper   paper clips   colored pencils

Procedure

1. Lay a sheet of tracing paper on top of a map of the United States.
2. Trace over the Pacific and Atlantic coasts of the United States with a blue pencil.
3. Using the blue pencil, trace all Great Lakes shorelines that reach nearby states.
4. Trace all state borders that go exactly north-south with a red pencil. (*Hint:* Some straight-line borders that appear to run north-south, such as the western border of Maine, do not follow lines of longitude.)
5. Use a green pencil to trace all state borders or sections of state borders that go exactly east-west. (*Hint:* Straight-line borders that are slanted, such as the southern border of Nevada, do not follow lines of latitude.)
6. Now use a blue pencil to trace the borders that follow rivers.
7. Use a brown pencil to trace any borders that are not straight lines or rivers.

Analyze and Conclude

1. How many state boundaries are completely defined by longitude and latitude? How many are partially defined by longitude and latitude?
2. What feature is used to define a state border when longitude and latitude are not used? Give examples of specific states.
3. Study the physical map of the United States in Appendix B. What other physical features are used to define borders? Which state borders are defined by these features?
4. Which was used more often in locating state borders: longitude or latitude?
5. How many states do not use longitude and latitude for the location of their borders?
6. **Apply** In which region of the country were lines of latitude and longitude most important in determining state borders? What do you think is the reason for this?

More to Explore

Research the history of your state to find out when and how its borders were established. Are your state's borders based on longitude and latitude, landforms and topography, or both?

Review a map of your county or state. Are any features, other than the state's border, related to longitude and latitude? Which features seem to follow landforms and topography?

A Borderline Case

Preparing for Inquiry

Key Concept Lines of latitude and longitude were used to draw the boundaries between many states.

Skills Objectives Students will be able to
◆ infer which state borders were drawn according to latitude and longitude;
◆ draw conclusions about what people used to locate borders between states.

Time 30 minutes

Advance Planning Make sure appropriate maps are available for all students. Gather tracing paper and pencils a day in advance.

Troubleshooting the Experiment

◆ If students do not have the colors called for in the procedure, advise them to make a color key at the bottom of their traced map.
◆ In some cases, students may have trouble deciding whether a border was drawn to a line of latitude or longitude. Advise them to make the best inference they can.

Expected Outcome

Students should be able to infer the basis for most state boundaries, whether lines of latitude and longitude or prominent physical features.

Extending the Inquiry

More to Explore Have students study a state map before they begin their research and make predictions about the basis on which the state borders were drawn. They can then use encyclopedias, maps, and state history books to confirm or invalidate their predictions.

Analyze and Conclude

1. Three states completely defined are Wyoming, Colorado, and Utah. All other states except those listed for Question 5 are partially defined.
2. Rivers are most often used, such as between Ohio and Kentucky.

3. A lake is used between New York and Vermont. Mountain ranges are also used, such as between Virginia and West Virginia. Oceans form borders of states on the coasts.
4. Latitude
5. Eight states—Hawaii, Delaware, New Jersey, and five of the New England states (except Maine)
6. The states west of the Mississippi make most use of latitude and longitude probably because the borders of these states were established by government surveys—but accept all reasonable responses.

Program Resources

◆ **Teaching Resources** Real-World Lab blackline masters, pp. 29–31

Media and Technology

 Lab Activity Videotape
Earth's Changing Surface, 1

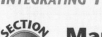
SECTION 3 Maps in the Computer Age

Objective

After completing the lesson, students will be able to
◆ describe how satellites and computers are used in mapmaking.

Key Terms satellite image, pixel, digitizing

1 Engage/Explore

Activating Prior Knowledge

Remind students that artificial satellites are launched to orbit Earth. Ask: **What functions do these satellites perform?** (*Students may mention a variety of functions, such as military spying and the collection of weather data.*) Explain that some satellites record data about Earth's surface and that these data are used to make maps.

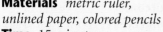

Skills Focus predicting
Materials *metric ruler, unlined paper, colored pencils*
Time 15 minutes
Tips Advise students to begin by drawing a horizontal line 6 cm long, marking each centimeter length along that line. Next they should draw a perpendicular line up from the left edge of the first line, marking each centimeter length along that line. When they complete the square and draw lines from each centimeter mark to the mark on the opposite line, they will have made a grid of 36 squares. You may want to provide a sheet of graph paper to each student to test their predictions.
Expected Outcome Students' will observe that the pixel picture and the original have a similar though not identical shape.
Think It Over If the squares remain the same size, then the smaller object will look less like the original. Conversely, using the smaller squares on graph paper would make the pixel picture look more like the original.

SECTION 3 Maps in the Computer Age

DISCOVER · ACTIVITY

Can You Make a Pixel Picture?

1. With a pencil, draw a square grid of lines spaced 1 centimeter apart. The grid should have 6 squares on each side.

2. On the grid, draw the outline of a simple object, such as an apple.

3. Using a different color pencil, fill in all squares that are completely inside the apple. If a square is mostly inside the apple, fill it in completely. If it is mostly outside, leave it blank.

4. Each square on your grid represents one pixel, or bit of information, about your picture. Looking at your pixel picture, can you recognize the shape you started with?

Think It Over
Predicting How would the pixel picture change if you drew the object smaller? How would the pixel picture look if you used graph paper with squares that are smaller than your grid?

GUIDE FOR READING

◆ How are satellites and computers used in mapmaking?

Reading Tip Before you read, preview Figures 12 and 13. In your notebook, describe how you think computers may have affected mapmaking.

Figure 11 A satellite image is made up of many pixels. This enlargement of a satellite image shows Tampa Bay and St. Petersburg, Florida.

For centuries, mapmakers slowly gathered data and then drew maps by hand. Explorers made maps by sketching coastlines as seen from their ships. Mapmakers sometimes drew the land based on reports from people who had traveled there. More accurate maps were made by locating points on the surface in a process called surveying.

During the twentieth century, people learned to make highly accurate maps using photographs taken from airplanes. These photographs are called aerial photographs. Aerial photographs are still important in many types of mapmaking.

Since the 1970s, information gathered by satellites has revolutionized mapmaking. Powerful computers use the satellite data to make maps quickly and accurately.

Satellite Mapping

Beginning in 1972, the United States launched a series of Landsat satellites designed to observe Earth's surface. Landsat uses electronic devices to collect information about the land surface in the form of computer data. **Satellite images** are pictures of the surface based on these data. As Landsat orbits Earth, it collects and stores information about a strip of the surface that is

---

READING STRATEGIES

Reading Tip For Figure 12, a typical prediction might suggest that computers have made it possible to send pictures from space, and maps can be made from those pictures. For Figure 13, a typical prediction might suggest that computers have made mapmaking faster and easier than before.

Vocabulary Call students' attention to the key term *digitizing* on page 28. Explain that a *digit* is any of the Arabic number symbols, 0 through 9. Because computer languages are based on combinations of the digits 0 and 1, entering data into a computer is a process of converting that data into numbers, or "digitizing." Students may have heard of the "digital revolution," which is a way of saying that many technologies now depend on computers.

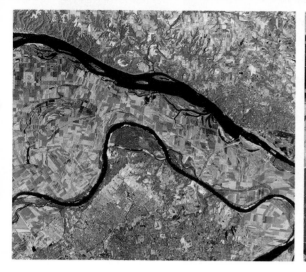
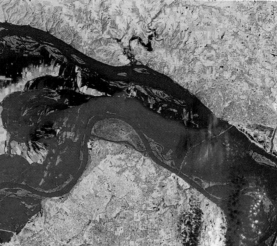

Figure 12 Landsat made these images of part of the Mississippi and Missouri rivers. They show an area just north of St. Louis, before (left) and during (right) a flood in 1993. The Mississippi is the wider river in each image. In both images, north is at the top.
Inferring What can you infer about the relief of the land between the Mississippi and Missouri rivers?

185 kilometers wide. The satellite relays the data back to a station on Earth, where computers create images of the surface.

Pictures made by Landsat show what covers the land surface—plants, soil, sand, rock, water, or snow and ice. Large human-made features, such as cities, are also visible.

Printing Satellite Images Unlike a photograph, a satellite image is made up of thousands of tiny dots called **pixels.** A painting made of pixels would have many separate dots of color. Each pixel in a satellite image contains information on the color and brightness of a small part of Earth's surface. This information is stored on a computer as a series of 0's and 1's. When the satellite image is printed, the computer translates these numbers into colors.

Interpreting Satellite Images Scientists learn to identify 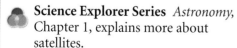 INTEGRATING ENVIRONMENTAL SCIENCE specific features by the "signature," or combination of colors and shapes, that the feature makes on a satellite image. In a satellite image, areas covered by grass, trees, or crops are often shown as red, water as black or blue, and cities as bluish gray. Landsat images may show features such as grasslands, forests, and agricultural crops, as well as desert areas, mountains, or cities. By comparing one image with another made at an earlier time, scientists can see changes due to drought, forest fires, or floods. Figure 12 shows satellite images taken before and during a flood in the Mississippi River valley.

✓ *Checkpoint* *What information does a pixel in a satellite image contain?*

Program Resources

- **Science Explorer Series** *Astronomy,* Chapter 1, explains more about satellites.
- ◆ **Teaching Resources** 1-3 Lesson Plan, p. 21; 1-3 Section Summary, p. 22
- ◆ **Guided Study Workbook** Section 1-3

Answers to Self-Assessment

Caption Question

Figure 12 You can infer that the relief is very low, because the image during the flood shows that the land is covered with water.

✓ *Checkpoint*

Each pixel contains information on the color and brightness of a small part of Earth's surface.

2 Facilitate

Satellite Mapping

Using the Visuals: Figure 11

Explain that *pixel* is an abbreviation for "picture element." Ask: **How would you describe this satellite image?** *(It is made up of small areas that differ in color and brightness.)* Explain that each of these small areas is made up of pixels. Also point out that although this picture may be difficult to interpret, an expert is able to see important features of the area.
learning modality: visual

Building Inquiry Skills: Drawing Conclusions

Materials *colored pencils, paper, magazine pictures*
Time 15 minutes

Give each student a photo of a landscape from a magazine. Then challenge students to make an image that is similar to their photos using only colored dots on a piece of paper. Display some of the pictures and ask: **Are pixels enough to make a recognizable image?** *(Students should draw the conclusion that they are enough.)* To emphasize the concept, show students a photo of a painting by the French artist Georges Seurat, who painted with small dabs of paint.
learning modality: visual

 Integrating Environmental Science

Explain that Landsat satellites collect data about where and how much rainforests are shrinking due to fires and clearing for agriculture. Ask students: **How could the collection of such data help prevent environmental disaster in the future?** *(Scientists would have the information to warn the public and governments where too much forest is being lost.)* **learning modality: logical/mathematical**

Ongoing Assessment

Skills Check Have students create a flowchart that shows the steps involved from the collection of data by a satellite to the printing of a satellite image.

Computer Mapping

Using the Visuals: Figure 13

Ask students: **What could this mapmaker be doing that involves digitizing?** *(She could be converting map points into numbers by entering their locations into the computer.)* **learning modality: visual**

3 Assess

Section 3 Review Answers

1. Landsat uses electronic devices to collect information about the land surface in the form of computer data. The satellite relays the data back to a station on Earth, where computers create images of the surface.

2. Computers can display maps on a computer screen or printed out. Computers can also automatically create three-dimensional views.

3. Mapmakers convert the location of map points to numbers in a process called digitizing.

4. Answers may vary. A typical answer might mention how mapmakers using computers can produce maps quickly and easily and how satellites can produce accurate images of Earth's surface.

Science at Home

Tips Students might find a variety of maps, including weather maps, political maps of areas of world interest, and any number of specialized maps, such as those showing population or distribution of natural resources. Review some of these kinds of maps in class, and then encourage students to convey their knowledge to family members at home.

Performance Assessment

Writing Have students explain in their own words how satellites and computers are changing mapmaking.

28 ◆ G

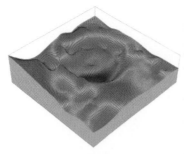

Figure 13 Today computers are an essential tool in making accurate maps. A computer produced the digital model shown above.

Computer Mapping

With computers, mapmakers have new ways of storing and displaying map data. Computer mapmakers use up-to-the-minute data to produce maps quickly and easily.

All of the data used in computer mapping must be in numbers, just like the pixels in a satellite image. The process by which mapmakers convert the location of map points to numbers is called **digitizing.** Once the map data have been digitized, they can be displayed on a computer screen, modified, and printed out in map form.

Computers can automatically create three-dimensional views that might take a person hundreds of hours to draw by hand. The computer image in Figure 13, for example, was made to help geologists search for oil.

Section 3 Review

1. Describe how Landsat collects data about Earth's surface.
2. What are the two ways in which computers are useful in making maps?
3. How are the data for a map put in a form that a computer can use?
4. **Thinking Critically** **Making Generalizations** In your own words, describe how computers and satellites have improved the accuracy of maps.

Science at Home

Most of the maps that you see today in newspapers and magazines are made using computers. With family members look through newspapers and news magazines. How many different types of maps can you find? Explain to your family the map's scale, symbols, and key. After you have studied the map, try to state the main point of the information shown on the map.

28 ◆ G

Background

Facts and Figures Digitizing is essentially a way of putting map information into a computer. This is often done by hand, using a mouse or similar tool to trace everything on an existing map, such as roads and boundaries. For a topographic map, digitizing involves tracing all contour lines and entering all symbols and figures. In some cases, these tasks can be accomplished with a scanner.

Program Resources

◆ **Teaching Resources** 1-3 Review and Reinforce, p. 23; 1-3 Enrich, p. 24

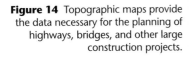 **DISCOVER** •••ACTIVITY••••

Can a Map Show Relief?

1. ✂ Carefully cut the corners off 8 pieces of cardboard so that they look rounded. Each piece should be at least 1 centimeter smaller than the one before.

2. Trim the long sides of the two largest pieces so that the long sides appear wavy. Don't cut any more than one-half centimeter into the cardboard.

3. Trace the largest cardboard piece on a sheet of paper.

4. Trace the next largest piece inside the tracing of the first. Don't let any lines cross.

5. Trace the other cardboard pieces, from largest to smallest, one inside the other, on the same paper.

6. Stack the cardboard pieces in the same order they were traced beside the paper. Compare the stack of cardboard pieces with your drawing. How are they alike? How are they different?

Think It Over
Making Models If the cardboard pieces are a model of a landform, what do the lines on the paper represent?

You are an engineer planning a route for a highway over a mountain pass. You need to consider many different factors. To design a safe highway, you need a route that avoids the steepest slopes. To protect the area's water supply, the highway must stay a certain distance from rivers and lakes. You also want to find a route that avoids houses and other buildings. How would you find the best route? You could start by studying a topographic map.

Mapping Earth's Topography

A **topographic map** is a map showing the surface features of an area. Topographic maps use symbols to portray the land as if you were looking down on it from above. **Topographic maps provide highly accurate information on the elevation, relief, and slope of the ground surface.**

> **GUIDE FOR READING**
>
> ◆ What is a topographic map?
> ◆ How do mapmakers represent elevation, relief, and slope?
> ◆ What is the Global Positioning System?
>
> *Reading Tip* As you read, make a list of main ideas and supporting details about topographic maps.

Figure 14 Topographic maps provide the data necessary for the planning of highways, bridges, and other large construction projects.

SECTION
4 Topographic Maps

Objectives

After completing the lesson, students will be able to
◆ describe a topographic map;
◆ explain how elevation, relief, and slope are shown on topographic maps;
◆ identify the Global Positioning System.

Key Terms topographic map, contour line, contour interval, Global Positioning System

1 Engage/Explore

Activating Prior Knowledge

Draw a large circle on the board. Then draw a circle inside the first circle, another circle inside the second circle, and another inside the third circle. Write numbers on the circles: 10 on the outermost, 20 on the circle inside that, and so on. Ask: **What do the numbers suggest about this shape?** *(Many students will infer that the numbers suggest height and thus also infer that the circles represent a hill as seen from above.)*

•••••••• **DISCOVER** •••••••••

Skills Focus making models

Materials *scissors, 8 pieces of cardboard of increasing dimensions, metric ruler, unlined paper*
Time 20 minutes
Tips Cut the cardboard pieces in advance. Suggested sizes of cardboard squares, in centimeters: 4×4, 6×8, 8×10, 10×12, 12×14, 16×18, 18×22, 20×26. The thicker the cardboard, the better.
Expected Outcome Students will trace a series of lines that finally show the "topography" that results when the cardboard pieces are stacked.
Think It Over Answers may vary. A typical answer might suggest that the lines represent lines around the stack at various heights.

2 Facilitate

Mapping Earth's Topography

Math TOOLBOX

Tips Because the figures in the calculation are so large, provide access to a calculator for those students who don't have one. Make sure students understand how to convert between units in the metric system.

Expected Outcome The distance in kilometers is 5,875,000 ÷ 100,000 = 58.75. Have students round to the nearest tenth, or 58.8 km.

Extend Provide problems for students to solve with the scales used by the USGS on topographic maps. *Examples:* **1.** Find the actual distance in kilometers on a map with a scale of 1:24,000 between two points that are 13.2 cm apart. *(1/24,000 = 13.2 cm/d, 1 × d = 24,000 × 13.2, d = 316,800 cm, or 3.2 km)* **2.** Find the actual distance in kilometers on a map with a scale of 1:25,000 between two points that are 25.6 cm apart. *(1/25,000 = 25.6 cm/d, 1 × d = 25,000 × 25.6, d = 640,000 cm, or 6.4 km)* **learning modality: logical/mathematical**

Using the Visuals: Figure 15

After students have examined the symbols, ask: **Which of these symbols could you recognize even without an explanation?** *(Students might mention the symbols for church, campground, divided highway, and railroad tracks.)* Explain that the symbols were created to make sense even to those who have no specialized knowledge. Ask: **Are the symbols for woods and built-up areas always a rectangle?** *(No, these symbols are showing what the colors on the maps mean. Green is used for wooded areas, while gray or pink is used for built-up areas.)* **What can you infer about topographic maps from the last three symbols on the table?** *(Topographic maps are used for watery areas as well as for land.)* **learning modality: visual**

Math TOOLBOX

Scale and Ratios

A ratio compares two numbers by division. For example, the scale of a map given as a ratio is 1 : 250,000. At this scale, the distance between two points on the map measures 23.5 cm. How would you find the actual distance? Begin by writing the scale as a fraction.

$$\frac{1}{250,000}$$

Next, write a proportion. Let d represent the actual distance between the two points.

$$\frac{1}{250,000} = \frac{23.5 \text{ cm}}{d}$$

Then write the cross products.

$$1 \times d = 250,000 \times 23.5 \text{ cm}$$
$$d = 5,875,000 \text{ cm}$$

(*Hint:* To convert cm to km, divide d by 100,000.)

Figure 15 Maps made by the U. S. Geological Survey use more than 150 symbols.

Uses of Topographic Maps People find many uses for topographic maps. Businesses use them to help decide where to build new stores, housing, or factories. Cities and towns use them to decide where to build new schools. Topographic maps have recreational uses, too. If you were planning a bicycle trip, you could use a topographic map to see whether your trip would be flat or hilly.

Scale Topographic maps usually are large-scale maps. A large-scale map is one that shows a close-up view of part of Earth's surface. In the United States, most topographic maps are at a scale of 1 : 24,000, or 1 centimeter equals 0.24 kilometers. At this scale, a map can show the details of elevation and features such as rivers and coastlines. Large buildings, airports, and major highways appear as outlines at the correct scale. Symbols are used to show houses and other small features.

Coverage Most nations have a government agency that is responsible for making topographic maps. In the United States, that agency is the U. S. Geological Survey, or USGS. The USGS has produced about 57,000 topographic maps at scales of either 1 : 24,000 or 1 : 25,000. The maps cover all of the United States, except for parts of Alaska. Each map covers an area of roughly 145 square kilometers.

Symbols Mapmakers use a great variety of symbols on topographic maps. If you were drawing a map, what symbols would you use to represent woods, a campground, an orchard, a swamp, or a school? Look at Figure 15 to see the symbols that the USGS uses for these and other features.

☑ *Checkpoint* *In the United States, what agency is responsible for producing topographic maps?*

Commonly Used Map Symbols

Symbol		Symbol		Symbol	
Contour line: elevation	⬭	Primary highway	▬▬	River	〰
Contour line: depression	⬭	Secondary highway	▬ ▬	Stream	⌇
Building	■ □ ▦ ▨	Divided highway	▬▬	Waterfall or rapids	▨
School; church	⚑ ⛪	Railroad tracks	┼┼┼	Marsh or swamp	⠿
Built-up area	▨ ▨	Airport	✕	Rock or coral reef	Reef
Campground; picnic area	⛺ ⛱	Woods	▨	Breakwater; wharf	⌐⌐
Cemetery	Cem	Orchard	⁞⁞⁞	Exposed wreck	⛵

Background

Facts and Figures Many USGS topographic maps are at a scale of 1 : 24,000, or 1 in. = 2,000 ft. These maps are known as 7.5-minute quadrangle maps, because each covers a rectangle of 7.5 minutes of latitude and 7.5 minutes of longitude. (There are 60 minutes in each degree of latitude and longitude.) Maps for Alaska cover double that area; the scale is 1 : 63,360, or 1 in. = 1 mi.

The larger the scale of a map, the smaller the area covered. Thus, a large-scale map shows more detail than a small-scale map. Maps with scales larger than 1 : 63,360 are considered large-scale maps; small-scale maps are those with scales smaller than 1 : 1,000,000. Maps with scales in between are called medium-scale maps.

Figure 16 The contour lines on a topographic map represent elevation and relief. *Comparing and Contrasting What information does the topographic map provide that the photograph does not?*

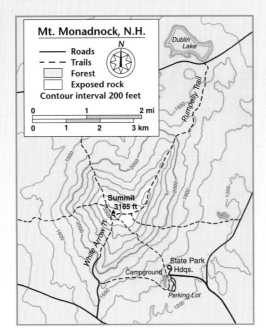

Mt. Monadnock, N.H.

— Roads
--- Trails
☐ Forest
☐ Exposed rock
Contour interval 200 feet

0   1   2 mi
0   1   2   3 km

Dublin Lake

Pumpelly Trail

White Arrow Tr.

Summit
3165 ft

State Park
Hdqs.

Campground

Parking Lot

Showing Relief on Topographic Maps

To represent elevation, relief, and slope on topographic maps, mapmakers use contour lines. On a topographic map, a **contour line** connects points of equal elevation.

The change in elevation from contour line to contour line is called the **contour interval.** The contour interval for a given map is always the same. For example, the map in Figure 16 has a contour interval of 200 feet. If you start at one contour line and count up 10 contour lines, you have reached an elevation 2,000 feet above where you started. Usually, every fifth contour line is darker and heavier than the others. These lines are labeled with the elevation in round units, such as 1,600 or 2,000 feet above sea level. Most USGS maps give contour intervals in feet rather than meters.

Looking at a topographic map with many squiggly contour lines, you may feel as if you are gazing into a bowl of spaghetti. But if you follow the rules listed in *Exploring Topographic Maps* on the following page, you can learn to read contour lines. Reading contour lines is the first step toward "seeing" an area's topography by looking at a topographic map.

EXPLORING

Topographic Maps

Call on students to read the descriptions of the various features on the map and explain what the contour interval is. Students should practice finding high and low points on the map, steep and gentle slopes, and ridges and valleys. Also, have students use rulers to measure the scale and determine how much area the map covers. **learning modality: logical/mathematical**

Building Inquiry Skills: Making Models

Materials *topographic map, modeling compound, board*

Time 20 minutes

To reinforce how a topographic map represents elevation and relief, divide students into small groups and provide each group with a topographic map. Then challenge each group to make a three-dimensional model of a section of the map that contains more than one feature. **learning modality: kinesthetic**

Global Positioning System

Integrating Technology

Direct students' attention to Figure 17 and ask: What is the advantage of positioning with three satellites instead of only one? *(Since each satellite is in a different orbit, each has a different angle on Earth's surface. The point at which the different angles intersect pinpoints the location.)* Explain that this is similar to how geologists find the epicenter of an earthquake by using data from three different points. **learning modality: visual**

EXPLORING *Topographic Maps*

Topographic maps provide data on elevation, relief, slopes, and the shapes of landforms. This USGS map shows part of Tennessee.

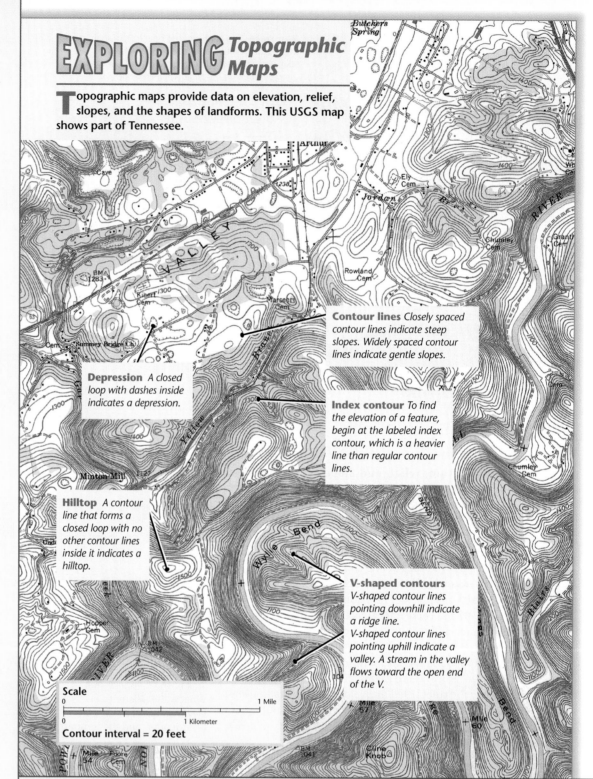

Contour lines *Closely spaced contour lines indicate steep slopes. Widely spaced contour lines indicate gentle slopes.*

Depression *A closed loop with dashes inside indicates a depression.*

Index contour *To find the elevation of a feature, begin at the labeled index contour, which is a heavier line than regular contour lines.*

Hilltop *A contour line that forms a closed loop with no other contour lines inside it indicates a hilltop.*

V-shaped contours *V-shaped contour lines pointing downhill indicate a ridge line. V-shaped contour lines pointing uphill indicate a valley. A stream in the valley flows toward the open end of the V.*

Scale

0 ———————— 1 Mile

0 ———————— 1 Kilometer

Contour interval = 20 feet

Background

History of Science The USGS was founded in 1879. Until the aerial photography of the 1930s, most maps were made using plane table surveying. A topographer would climb to the top of an area's highest point carrying a plane table, a drawing board on a tripod with a sighting device attached. Then, the topographer would sketch any prominent features that could be seen. Since the 1930s, aerial photography has been central to the making of these maps. For each area, two photographs are used, taken from different angles. The planes always fly at a certain altitude to make sure the scale remains the same. But the USGS doesn't rely exclusively on photos. Field workers on the ground carefully determine the position and elevation of particular points on the ground. These control points help mapmakers position map features accurately.

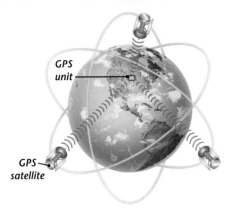

GPS unit

GPS satellite

Figure 17 The GPS network includes 24 satellites. Three satellites (left) must be above the horizon to pinpoint the location of the user (right). The user's latitude and longitude appear on the screen of a portable GPS unit like the one in the photograph.

Global Positioning System

 INTEGRATING TECHNOLOGY Today, surveyors, pilots, and mapmakers around the world rely on the **Global Positioning System,** or GPS, to determine locations precisely. **The Global Positioning System is a method of finding latitude, longitude, and elevation of points on Earth's surface using a network of satellites.** At any given moment, there are between five and eight GPS satellites above the horizon in a given area. A hand-held unit the size of a cellular phone picks up signals broadcast by these satellites. A computer inside the GPS unit then calculates the user's location and elevation.

Engineers can use GPS to locate points on the ground for a construction project. Airplanes, ships, and hikers can use GPS to navigate. Some cars now contain both a GPS unit and a digital road map stored in a computer. Using GPS, the computer determines the car's location and suggests a route to your destination.

Section 4 Review

1. What kind of information does a topographic map provide about landforms?
2. How do topographic maps represent elevation and relief?
3. What would the highest and lowest points in an area look like on a topographic map?
4. What is the role of satellites in the Global Positioning System?
5. **Thinking Critically Interpreting Maps** Look at the map on page 32. Where is the highest elevation? Where do you find the steepest slopes? The gentlest slopes?

Check Your Progress

CHAPTER PROJECT 1

On a large piece of paper, draw your map to scale. Locate all natural and human-made features on the map using the measurements you recorded on your rough sketch and the symbols you brainstormed earlier. Include a north arrow, a legend, and scale on your map. Show the topography of the land by using contour lines or other symbols that show how the land slopes.

Section 4 Review Answers

1. A topographic map provides information on the elevation, relief, and slope of the ground surface of an area.
2. Topographic maps represent elevation and relief with contour lines.
3. The highest point would be a closed loop with no other lines inside it that is surrounded by more contour lines than any other on the map. If the lowest point is a depression, it would be shown as a closed loop with dashes inside. Otherwise, the lowest point would be in the area below the lowest contour line. Often, the lowest point on a map is the surface of a lake, river, or the ocean.
4. A network of satellites broadcast signals that can be picked up by a hand-held unit with a computer inside that can calculate a user's location and elevation.
5. The highest elevation is Cline Knob, at about 1,840 feet, near the bottom of the page. The steepest slopes are the sides of the valley through which the river flows. The gentlest slopes are in the upper left area of the map.

Check Your Progress

CHAPTER PROJECT 1

Review each student's work up to this point. Make sure all students have made a scale and an initial sketch, brainstormed a list of symbols to use, and begun thinking about making the final map. Talk with students about how to show the topography at their site on the map. Encourage students to make a revised map if the first one does not turn out the way they envisioned it would.

Program Resources

◆ **Teaching Resources** 1-4 Review and Reinforce, p. 27; 1-4 Enrich, p. 28

Media and Technology

Transparencies "Exploring Topographic Maps," Transparency 4

Performance Assessment

Writing Provide each student with a section of a topographic map, then challenge students to describe all the information they can interpret from the map.

G ◆ 33

A Map in a Pan

Preparing for Inquiry

Key Concept A mapmaker can represent a three-dimensional landform on a two-dimensional topographic map.

Skills Objectives Students will be able to
◆ measure the depth of water in the bottom of a pan;
◆ make a two-dimensional model of a three-dimensional model hill;
◆ compare and contrast a topographic map with the model landform from which it was made.

Time 40 minutes

Advance Planning An aluminum baking pan is a good choice for the deep-sided pan; gather enough pans for each student or group. Cut a rectangular piece of clear plastic for each student or group. This plastic is available at building or hardware stores; it could be cut to order or cut from large sheets with a utility knife. The activity can be done with clear tap water, but water colored with food coloring is easier to see. Prepare enough colored water ahead of time.

Alternative Materials Alternatives to the deep-sided baking pan include an aquarium, a plastic shoebox, or a metal box. If clear, hard plastic is unavailable, students can use clear plastic wrap, though they will have to be very precise in its placement each time.

Guiding Inquiry

Introducing the Procedure
◆ Give students time to read the whole procedure. Then ask: **What will the outline you trace onto the plastic become on the sheet of paper?** *(contour lines)*
◆ **How will adding 1 cm of water each time be reflected on the map you make?** *(The addition of 1 cm will become a 1-cm contour interval between contour lines on the map.)*

Troubleshooting the Experiment
◆ Encourage students to be creative in making the shape of the clay hill, such as by varying the steepness of the slopes.

A Map in a Pan

A topographic map is a two-dimensional model of three-dimensional landforms.

Problem

How can you make a topographic map?

Materials

deep-sided pan
marking pencil
clear, hard sheet of plastic
sheet of unlined white paper

water
modeling clay
metric ruler
food coloring

Procedure

1. Place a lump of clay on the bottom of a deep-sided pan. Shape the clay into a model of a hill.
2. Pour colored water into the pan to a depth of 1 centimeter to represent sea level.
3. Place a sheet of hard, clear plastic over the container.
4. Trace the outline of the pan on the plastic sheet with a marking pencil. Then, looking straight down into the pan, trace the outline the water makes around the edges of the clay model. Remove the plastic sheet from the pan.

5. Add another centimeter of water to the pan, bringing the depth of the water to 2 centimeters. Replace the plastic sheet exactly as before, then trace the water level again.
6. Repeat Step 5 several times. Stop when the next addition of water would completely cover your model.
7. Remove the plastic sheet. Trace the outlines that you drew on the plastic sheet onto a sheet of paper.

Analyze and Conclude

1. Looking at your topographic map, how can you tell which parts of your model hill have a steep slope? A gentle slope?
2. How can you tell from the map which point on the hill is the highest?
3. Where on your map would you be likely to find a stream? Explain.
4. Is there any depression on your map where water would collect after it rained? What symbol should you use to identify this depression?
5. **Think About It** Compare your map with the clay landform. How are they alike? How are they different? How could you improve your map as a model of the landform?

More to Explore

Obtain a topographic map that includes an interesting landform such as a mountain, canyon, river valley, or coastline. After studying the contour lines on the map, make a sketch of what you think the landform looks like. Then build a scale model of the landform using clay or layers of cardboard or foamboard. How does your model landform compare with your sketch?

◆ For Step 1, students' clay models must not be higher than the sides of the deep-sided pans. Advise students to measure the pan's side, and then make the top of the model hill a few centimeters shorter.
◆ Advise students to use the metric ruler to make sure they add only 1 cm to the depth of water in the pan each time.

Program Resources
◆ **Teaching Resources** Skills Lab blackline masters, pp. 32–33

Media and Technology
 Lab Activity Videotape
Earth's Changing Surface, 2

SECTION 1 Exploring Earth's Surface

Key Ideas
- ◆ Earth's topography is made up of landforms that have elevation and relief, such as plains, mountains, and plateaus.
- ◆ The atmosphere, hydrosphere, and biosphere surround Earth's rocky outer layer, the lithosphere.

Key Terms

topography	landform	plateau
elevation	region	lithosphere
relief	plain	atmosphere
landform	mountain	hydrosphere
	mountain range	biosphere

SECTION 2 Mapping Earth's Surface

Key Ideas
- ◆ Maps and globes are drawn to scale to show features on Earth's surface as seen from above.
- ◆ The grid of latitude and longitude lines can be used to locate points on Earth's surface.

Key Terms

map	key	degree
globe	equator	latitude
scale	hemisphere	longitude
symbols	prime meridian	map projection

SECTION 3 Maps in the Computer Age

INTEGRATING TECHNOLOGY

Key Ideas
- ◆ Instruments carried aboard satellites in orbit around Earth make pictures of the surface called satellite images.
- ◆ Computers are used to store and display the information used in making maps.

Key Terms

satellite image	digitizing
pixel	

SECTION 4 Topographic Maps

Key Ideas
- ◆ Topographic maps portray the elevation, relief, and slope of the landforms in an area.
- ◆ Contour lines are used on a topographic map to show elevation and relief.
- ◆ The contour interval of a topographic map is the amount that elevation increases or decreases between contour lines.
- ◆ In addition to showing elevation and relief, topographic maps include a variety of other natural and human-made features.

Key Terms

topographic map	contour interval
contour line	Global Positioning System

Organizing Information

Concept Map Copy the concept map about landforms onto a separate piece of paper. Then complete it and add a title. (For more on concept maps, see the Skills Handbook.)

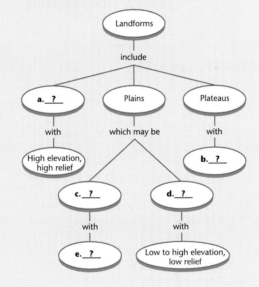

Chapter 1 **G ◆ 35**

Safety

Caution students to be careful when using scissors to cut the cardboard. Review the safety guidelines in Appendix A.

Media and Technology

Interactive Student Tutorial CD-ROM G-1

Computer Test Bank *Earth's Changing Surface*, Chapter 1 Test

Program Resources

- ◆ **Teaching Resources** Chapter 1 Project Scoring Rubric, p. 12; Chapter 1 Performance Assessment, pp. 138–140; Chapter 1 Test, pp. 141–144

- ◆ When students place the sheet of plastic over the pan in Step 3, they should use the marking pencil to mark the corners of the pan on the plastic. In this way, they can always place the plastic in the same position.
- ◆ Advise students to keep the sheet of plastic as dry as possible. Students can use paper towels to gently dry any wet spots on the plastic.

Expected Outcome
Students should be able to represent the shape, slope, and elevation of the model hill by drawing contour lines on the unlined paper, culminating with a closed loop at the top of the hill.

Analyze and Conclude
1. The map shows a steep slope where the contour lines are closely spaced, while it shows a gentle slope where the contour lines are widely spaced.
2. The highest point is indicated by a closed loop with no other contour lines inside it.
3. You might find a stream where a series of V-shaped contour lines point uphill, indicating a valley.
4. There may or may not be a depression on the hill. If there is, it will be shown with a closed loop with dashes inside.
5. They are alike in that they are both models of a natural landform. A main difference between them is that the clay hill is three-dimensional, while the map is two-dimensional. Also, the map does not show every detail of the hill. One way to improve the map is to make the interval between contour lines smaller, such as by adding 0.5 cm of water each time.

Extending the Inquiry

More to Explore State and national parks make topographic maps readily available; often public libraries have these maps on file. Maps can also be obtained from the USGS or from county offices. Encourage students to search for such maps, and then help them collect the materials necessary to build the model landform from the map.

Organizing Information

Concept Map Sample Title: *Types of Landforms* **a.** mountains **b.** high elevation, low relief **c.** coastal **d.** interior **e.** low elevation, low relief

G ◆ 35

Reviewing Content

Multiple Choice

1. d 2. c 3. b 4. c 5. d

True or False

6. Elevation 7. equator 8. true 9. close together 10. true

Checking Concepts

11. A large area of land where the topography is similar is called a landform region.

12. A mountain range is a series of mountains that have the same general shape and structure.

13. A coastal plain has low elevation, while an interior plain may have high or low elevation.

14. It is in the Eastern Hemisphere because it lies 170 degrees east of the prime meridian.

15. Contour lines never cross because a contour line connects points of equal elevation, but they do come together at a perfectly vertical cliff.

16. A 1.5-meter deep depression would not show on a map with a 5-meter contour interval, because that interval shows only changes in elevation greater than 5 meters. The depression would show on a map with a 1-meter contour interval because the depression is greater than the interval.

17. Answers will vary. A typical answer should describe the landforms associated with the Atlantic coastal plain, the Piedmont Plateau, the Appalachian Mountains, the Oachita Mountains, The Great Plains, the Rocky Mountains, the Colorado Plateau, the Mojave Desert, and the Coastal Range.

Thinking Critically

18. The globe has a scale of 1: 26,000,000. A distance of 1 centimeter on the globe would represent 260 kilometers.

19. To return to its starting place without changing direction, the plane had to have traveled 360 degrees of longitude, the total around the entire Earth. But since it traveled only 1,000 kilometers—flying 1,000 kilometers per hour—it must have flown around the world at a very high latitude, either north or south.

Reviewing Content

 For more review of key concepts, see the Interactive Student Tutorial CD-ROM.

Multiple Choice

Choose the letter of the best answer.

1. A landform that has high elevation but a mostly flat surface is a
   a. coastal plain. **b.** mountain.
   c. mountain belt. **d.** plateau.
2. Of the Earth's four "spheres," the one that extends into all the others is the
   a. lithosphere. **b.** hydrosphere.
   c. biosphere. **d.** atmosphere.
3. Latitude is a measurement of distance north or south of the
   a. hemispheres. **b.** equator.
   c. axis. **d.** prime meridian.
4. To show the continents without distorting their relative sizes and shapes, a mapmaker would choose a
   a. Mercator projection.
   b. globe.
   c. equal-area projection.
   d. topographic map.
5. On a topographic map, the contour lines form a V at a
   a. hilltop. **b.** level area.
   c. depression. **d.** valley.

True or False

If the statement is true, write true. If it is false, change the underlined word or words to make the statement true.

6. <u>Relief</u> measures a landform's height above sea level.
7. Going north or south from the <u>prime meridian</u>, the distance to one of the poles is 90 degrees.
8. Computers use data about Earth's surface that has been <u>digitized</u>, or put in the form of numbers.
9. If contour lines on a slope are spaced <u>wide apart</u>, then the slope is very steep.
10. Contour lines that form a closed loop marked with dashes indicate a <u>depression</u>.

Checking Concepts

11. What do geologists call an area where there is mostly one kind of topography?
12. What is a mountain range?
13. Compare the elevation of a coastal plain to that of an interior plain.
14. The South Island of New Zealand lies at about 170° E. What hemisphere is it in?
15. Could contour lines on a map ever cross? Explain.
16. Which would be more likely to show a shallow, 1.5-meter-deep depression in the ground: a 1-meter contour interval or a 5-meter contour interval? Explain.
17. **Writing to Learn** With your family, you make a car trip across the United States along the latitude line 35° N. Write a series of postcards to friends describing the landforms that you see on your trip. Use Appendix B to determine what the land is like along your route.

Thinking Critically

18. **Applying Concepts** Earth's diameter is about 13,000 kilometers. If a globe has a diameter of 0.5 meter, write the globe's scale as a ratio. What distance on Earth would 1 centimeter on the globe represent?
19. **Inferring** An airplane flies directly west at 1,000 kilometers per hour. Without changing direction, the plane returns to its starting point in just one hour. What can you infer about the plane's route with regard to lines of latitude and longitude? Explain.
20. **Observing** Using an atlas, find the latitude and longitude of San Francisco, California; Wichita, Kansas; and Richmond, Virginia. What do these three cities have in common?
21. **Comparing and Contrasting** How is mapmaking with computers different from earlier mapmaking techniques?
22. **Problem Solving** Your community has decided to build a zoo for animals from many regions of Earth. How could you use topographic maps of your area to help decide on the best location for the zoo?

---

20. San Francisco, California, is at 38° N 122° W; Wichita, Kansas, is at 38° N 97° W; Richmond, Virginia, is at 38° N 77° W. All three cities are at 38° N latitude.

21. Earlier mapmaking techniques depended on a slow gathering of data and then drawing the maps by hand. Mapmaking with computers depends on digitizing map data, and then the maps can be displayed, modified, printed out, or made into three-dimensional views.

22. Answers will vary. A typical answer might suggest the use of topographic maps to find an area that has a variety of landforms and water environments in a relatively small area in order to accommodate the animals from many regions. In addition, these maps might be used to avoid building in residential areas and other heavily used areas.

Applying Skills

This map shows part of Acadia National Park in Maine. The contour interval is 20 feet. Use the map to answer Questions 23–25.

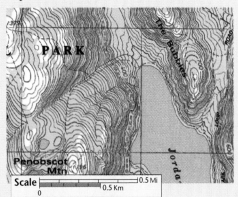

Scale
0.5 Mi
0
0.5 Km

23. Interpreting Maps
A. What is the elevation of the large lake?
B. Which of the two Bubbles is higher?

24. Calculating Use the map scale to calculate the distance from the top of Penobscot Mountain to the large lake.

25. Inferring How can you tell whether the streams flow into or out of the large lake?

Performance — CHAPTER PROJECT 1 — Assessment

Project Wrap Up Present your map to the class. Discuss the natural and physical features found on your site. What symbols did you use to represent these features? How did you measure and locate them on your map? How accurate is your map? Ask your classmates how you could improve your map.

Reflect and Record Write an evaluation of your map. What would you change about it? What would you keep the same? Does your map give others a clear idea of what the land looks like?

Applying Skills

23. a. between 260 and 280 feet
b. The north Bubble has an elevation of 860 feet, which is higher than the south Bubble's 760 feet.
24. The distance is 0.5 km.
25. Into the large lake; the V-shaped contours point uphill and the streams flow in the opposite direction.

Performance — CHAPTER PROJECT 1 — Assessment

Project Wrap Up Talk with each student about his or her map, and have each briefly explain what the presentation will entail. Help students think about what they should present and the order in which they should present it. Then, as each student presents the map, assess how well it is made, how much detail it includes, and how well the student presents it to the class.

Reflect and Record In assessing the quality of their maps, students should compare their maps with the maps others have made. They should write a critique that includes both features they would change and features they would keep if they could do it over again.

Test Preparation
26. b 27. d 28. a 29. b 30. a

Test Preparation

Use these questions to prepare for standardized tests.

The map shows part of Earth's surface with a grid of latitude and longitude lines. Study the map. Then answer Questions 26–30.

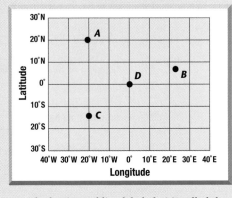

26. The horizontal line labeled 0° is called the
a. horizon line.   b. equator.
c. prime meridian.   d. contour line.

27. The latitude and longitude of point B is best given by
a. 25°S 7°W.   b. 7°N 25°W.
c. 7°E 25°N.   d. 7°N 25°E.

28. In which two hemispheres is point C located?
a. western and southern hemispheres
b. northern and eastern hemispheres
c. eastern and western hemispheres
d. western and northern hemispheres

29. The north-south distance in degrees from point A to Point C is about
a. 15°.   b. 35°.
c. 25°.   d. 0°.

30. Suppose you start at point D and travel southwest to point C. Through how many degrees of longitude have you traveled?
a. 20°   b. 15°
c. 60°   d. 30°

Program Resources

◆ **Inquiry Skills Activity Book** Provides teaching and review of all inquiry skills
◆ **Standardized Test Preparation Book** Provides standardized test practice
◆ **Reading in the Content Area** Provides strategies to improve science reading skills
◆ **Teacher's ELL Handbook** Provides multiple strategies for English language learners

Weathering and Soil Formation

Sections	Time	Student Edition Activities	Other Activities
Soils for Seeds CHAPTER PROJECT 2 p. G39	Ongoing (2 weeks)	Check Your Progress, p. G55 Check Your Progress, p. G60 Project Wrap Up, p. G63	
1 Rocks and Weathering pp. G40–48 ◆ 2.1.1 Identify what causes mechanical weathering. ◆ 2.1.2 Identify what causes chemical weathering. ◆ 2.1.3 Describe the factors that determine how fast weathering occurs.	4–5 periods/ 2–2½ blocks	**Discover** How Fast Can It Fizz, p. G40 **Try This** Rusting Away, p. G44 **Science at Home,** p. G45 **Skills Lab: Controlling Variables** Rock Shake, pp. G46–47	TE Demonstration, p. G41 TE Integrating Physics, p. G42 TE Building Inquiry Skills: Designing Experiments, p. G42 TE Real-Life Learning, p. G43 TE Demonstration, p. G43 TE Inquiry Challenge, p. G45 ISLM G-2, "Investigating Soils and Drainage"
2 Soil Formation and Composition pp. G49–56 ◆ 2.2.1 Describe the composition of soil. ◆ 2.2.2 Explain how soil is formed and how soil horizons develop. ◆ 2.2.3 Identify the roles of plants and animals in soil formation.	3–4 periods/ 1½–2 blocks	**Discover** Is Soil?, p. G49 **Sharpen Your Skills** Predicting, p. G51 **Try This** A Square Meter of Soil, p. G54 **Real-World Lab: Careers in Science** Getting to Know the Soil, p. G56	TE Building Inquiry Skills: Comparing and Contrasting, p. G51 TE Using the Visuals: Figure 7, p. G51 TE Integrating Life Science, p. G52 TE Including All Students, p. G52 TE Building Inquiry Skills: Calculating, p. G53 TE Inquiry Challenge, p. G53
3 *INTEGRATING ENVIRONMENTAL SCIENCE* **Soil Conservation** pp. G57–60 ◆ 2.3.1 Explain why soil is a valuable resource. ◆ 2.3.2 List ways that soil can be lost or destroyed. ◆ 2.3.3 Identify some ways that soil can be conserved.	2 periods/ 1 block	**Discover** How Can You Keep Soil From Washing Away?, p. G57	TE Inquiry Challenge, p. G58
Study Guide/Assessment pp. G61–63	1 period/ ½ block		ISAB Provides teaching and review of all inquiry skills

 For Standard or Block Schedule The Resource Pro® CD-ROM gives you maximum flexibility for planning your instruction for any type of schedule. Resource Pro® contains Planning Express®, an advanced scheduling program, as well as the entire contents of the Teaching Resources and the Computer Test Bank.

Key: **SE** Student Edition
PLM Probeware Lab Manual
ISAB Inquiry Skills Activity Book

Program Resources	Assessment Strategies	Media and Technology
TR Chapter 2 Project Teacher Notes, pp. G34–35 **TR** Chapter 2 Project Overview and Worksheets, pp. G36–39	**TE** Performance Assessment: Chapter 2 Project Wrap Up, p. G63 **TE** Check Your Progress, pp. G55, G60 **TR** Chapter 2 Project Scoring Rubric, p. G40	Science Explorer Internet Site Audio CDs and Audiotapes, English-Spanish Section Summaries
TR 2-1 Lesson Plan, p. G41 **TR** 2-1 Section Summary, p. G42 **TR** 2-1 Review and Reinforce, p. G43 **TR** 2-1 Enrich, p. G44 **TR** Skills Lab blackline masters, pp. G53–55 **SES** Book H, *Earth's Waters,* Chapters 1 and 3 **SES** Book L, *Chemical Interactions,* Chapter 3	**SE** Section 1 Review, p. G45 **SE** Analyze and Conclude, p. G47 **TE** Ongoing Assessment, pp. G41, G43 **TE** Performance Assessment, p. G45	Lab Activity Videotape, *Earth's Changing Surface,* 3 Transparency 5, "Exploring the Forces of Mechanical Weathering"
TR 2-2 Lesson Plan, p. G45 **TR** 2-2 Section Summary, p. G46 **TR** 2-2 Review and Reinforce, p. G47 **TR** 2-2 Enrich, p. G48 **TR** Real-World Lab blackline masters, pp. G56–57 **SES** Book A, *From Bacteria to Plants,* Chapters 2 and 3 **SES** Book F, *Inside Earth,* Chapter 5	**SE** Section 2 Review, p. G55 **SE** Analyze and Conclude, p. G56 **TE** Ongoing Assessment, pp. G51, G53 **TE** Performance Assessment, p. G55	Lab Activity Videotape, *Earth's Changing Surface,* 4 Transparencies 6, "Soil Composition and Soil Horizons"; 7, "Exploring Living Organisms in Soil"; 8, "Soils of North America"
TR 2-3 Lesson Plan, p. G49 **TR** 2-3 Section Summary, p. G50 **TR** 2-3 Review and Reinforce, p. G51 **TR** 2-3 Enrich, p. G52 **SES** Book I, *Weather and Climate,* Chapter 2	**SE** Section 3 Review, p. G60 **TE** Ongoing Assessment, p. G59 **TE** Performance Assessment, p. G60	Exploring Earth Science Videodisc, Unit 3 Side 1, "Is Our Soil Endangered?"
GSW Provides worksheets to promote student comprehension of content **RCA** Provides strategies to improve science reading skills **ELL** Provides multiple strategies for English language learners	**SE** Study Guide/Assessment, pp. G61–63 **TR** Chapter 2 Performance Assessment, pp. G145–147 **TR** Chapter 2 Test, pp. G148–151 **CTB** *Earth's Changing Surface,* Chapter 2 Test **STP** Provides standardized test practice	Interactive Student Tutorial CD-ROM, G-2 Computer Test Bank, *Earth's Changing Surface,* Chapter 2 Test

TE Teacher's Edition
RCA Reading in the Content Area
GSW Guided Study Workbook

TR Teaching Resources
ISLM Integrated Science Laboratory Manual
ELL Teacher's ELL Handbook

CTB Computerized Test Bank
STP Standardized Test Preparation Book
SES Science Explorer Series Text

Meeting the National Science Education Standards and AAAS Benchmarks

National Science Education Standards	Benchmarks for Science Literacy	Unifying Themes
Science As Inquiry (Content Standard A) ◆ **Design and conduct a scientific investigation** Students investigate how soil composition affects plant growth. Students compare the rates of weathering that take place under different conditions. *(Chapter Project; Skills Lab)* ◆ **Develop descriptions, explanations, predictions, and models using evidence** Students observe a sample of soil to determine its characteristics. *(Real-World Lab)* **Life Science** (Content Standard C) ◆ **Populations and ecosystems** Some soil organisms mix the soil and make spaces in it for air and water; others make humus. *(Section 2)* **Earth and Space Science** (Content Standard D) ◆ **Structure of the Earth system** Weathering is the process that breaks down rock and other materials at Earth's surface. Soil forms as rock is broken down by weathering and mixes with other materials. Soil is one of Earth's most valuable resources. *(Sections 1, 2, 3; Chapter Project; Skills Lab; Real-World Lab)* **Science in Personal and Social Perspectives** (Content Standard F) ◆ **Science and technology in society** Students examine the issue of preserving stone monuments. *(Science and Society)*	**1B Scientific Inquiry** Students investigate how soil composition affects plant growth. Students compare the rates of weathering that take place under different conditions. Students observe a sample of soil to determine its characteristics. *(Chapter Project; Skills Lab; Real-World Lab)* **3C Issues in Technology** Students examine the issue of preserving stone monuments. Soil conservation is the management of soil to prevent its destruction. *(Science and Society; Section 3)* **4B The Earth** Soil is one of Earth's most valuable resources. *(Section 3)* **4C Processes That Shape the Earth** Weathering is the process that breaks down rock and other materials at Earth's surface. Soil forms as rock is broken down by weathering and mixes with other materials. Plowing removed the grass from the Great Plains and exposed the soil, which led to the Dust Bowl. *(Sections 1, 2, 3; Skills Lab; Real-World Lab)* **5D Interdependence of Life** Some soil organisms mix the soil and make spaces in it for air and water; others make humus. *(Section 2)*	◆ **Energy** The forces of weathering break rocks. Many burrowing animals break up compacted soil and mix humus through it. Wind blew away the soil in the Dust Bowl. *(Sections 1, 2, 3; Skills Lab)* ◆ **Evolution** Over time, weathering breaks down even the biggest, hardest rocks. Soil formation continues over a long period of time, and gradually soil horizons develop. *(Sections 1, 2)* ◆ **Patterns of Change** Once rocks become exposed at Earth's surface, they begin to undergo weathering. Soil forms as rock is broken down and mixes with other materials. *(Sections 1, 2; Science and Society)* ◆ **Scale and Structure** Soil is a mixture of rock particles, minerals, decayed organic material, air, and water. *(Section 2; Real-World Lab)* ◆ **Systems and Interactions** Soil composition can affect how plants grow. Weathering breaks rock down into particles of soil. Some soil organisms mix the soil and make spaces in it for air and water. Two ways that soil can be conserved include contour plowing and conservation plowing. *(Chapter Project; Sections 1, 2, 3)* ◆ **Unity and Diversity** The two kinds of weathering are mechanical weathering and chemical weathering. Soil is classified into three horizons. *(Sections 1, 2; Skills Lab)* ◆ **Stability** Weathering and erosion work together continuously to wear down and carry away the rocks at Earth's surface. *(Section 1)*

Take It to the Net

 Interactive text at www.phschool.com

Science Explorer comes alive with iText.

- **Complete student text** is accessible from any computer with a browser.

- **Animations, simulations, and videos** enhance student understanding and retention of concepts.

- **Self-tests** and **online study tools** assess student understanding.

- **Teacher management tools** help you make the most of this valuable resource.

STAY CURRENT with **SCIENCE NEWS** ®

Find out the latest research and information about Earth's surface at:
www.phschool.com

Go to **www.phschool.com** and click on the Science icon. Then click on Science Explorer under PH@school.

ACTIVITY	Time (minutes)	Materials *Quantities for one work group*	Skills
Section 1			
Discover, p. 40	10	**Consumable** 2 fizzing antacid tablets, warm water **Nonconsumable** 2 beakers, plastic stirring rod, plastic bowl, stopwatch	Inferring
Try This, p. 44	5; 5	**Consumable** 2 pads of steel wool, water **Nonconsumable** jar with lid	Predicting
Science at Home, p. 45	Home	**Consumable** plastic drinking straw, modeling clay, water **Nonconsumable** freezer	Drawing Conclusions
Skills Lab, pp. 46–47	30; 30	**Consumable** 300 mL of water, paper towels, masking tape, 2 pieces of thin cloth, 300 mL of vinegar, 80 small pieces of limestone **Nonconsumable** balance, marking pen or pencil, 250-mL plastic graduated cylinder, 4 500-mL watertight plastic containers with screw-on caps	Measuring, Predicting, Controlling Variables, Creating Data Tables, Drawing Conclusions
Section 2			
Discover, p. 49	15	**Consumable** soil sample, paper cup, paper towel, toothpick **Nonconsumable** hand lens	Forming Operational Definitions
Sharpen Your Skills, p. 51	5	No special materials are required.	Predicting
Try This, p. 54	30	**Consumable** string **Nonconsumable** metric ruler, stakes, trowel, hand lens	Drawing Conclusions
Real-World Lab, p. 56	40	**Consumable** 20–30 grams of soil, toothpick, water, graph paper ruled with 1- or 2-mm spacing **Nonconsumable** plastic spoon, plastic dropper, stereomicroscope, plastic petri dish or jar lid	Observing, Inferring, Posing Questions
Section 3			
Discover, p. 57	15	**Consumable** soil, water, craft sticks, paper clips, pebbles, modeling clay, paper **Nonconsumable** pie plate, container	Observing

A list of all materials required for the Student Edition activities can be found beginning on page T15. You can obtain information about ordering materials by calling 1-800-848-9500 or by accessing the Science Explorer Internet site at: **www.phschool.com**

Soils for Seeds

Many students may think that all soil is a substance that varies little from place to place, especially if they have always lived in the same general area. Students may not realize how important the composition of soil is to the growth and health of plants.

Purpose In the Chapter 2 Project, students will work in small groups to examine soils, plant bean seeds in different kinds of soils, collect and record data about the growth of the bean plants, compare how the plants fared in different soils, and draw conclusions about how much effect a soil has on the plants it holds. By doing this project, students will gain a better understanding of soil composition and fertility.

Skills Focus Students will be able to:
- design an experiment that investigates different soils and their effects on plant growth;
- control variables in setting up an experiment that isolates soil as the only variable among different plants;
- make measurements of plant growth over the course of the project;
- create a data table to record observations about the growth and health of the plants;
- draw conclusions about how soil composition affects plant growth.

Project Time Line The entire project will require about two to three weeks. Depending on how much class time students can spend working on the project, planning and setup should take only one or two days. Observing plant growth requires a minimum of two weeks. The presentations can be done in a day. The project will require groups to carry out the following phases.
- Meet to decide on which soils to use and how to set up the experiment.
- Examine the different soils and note their characteristics.
- Plant the seeds and set up the experiment.
- Create a data table to record growth data.
- Observe and record the growth and health of the plants in different soils.

Gargoyle statue overlooking a city

CHAPTER 2
Weathering and Soil Formation

WEB ACTIVITY www.phschool.com

Integrating Environmental Science

SECTION **1** Rocks and Weathering

Discover **How Fast Can It Fizz?**
Try This **Rusting Away**
Skills Lab **Rock Shake**

SECTION **2** Soil Formation and Composition

Discover **What Is Soil?**
Sharpen Your Skills **Predicting**
Try This **A Square Meter of Soil**
Real-World Lab **Getting to Know the Soil**

SECTION **3** Soil Conservation

Discover **How Can You Keep Soil From Washing Away?**

- Draw conclusions about the effect soil had on the data collected.
- Present the results and conclusions to the class.

For more detailed information on planning and supervising the Chapter 2 Project, see Chapter 2 Project Teacher Notes, pages 34–35 in Teaching Resources.

Suggested Shortcuts
- You can make this project shorter and less involved by explaining the experiment to students and having them observe the growth of plants in sand, gravel, vermiculite, potting soil, and local topsoil over a two-week period. Each student can make individual observations and create a data table to record those observations.
- You can make this project shorter by planting bean seeds about a week in advance. You can give each student group three or four pots to observe, each pot containing plants in a different type of soil.

Possible Materials Sand, gravel, vermiculite, and potting soil can be purchased from any

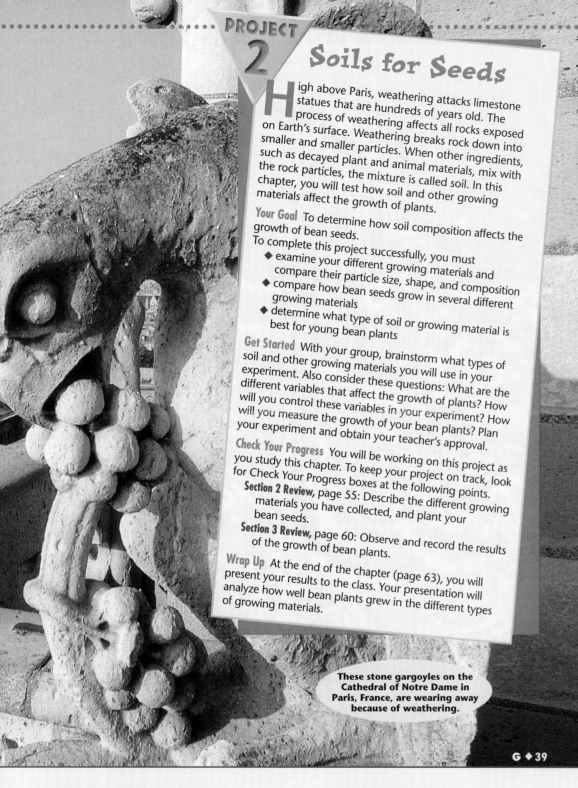

Soils for Seeds

High above Paris, weathering attacks limestone statues that are hundreds of years old. The process of weathering affects all rocks exposed on Earth's surface. Weathering breaks rock down into smaller and smaller particles. When other ingredients, such as decayed plant and animal materials, mix with the rock particles, the mixture is called soil. In this chapter, you will test how soil and other growing materials affect the growth of plants.

Your Goal To determine how soil composition affects the growth of bean seeds.

To complete this project successfully, you must

- ◆ examine your different growing materials and compare their particle size, shape, and composition
- ◆ compare how bean seeds grow in several different growing materials
- ◆ determine what type of soil or growing material is best for young bean plants

Get Started With your group, brainstorm what types of soil and other growing materials you will use in your experiment. Also consider these questions: What are the different variables that affect the growth of plants? How will you control these variables in your experiment? How will you measure the growth of your bean plants? Plan your experiment and obtain your teacher's approval.

Check Your Progress You will be working on this project as you study this chapter. To keep your project on track, look for Check Your Progress boxes at the following points.

Section 2 Review, page 55: Describe the different growing materials you have collected, and plant your bean seeds.

Section 3 Review, page 60: Observe and record the results of the growth of bean plants.

Wrap Up At the end of the chapter (page 63), you will present your results to the class. Your presentation will analyze how well bean plants grew in the different types of growing materials.

These stone gargoyles on the Cathedral of Notre Dame in Paris, France, are wearing away because of weathering.

G ◆ 39

local garden or large hardware store. Students can collect local topsoil; they will need a trowel and a bucket. Each group will also need 12 to 15 pinto bean seeds and three or four small pots in which to plant their beans. (Plastic foam cups with a small hole punched in the bottom can be used for pots.) To make measurements of plant growth, students should use metric rulers.

Launching the Project Introduce the Chapter 2 Project by displaying a healthy potted plant. Ask: **If you wanted to grow a healthy plant like this, how could you meet the plant's requirements?** *(Answers will vary. Most students will mention the right amount of sunlight and water. Some may mention good soil.)* Point out that each one of these factors could be investigated to find out what effect it has on plant growth. In this project, students will investigate only one factor—how soil affects plants. Thus, type of soil will be the variable in the experiment they will design. They will have to control other factors so that only soil makes a difference in how plants grow. To help students get started, pass out Chapter 2 Project Overview and Worksheets, pages 36–39 in Teaching Resources. You may also wish to pass out the Chapter 2 Project Scoring Rubric, page 40, at this time.

Program Resources

◆ **Teaching Resources** Chapter 2 Project Teacher Notes, pp. 34–35; Project Overview and Worksheets, pp. 36–39; Project Scoring Rubric, p. 40

Media and Technology

 Audio CDs and **Audiotapes** English-Spanish Section Summaries

WEB ACTIVITY www.phschool.com

You will find an Internet activity, chapter self-tests for students, and links to other chapter topics at this site.

Performance Assessment

Use the Chapter 2 Project Scoring Rubric to assess students' work. Students will be assessed on

- ◆ how well they examine various soils and set up the experiment;
- ◆ how well they observe and record the growth of their plants in a data table;
- ◆ how effectively they present their results and conclusions to the class;
- ◆ how much they contribute to their group's effort.

Objectives

After completing the lesson, students will be able to

◆ identify what causes mechanical weathering;

◆ identify what causes chemical weathering;

◆ describe the factors that determine how fast weathering occurs.

Key Terms weathering, erosion, mechanical weathering, abrasion, ice wedging, chemical weathering, permeable

1 Engage/Explore

Activating Prior Knowledge

Many students have probably seen old headstones in cemeteries. Ask: **How would you describe the difference between a new headstone and one that is a hundred years old?** (*A typical answer might describe the old headstone as rounded and crumbling with a faded inscription.*) Invite students to speculate about what processes change a headstone through the years.

········ **DISCOVER** ········

Skills Focus inferring
Materials *2 fizzing*
antacid tablets, 2 beakers, warm water, plastic stirring rod, plastic bowl, stopwatch
Time 10 minutes
Tips Demonstrate how to grind up a tablet by using the stirring rod in a plastic bowl. Have students use warm water from the tap. If stopwatches are unavailable, students can observe a second hand on a watch or wall clock.
Expected Outcome Typical dissolving times are 30 seconds for the whole tablet, 10 seconds for the ground-up tablet.
Think It Over The ground-up tablet dissolved faster than the whole tablet. Inferences may vary. Some students might correctly suggest that the ground-up tablet had more surface area exposed to the water than the whole tablet, and therefore dissolved faster.

SECTION 1 **Rocks and Weathering**

DISCOVER ·····················**ACTIVITY**····

How Fast Can It Fizz?

1. Place a fizzing antacid tablet in a small beaker. Then grind up a second tablet and place it in another beaker. The whole tablet is a model of solid rock. The ground-up tablet is a model of rock fragments.

2. Add 100 mL of warm water to the beaker containing the whole tablet. Then stir with a stirring rod until the tablet dissolves completely. Use a stopwatch to time how long it takes.

3. Add 100 mL of warm water to the beaker containing the ground-up tablet. Then stir until all of the ground-up tablet dissolves. Time how long it takes.

Think It Over

Inferring Which dissolved faster, the whole antacid tablet or the ground-up tablet? What difference between the two affected how long it took them to dissolve?

GUIDE FOR READING

◆ What causes mechanical weathering?

◆ What causes chemical weathering?

◆ What determines how fast weathering occurs?

Reading Tip As you read, use the headings to make an outline about weathering.

Imagine a hike that lasts for months and covers hundreds of kilometers. Each year, many hikers go on such treks. They hike trails that run the length of America's great mountain ranges. For example, the John Muir Trail follows the Sierra Nevada mountains. The Sierras extend about 640 kilometers along the eastern side of California. In the east, the Appalachian Trail follows the Appalachian Mountains. The Appalachians stretch more than 2,000 kilometers from Alabama to Maine.

The two trails cross very different landscapes. The Sierras are rocky and steep, with many peaks rising 3,000 meters above sea level. The Appalachians are more rounded and gently sloping, and are covered with soil and plants. The highest peaks in the Appalachians are less than half the elevation of the highest peaks in the Sierras. Which mountain range do you think is older? The Appalachians formed more than 250 million years ago. The Sierras formed only within the last 10 million years. The forces that wear down rock on Earth's surface have had much longer to grind down the Appalachians.

The Effects of Weathering

The process of mountain building thrusts rock up to the Earth's surface. There, the rock becomes exposed to weathering. **Weathering** is the process that breaks down rock and other substances at Earth's surface. Heat, cold, water, and ice all contribute to weathering. So do the oxygen and carbon dioxide in the atmosphere. Repeated freezing

---

READING STRATEGIES

Reading Tip Students should use the main headings: "The Effects of Weathering," "Mechanical Weathering," "Chemical Weathering," and "Rate of Weathering." They can use any subheadings for the next level in their outlines. As they read the material under each heading, they should summarize the main points in a few words and add those to their outlines. Suggest students use their outlines as a study guide.

Vocabulary Help clarify the difference between the terms *mechanical weathering* and *chemical weathering* by referring to physical change and chemical change. Physical changes include changes in size, shape, phase, and so on. Such changes don't alter the basic substance. Chemical changes, by contrast, refer to changes from chemical reactions, in which substances change into other substances.

and thawing, for example, can crack rock apart into smaller pieces. Rainwater can dissolve minerals that bind rock together. You don't need to go to the mountains to see examples of weathering. The forces that wear down mountains also cause bicycles to rust, paint to peel, sidewalks to crack, and potholes to form.

The forces of weathering break rocks into smaller and smaller pieces. Then the forces of erosion carry the pieces away. **Erosion** (ee ROH zhun) is the movement of rock particles by wind, water, ice, or gravity. Weathering and erosion work together continuously to wear down and carry away the rocks at Earth's surface.

There are two kinds of weathering: mechanical weathering and chemical weathering. Both types of weathering act slowly, but over time they break down even the biggest, hardest rocks.

☑ *Checkpoint* *What is the difference between weathering and erosion?*

Mechanical Weathering

If you hit a rock hard enough with a hammer, the rock will break into pieces. Some forces of weathering can also break rock into pieces. The type of weathering in which rock is physically broken into smaller pieces is called **mechanical weathering.** These smaller pieces of rock have the same composition as the rock they came from. If you have seen rocks that are cracked or peeling in layers, then you have seen rocks that are undergoing mechanical weathering.

Mechanical weathering breaks rock into pieces by freezing and thawing, release of pressure, growth of plants, actions of animals, and abrasion. The term **abrasion** (uh BRAY zhun) refers to the grinding away of rock by rock particles carried by water, ice, wind, or gravity. Mechanical weathering works slowly. But over very long periods of time, it does more than wear down rocks. Mechanical weathering eventually wears away whole mountains.

Figure 1 The jagged, rocky peaks of the Sierra Nevadas (left) show that the mountains are young. The more gently sloping Appalachians (right) have been exposed to weathering for 250 million years.

---

2 Facilitate

The Effects of Weathering

Using the Visuals: Figure 1

Explain that the Sierra Nevada mountains formed less than 10 million years ago. Ask: **How much longer has weathering acted on the Appalachians?** *(250 million years)* **Do you think in another 250 million years the Sierra will look like the Appalachians?** *(Answers may vary. Many students will think they will.)* Advise students to keep this question in mind when they read about the causes of weathering and differences in the rate of weathering later in the section. **learning modality: logical/mathematical**

Mechanical Weathering

Demonstration

Materials *2 pieces of sandstone, newspaper*
Time 5 minutes

As students watch, have a volunteer rub two pieces of sandstone together over a spread-out newspaper. Students will observe particles fall onto the paper. Ask: **What kind of mechanical weathering does this model?** *(abrasion)* Ask: **How could such abrasion occur in nature?** *(Water or wind could carry sand particles into rock, grinding part of it away.)* **learning modality: visual**

Program Resources

◆ **Teaching Resources** 2-1 Lesson Plan, p. 41; 2-1 Section Summary, p. 42
◆ **Integrated Science Laboratory Manual** G-2, "Investigating Soils and Drainage"
◆ **Guided Study Workbook** Section 2-1

Answers to Self-Assessment

☑ *Checkpoint*

Weathering is the process that breaks down rock and other materials at Earth's surface, while erosion is the movement of rock particles by wind, water, ice, or gravity.

Ongoing Assessment

Oral Presentation Call on students at random to classify examples as either weathering or erosion. Each time you call on a student, give a brief, general description of an agent of weathering or an instance of erosion, without using any technical terms.

Mechanical Weathering, continued

Materials *small steel mixing bowl, plastic saucer, 4–5 kg weight, water, freezer*

Time 5 minutes for setup; 5 minutes the next day for observation

As students observe, fill the bowl to the top with water. Place the saucer over the top of the bowl. On top of the saucer place a small weight. Then place this apparatus in a freezer overnight. The next day, students will see that the expansion of water as it turned to ice pushed the weight up. **learning modality: visual**

EXPLORING
the Forces of Mechanical Weathering

Ask students to describe any evidence they have seen of mechanical weathering, then ask: **With which of the five forces is the composition of rock different after mechanical weathering occurs?** *(None. In each case, the composition of the rock remains the same.)* **How are rocks changed after mechanical weathering?** *(Rocks are either cracked or broken into smaller pieces.)* **learning modality: verbal**

Building Inquiry Skills: Designing Experiments

Materials *charcoal briquettes, plastic sandwich bags, water, marking pen, freezer*

Time 20 minutes for design and setup; 5 minutes the next day

Challenge small groups to use the materials given to design an experiment that shows how freezing and thawing water affects rock. A typical experiment might include soaking one briquette with water while keeping the other dry, and then placing each in a plastic bag and freezing both overnight. The next day, the water-saturated briquette would be cracked or in pieces, while the other would not. Review each group's design before permitting them to proceed. **learning modality: kinesthetic**

 In cool climates, the most important force of mechanical weathering is freezing and thawing of water. Water seeps into cracks in rocks and then freezes when the temperature drops. Water expands when it freezes. Ice therefore acts like a wedge, a simple machine that forces things apart. Wedges of ice in rocks widen and deepen cracks. This process is called **ice wedging.** When the ice melts, the water seeps deeper into the cracks. With repeated freezing and thawing, the cracks slowly expand until pieces of rock break off. *Exploring the Forces of Mechanical Weathering* shows how this process weathers rock.

✓ *Checkpoint* How does ice wedging weather rock?

EXPLORING
the Forces of Mechanical Weathering

Mechanical weathering affects all the rock on Earth's surface. Given enough time, mechanical weathering can break down a massive mountain into tiny particles of sand.

Release of Pressure
As erosion removes material from the surface of a mass of rock, pressure on the rock is reduced. This release of pressure causes the outside of the rock to crack and flake off like the layers of an onion.

Freezing and Thawing
When water freezes in a crack in a rock, it expands and makes the crack bigger. The process of ice wedging also widens cracks in sidewalks and causes potholes in streets.

Background

Facts and Figures Ice wedging, or frost wedging, is a powerful force of mechanical weathering. When water freezes, it expands about 9 percent larger than it was as a liquid. When water freezes within a crack in rock, it exerts a pressure of about 110 kg/cm^2. Such pressure is roughly equal to the force of a 98-kg object dropped from a height of 3 m. Freezing and thawing over and over eventually breaks rock apart.

Chemical Weathering

In addition to mechanical weathering, another type of weathering attacks rock. **Chemical weathering** is the process that breaks down rock through chemical changes. **The agents of chemical weathering include water, oxygen, carbon dioxide, living organisms, and acid rain.**

Chemical weathering produces rock particles that have a different mineral makeup from the rock they came from. Each rock is made up of one or more minerals. For example, granite is made up of several minerals, including feldspar, quartz, and mica. But chemical weathering of granite eventually changes the feldspar minerals to clay minerals.

Plant Growth
Roots of trees and other plants enter cracks in rocks. As the roots grow, they force the cracks farther apart. Over time, the roots of even small plants can pry apart cracked rocks.

Abrasion
Sand and other rock particles that are carried by wind, water, or ice can wear away exposed rock surfaces like sandpaper on wood. Wind-driven sand helped shape the rocks shown here.

Animal Actions
Animals that burrow in the ground—including moles, gophers, prairie dogs, and some insects—loosen and break apart rocks in the soil.

Real-Life Learning

Time *15 minutes*

ACTIVITY

Have students look for examples of mechanical weathering caused by plant growth on or around the school grounds. Students can do this during lunch or after school. They should be able to find examples of plants growing up through cracks in the sidewalk or blacktop or plant roots displacing stones or concrete. Encourage students to sketch what they see and then tell the class about it. **learning modality: visual**

Chemical Weathering

Addressing Naive Conceptions

Many students may believe that weathering, especially chemical weathering, occurs as large and dramatic events. Ask: **Have any of you ever seen rock weather?** (*No one will probably have seen rock weather.*) Emphasize that weathering usually occurs slowly over great spans of time. A person's lifetime is not long enough to observe any dramatic changes caused by weathering, such as mountains being worn down. **learning modality: verbal**

Demonstration

Materials *samples of limestone and granite, 2 plates, dilute hydrochloric acid or vinegar, plastic dropper, gloves*

ACTIVITY

Time 5 minutes

Display two plates, with a limestone sample on one and a granite sample on the other. Then, as students observe, use the dropper to apply the acid to each rock. The limestone will dramatically fizz and deteriorate, while the granite will remain unchanged. Ask: **What does this demonstration model?** (*The way that carbonic acid weathers limestone*) **learning modality: visual**

Program Resources

🔵 **Science Explorer Series** *Earth's Waters*, Chapter 1, provides more information on the properties of water.

Media and Technology

📽 **Transparencies** "Exploring the Forces of Mechanical Weathering," Transparency 5

Answers to Self-Assessment

☑ *Checkpoint*

Water seeps into cracks in rock and then freezes. Because water expands when it freezes, the ice acts as a wedge, widening and deepening the cracks.

Ongoing Assessment

Writing Have students explain in their own words the difference between mechanical weathering and chemical weathering.

 Students can save their paragraphs in their portfolios.

Chemical Weathering, continued

Figure 2 As weathering breaks apart rock, the surface area exposed to further weathering increases.

Using the Visuals: Figure 2

To help students understand that more surface area means more weathering, propose that the faces of the unbroken cube in the figure are each 10 × 10 m and the rock is sitting on Earth's surface. Ask: **How many square meters of rock are exposed to the forces of chemical weathering?** *(600 m², 6 × 10², are exposed to weathering.)* **If the rock fractures into eight pieces as shown, how much surface area is exposed?** *(Now each face is 25 m². Thus, there would be 1,200 m² exposed to chemical weathering: 8 pieces × 6 sides each = 48; 48 × 25 m² = 1200 m².)* **learning modality: logical/mathematical**

Skills Focus predicting
Materials *2 pads of steel wool, water, jar with lid*
Time 5 minutes for setup; 5 minutes a few days later
Tips Don't use steel-wool pads that contain soap. To cut down on the cost of materials, cut each pad in half.
Expected Outcome The moistened steel wool left in the jar will rust. When squeezed, it will crumble and stay compacted, while the new piece will spring back to the original shape. Like the oxidation of rock, the steel wool becomes crumbly and turns reddish.
Extend Encourage interested students to set up a long-term experiment by placing half a steel-wool pad somewhere outside where it will not be disturbed and keeping the other half inside as a control. After a month, compare the two to observe the effects of weathering.
learning modality: kinesthetic

 Integrating Environmental Science

Ask students: **What do you and your family do to contribute to the problem of acid rain?** *(Students should mention driving and electricity use.)* **How could you reduce your contribution to this problem?** *(Students might mention using more efficient vehicles and electric appliances or using them less often.)*
learning modality: verbal

44 ◆ G

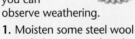

Rusting Away

Here's how you can observe weathering. **ACTIVITY**

1. Moisten some steel wool and place it in a closed container so it will not dry out.
2. Observe the steel wool after a few days. What has happened to the steel wool?
3. Take a new piece of steel wool and squeeze it between your fingers. Remove the steel wool from the container and squeeze it between your fingers. What happens? Wash your hands when you have finished.

Predicting If you kept the steel wool moist for a longer time, what would eventually happen to it? How is the weathering of steel wool like the weathering of a rock?

Chemical weathering creates holes or soft spots in rock, so the rock breaks apart more easily. Chemical and mechanical weathering often work together. As mechanical weathering breaks rock into pieces, more surface area becomes exposed to chemical weathering. The Discover activity in this section shows how increasing the surface area increases the rate of a chemical reaction.

Water Water is the most important agent of chemical weathering. Water weathers rock by dissolving it. When a rock or other substance dissolves in water, it mixes uniformly throughout the water to make a solution. Over time, many rocks will dissolve in water.

Oxygen The oxygen gas in air is an important cause of chemical weathering. If you have ever left a bicycle or metal tool outside in the rain, then you have seen how oxygen can weather iron. Iron combines with oxygen in the presence of water in a process called oxidation. The product of oxidation is rust. Rock that contains iron also oxidizes, or rusts. Rust makes rock soft and crumbly and gives it a red or brown color.

Carbon Dioxide Another gas found in air, carbon dioxide, also causes chemical weathering. Carbon dioxide becomes dissolved in rainwater and in water that sinks through air pockets in the soil. The result is a weak acid called carbonic acid. Carbonic acid easily weathers marble and limestone.

Living Organisms Imagine a seed landing on a rock face. As it sprouts, its roots push into cracks in the rock. As the plant's roots grow, they produce weak acids that slowly dissolve rock around the roots. Lichens—plantlike organisms that grow on rocks—also produce weak acids that chemically weather rock.

Acid Rain Over the past 150 years, people have been burning

INTEGRATING ENVIRONMENTAL SCIENCE large amounts of coal, oil, and gas for energy. Burning these fuels can pollute the air with sulfur, carbon, and nitrogen compounds. Such compounds react chemically with the water vapor in clouds, forming acids. These acids mix with raindrops and fall as acid rain. Acid rain causes very rapid chemical weathering.

Background

Facts and Figures Chemical weathering cannot take place without water. Some moisture is available for chemical weathering even in deserts, but the processes of chemical weathering are much more significant in wetter climates. Solution, oxidation, formation of carbonic acid, and acid rain all require water.

Chemical weathering works to prepare rock for erosion. First, such weathering often results in softer and smaller rocks that erode more easily. Second, chemical weathering often involves dissolving minerals in solution. Such dissolved minerals are easily transported by the flow of water, a process called chemical erosion.

Rate of Weathering

Visitors to New England's historic cemeteries may notice a surprising fact. Slate tombstones from the 1700s are less weathered and easier to read than marble gravestones from the 1800s. Why is this so? **The most important factors that determine the rate at which weathering occurs are type of rock and climate.**

Type of Rock Some kinds of rocks weather more rapidly than others. The minerals that make up the rock determine how fast it weathers. Rock made of minerals that do not dissolve easily in water weathers slowly. Rock made of minerals that dissolve easily in water weathers faster.

Some rock weathers easily because it is permeable. **Permeable** (PUR mee uh bul) means that a material is full of tiny, connected air spaces that allow water to seep through it. Permeable rock weathers chemically at a fast rate. Why? As water seeps through the spaces in the rock, it removes dissolved material formed by weathering.

Climate Climate refers to the average weather conditions in an area. Both chemical and mechanical weathering occur faster in wet climates. Rainfall provides the water needed for chemical changes as well as for freezing and thawing.

Chemical reactions occur faster at higher temperatures. That is why chemical weathering occurs more quickly where the climate is both hot and wet. Granite, for example, is a very hard rock that forms when molten material cools inside Earth. Granite weathers so slowly in cool climates that it is often used as a building stone. But in hot and wet climates, granite weathers faster and eventually crumbles apart.

Figure 3 The rate of weathering of these tombstones depends on the type of rock. Slate (top) resists weathering better than marble (bottom). *Inferring What type of weathering probably wore away the letters on the marble tombstone?*

Section 1 Review

1. What factors cause mechanical weathering?
2. Describe three causes of chemical weathering.
3. What factors affect the rate of weathering?
4. Explain why chemical weathering occurs faster in hot, wet climates than in cool, dry climates.
5. **Thinking Critically** **Predicting** Suppose you see a large boulder with several cracks in it. What would you expect to see if you could observe the boulder again in several hundred years? Explain.

Science at Home

Here's how to demonstrate one type of weathering for your family. Plug one end of a drinking straw with a small piece of clay. Fill the straw with water. Now plug the top of the straw with clay. Make sure that the clay plugs do not leak. Lay the straw flat in the freezer overnight. Remove the straw the next day. What happened to the clay plugs? What process produced this result? Be sure to dispose of the straw so that no one will use it for drinking.

Program Resources

◆ **Teaching Resources** 2-1 Review and Reinforce, p. 43; 2-1 Enrich, p. 44
  Science Explorer Series *Chemical Interactions*, Chapter 3, provides more information about solutions.
  Science Explorer Series *Earth's Waters*, Chapter 3, provides more information about acid rain.

Answers to Self-Assessment

Caption Question

Figure 3 A typical answer might correctly suggest that chemical weathering probably wore away the letters.

Rate of Weathering

Inquiry Challenge

Divide students into small groups and challenge each group to develop a hypothesis about which factor plays the greater role in rate of weathering, type of rock or climate. Then have students design an experiment that could test their hypothesis. Finally, have a member of each group describe the experiment to the class.
cooperative learning

3 Assess

Section 1 Review Answers

1. Freezing and thawing, heating and cooling, growth of plants, actions of animals, and abrasion
2. Answers may vary. Students should describe any three of the following: the presence of water to dissolve rocks, the presence of oxygen to cause oxidation, the presence of carbon dioxide dissolved in rainwater, the presence of living organisms, and the presence of acid rain.
3. The most important factors are type of rock and climate.
4. In hot, wet climates, rainfall provides the water needed for chemical changes and higher temperatures cause chemical reactions to occur faster.
5. Answers may vary. Students might suggest that they would see a crumbled rock, a rock with much larger cracks, or a rock with plants growing in the cracks.

Science at Home

Encourage students to try this model of ice wedging at home. Use a plastic straw. After freezing the straw overnight, students should observe that the ice has forced one or both of the clay plugs out of the straw because water expands when it freezes.

Performance Assessment

Skills Check Have students make a compare/contrast table that includes every agent of mechanical and chemical weathering.

G ◆ 45

Rock Shake

Preparing for Inquiry

Key Concept Both mechanical weathering and chemical weathering break down rocks into smaller pieces.

Skills Objectives Students will be able to:
- make predictions about whether an acid or water will weather limestone pieces more;
- control variables by setting up four different variations of weathering;
- create a data table by recording data related to change in mass and percent change in mass;
- draw conclusions about weathering from their data.

Time 30 minutes on Day 1; 30 minutes on Day 2

Advance Planning Collect and prepare the pieces of limestone at least a day in advance. Each student will need 80 pieces. Small limestone gravel is the best material to use. Use a hammer to break up any large pieces. Soak the limestone pieces in water 24 hours in advance.

The cloth students use should be about 10 × 10 centimeters; cheesecloth will work the best. The vinegar should be a vinegar-water solution. Make this in advance by using 75 percent white vinegar and 25 percent distilled water. The water used in containers A and B should be distilled water, because tap water is slightly acidic.

Since there are many varieties of limestone, you should perform the activity in advance at least once. Some limestone is very susceptible to change from acid, while other limestone is resistant to such change. Some limestone may break up more from shaking. By doing the activity in advance, you can determine likely changes in mass for the pieces in each container.

Designate a space for students to place their containers overnight. Have students write their initials on the masking tape label of each container to avoid confusion.

Alternative Materials If standard plastic containers are unavailable, use small plastic soft-drink bottles.

ROCK SHAKE

Which do you think would weather faster, a rock attacked by plant acids or a rock in the rushing waters of a stream? Many factors affect the rate at which rock weathers. In this lab, you will compare the rates of weathering that take place under different conditions.

Problem

How will shaking and acid conditions affect the rate at which limestone weathers?

Materials

300 mL of water
balance
paper towels
masking tape
2 pieces of thin cloth
marking pen or pencil
300 mL of vinegar, an acid
plastic graduated cylinder, 250 mL
80 small pieces of water-soaked limestone
4 watertight plastic containers with screw-on caps, 500-mL

Procedure

Part 1— Day 1

1. Using masking tape, label the four 500-mL containers A, B, C, and D.
2. Separate the 80 pieces of limestone into four sets of 20.
3. Copy the data table in your notebook. Then place the first 20 pieces of limestone on the balance and record their mass in the data table. Place the rocks in Container A.
4. Repeat Step 3 for the other sets of rocks and place them in containers B, C, and D.
5. Pour 150 mL of water into container A and container B. Put caps on both containers.
6. Pour 150 mL of vinegar into container C and also into container D. Put caps on both containers.
7. Predict the effect of weathering on the mass of the limestone pieces. Which will weather more: the limestone in water or the limestone in vinegar? (*Hint:* Vinegar is an acid.) Also predict the effect of shaking on the limestone in containers B and D. Record your predictions in your notebook.
8. Allow the pieces to soak overnight.

Container	Total Mass Start	Total Mass Next Day	Change in Mass	Percent Change in Mass
A (water, no shaking)				
B (water, shaking)				
C (vinegar, no shaking)				
D (vinegar, shaking)				

Guiding Inquiry

Introducing the Procedure

- After students have read the procedure, ask: **What variables are you testing in this experiment?** (*The effect of acid and the effect of shaking on limestone*)
- **What is the purpose of container A?** (*Since container A contains no acid and the pieces are not shaken, it is the control.*)

Troubleshooting the Experiment

- On Day 1, make sure students write their predictions in their journals.

- On Day 2, students should be able to see a clock so they can time how long they shake containers B and D. Students can work in pairs, with each student shaking one container. If students get tired, they can rest, as long as each container is shaken the same total amount of time.
- Demonstrate how to pour the water through the cloth. Advise students to pick out the 20 largest pieces, ignoring any tiny sediment.
- Help students determine percent change by doing an example problem on the board.

Part 2—Day 2

9. Screw the caps tightly on containers B and D. Shake both containers for 10 to 15 minutes. Make sure that each container is shaken for exactly the same amount of time and at the same intensity. After shaking, set the containers aside. Do not shake containers A and C.

10. Open the top of container A. Place one piece of thin cloth over the opening of the container. Carefully pour all of the water out through the cloth into a waste container. Be careful not to let any of the pieces flow out with the water. Dry these pieces carefully and record their mass in your data table.

11. Next, determine how much limestone was lost through weathering in container A. (*Hint:* Subtract the mass of the limestone pieces remaining on Day 2 from the mass of the pieces on Day 1.)

12. Repeat Steps 10 and 11 for containers B, C, and D.

Analyze and Conclude

1. Calculate the percent change in mass of the 20 pieces for each container.

$$\% \text{ change} = \frac{\text{Change in mass} \times 100}{\text{Total mass start}}$$

Record the results in the data table.

2. Do your data show a change in mass of the 20 pieces in each of the four containers?

3. Is there a greater change in total mass for the pieces in one container than for the pieces in another? Explain.

4. How correct were your predictions of how shaking and acid would affect the weathering of limestone? Explain.

5. If your data showed a greater change in the mass of the pieces in one of the containers, how might this change be explained?

6. **Think About It** Based on your data, which variable do you think was more responsible for breaking down the limestone: the vinegar or the shaking? Explain.

Design an Experiment

Would your results for this experiment change if you changed the variables? For example, you could soak or shake the pieces for a longer time, or test rocks other than limestone. You could also test whether adding more limestone pieces (30 rather than 20 in each set) would make a difference in the outcome. Design an experiment on the rate of weathering to test the effects of changing one of these variables. Have your teacher approve your plan before you begin.

Expected Outcome

The pieces in container D will show the greatest change in mass, because those pieces were subjected to both chemical and mechanical weathering (acid and shaking). The pieces in container A will show little or no change in mass, because they were subjected to neither chemical nor mechanical weathering. The pieces in container C will probably show a greater change in mass than the pieces in container B, depending on the type of limestone students use.

Program Resources

◆ **Teaching Resources** Skills Lab blackline masters, pp. 53–55

Media and Technology

 Lab Activity Videotape
Earth's Changing Surface, 3

Analyze and Conclude

1. The percent change in mass of the 20 pieces in each container will vary significantly, depending on the variety of limestone used, the original mass of the pieces, the strength of the acid, and the amount of shaking. The exact figures are unimportant. How the figures compare with one another will be telling.

2. Answers will vary. Students should see a change in mass of the pieces in containers B, C, and D. There should be little or no change in mass of the pieces in container A.

3. The pieces in container D should show the greatest change in total mass, because they were subjected to both the acid and the shaking. The pieces in container A should show little change in total mass, because they were not subject to acid or shaking.

4. Answers will vary according to predictions. Most students will probably have correctly predicted that the acid and shaking will cause the mass of the limestone pieces to change more than the mass of the pieces not exposed to these forms of "weathering."

5. The mass of the pieces in container D showed the greatest change because those pieces of limestone were both soaked overnight in acid and shaken the next day, while none of the pieces in the other containers were subjected to both types of weathering.

6. Answers will vary. Most students will suggest that the acid was more responsible for breaking down the limestone, because the change in mass of the pieces in container C was greater than the change in mass of the pieces in container B.

Extending the Inquiry

Design an Experiment Encourage students to continue testing limestone or other types of rock. Granite, for example, is more resistant to both acid and shaking. Different students can test different kinds of rocks, and then collaborate in a compare/contrast table.

Safety

Caution students to wear their goggles when pouring the vinegar and shaking the containers. Have them make sure the caps are screwed on tightly. Review the safety guidelines in Appendix A.

SCIENCE AND SOCIETY

Preserving Stone Monuments

Purpose Students will become more familiar with the pros and cons of preserving stone monuments.

Role Play

Time 40 minutes

After students have read the feature, divide the class into small groups and have them meet for 10 minutes to prepare for a panel discussion. Assign each group a position to support. One group could advocate restoring stone monuments whatever the cost. Another group could focus on instituting regulations to diminish air pollution around the world. Another group could advance the notion that there are much better ways to spend money, such as for famine relief. A fourth group could advocate covering important monuments until techniques can be developed to save them. Then invite all groups to participate in a UN-sponsored assembly where these matters can be discussed. Have a student volunteer moderate the discussion, and encourage groups to strongly express their positions though avoid any personal attacks.

Extend Encourage interested students to contact a local historical society to find out what stone structures in their area are threatened by weathering and pollution. Students could make a list of these structures, complete with locations, descriptions of the problems, and possible solutions. Consider having student volunteers meet and develop this list before the panel discussion.

You Decide

After the panel discussion has concluded, encourage students to reflect on what they've said and heard as they identify the problem and analyze the options. Then encourage each student to take a position by writing an advocacy letter to a public official. Assess these letters on the soundness of their argument, not on the position a student takes on the issue.

SCIENCE AND SOCIETY

Preserving Stone Monuments

A statue with a human head and a lion's body crouches in the desert beside the pyramids of Egypt. This is the great Sphinx. It was carved out of limestone about 4,500 years ago. Thousands of years of weathering by water, wind, and sand have worn away much of the Sphinx's face. In the 1800s, sand that had protected the Sphinx's body was cleared away. Weathering attacked the newly exposed parts of the Sphinx. Flakes and even chunks of stone fell from the statue. Workers tried to repair the Sphinx with cement. But the repairs weakened the statue and changed its shape.

The Issues

Should Structures Be Restored?
Weathering threatens many ancient stone monuments throughout the world. Pollutants in air and rain make stone weather faster. But there are ways to slow the weathering of a monument without changing or damaging it. In 1998, workers in Egypt completed a new restoration of the Sphinx. They removed the added cement. They replaced the damaged stones with new, hand-cut limestone blocks of the same size and weight. The new stone will help protect what remains of the monument. Visitors to the Sphinx will now see only the original statue and repairs made with original materials. The new repairs preserve the statue's original shape.

Most people want the Sphinx and other monuments to be restored. But restoration is time-consuming and very expensive. And in some cases, repair work can damage or change the original structure.

Can New Technology Slow Weathering?
Advances in technology may provide some solutions. At the Sphinx, scientists measure wind direction, wind speed, and moisture in the air. This information helps scientists follow the weathering process and provides data that will help prevent more damage. Similar instruments are used at other monuments.

Other scientists are working on a way of coating stone with a chemical compound to strengthen and repair the surface. So far, they have found a compound that sticks well to sandstone, but not to marble or limestone.

What Else Can People Do? Repair and restoration are not the only options. Some say that ancient monuments should be buried again after being uncovered by archaeologists. Some people suggest that the Sphinx itself should be reburied in the sand that protected it for so many centuries. But scholars, archaeologists, and tourists disagree. Meanwhile, as people seek solutions, rain, wind, sun, and polluted air continue to take their toll.

You Decide

1. Identify the Problem
In your own words, explain the difficulties involved in preserving ancient monuments.

2. Analyze the Options
List methods for preserving ancient buildings and monuments. Note the advantages and disadvantages of repair work, technology, and other approaches.

3. Find a Solution
Make a plan to preserve a monument in your city. Write your recommendations in the form of a letter to a city mayor or town council.

Background

Facts and Figures The deterioration of the Sphinx is not all modern. The nose has been missing since the fourteenth century, and the first repairs of the structure date from ancient times. In the 1990s, the Egyptian government undertook to repair the structure as best it could, keeping in mind that it will remain an ancient ruin.

The Sphinx is far from the only concern for those wanting to save ancient monuments. The Acropolis in Athens, Greece, is deteriorating at an alarming rate, in no small part because of the polluted Athens air. The acid precipitation in large cities takes a toll on all monuments. For example, a large granite obelisk, called Cleopatra's Needle, lasted over 3,000 years in Egypt. For most of this century, it has stood in New York City's Central Park. Now its hieroglyphics are almost obliterated.

2 Soil Formation and Composition

SECTION

Soil Formation and Composition

DISCOVER ·····················ACTIVITY···

What Is Soil?

1. Use a toothpick to separate a sample of soil into individual particles. With a hand lens, try to identify the different types of particles in the sample. Wash your hands when you are finished.

2. Write a "recipe" for the sample of soil, naming each of the "ingredients" that you think the soil contains. Include what percentage of each ingredient would be needed to make up the soil.

3. Compare your recipe with those of your classmates.

Think It Over
Forming Operational Definitions Based on your observations, how would you define *soil*?

A bare rock surface does not look like a spot where a plant could grow. But look more closely. In that hard surface is a small crack. Over many years, mechanical and chemical weathering will slowly enlarge the crack. Rain and wind will bring bits of weathered rock, dust, and dry leaves. The wind also may carry tiny seeds. With enough moisture, a seed will sprout and take root. Then, when the plant blossoms a few months later, the rock itself will seem to have burst into flower.

Soil Formation

The crack in the rock seems to have little in common with a flower garden containing thick, rich soil. But soil is what the weathered rock and other materials in the crack have started to become. **Soil** is the loose, weathered material on Earth's surface in which plants can grow. **Soil forms as rock is broken down by weathering and mixes with other materials on the surface.**

Soil is constantly being formed wherever bedrock is exposed. **Bedrock** is the solid layer of rock beneath the soil. Once exposed at the surface, bedrock gradually weathers into smaller and smaller particles that are the basic material of soil.

Figure 4 A crack between rocks holds just enough soil for this plant.

GUIDE FOR READING

◆ How does soil form?
◆ What is soil made of?
◆ What is the role of plants and animals in soil formation?

Reading Tip Before you read, rewrite the headings as *how, what, where,* and *why* questions. Then look for answers as you read.

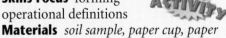 G ◆ 49

READING STRATEGIES

Vocabulary Call students' attention to the key term *soil horizon*. Most students know that *horizon* generally refers to where Earth and the sky meet. Explain that *horizon* comes from a Greek word for "boundary." The intersection of Earth and the sky is a boundary between the two. A soil horizon designates a boundary between two different layers in the soil.

Program Resources

◆ **Teaching Resources** 2-2 Lesson Plan, p. 45; 2-2 Section Summary, p. 46
◆ **Guided Study Workbook** Section 2-2

Objectives

After completing the lesson, students will be able to
◆ describe the composition of soil;
◆ explain how soil is formed and how soil horizons develop;
◆ identify the roles of plants and animals in soil formation.

Key Terms soil, bedrock, humus, loam, soil horizon, topsoil, subsoil, litter, decomposer

1 Engage/Explore

Activating Prior Knowledge

Ask students: **How would you describe the soil of this area in terms of color, feel, and makeup?** *(Answers will vary, depending on the local soil type. Students should mention whether the local soil is black, brown, or red; sandy or clayey; and so on.)* Then let students examine and feel a commercial potting soil. Challenge students to explain why that soil is different from the local soil.

········· DISCOVER ·········

Skills Focus forming operational definitions
Materials *soil sample, paper cup, paper towel, toothpick, hand lens*
Time 15 minutes
Tips Provide each student with about 50 mL of soil in a paper cup. You can collect this soil from your local area or buy commercial topsoil. Advise students to pour the sample onto a paper towel for examination.
Expected Outcome Students should observe a variety of different substances in the soil, including rock particles and organic matter. Their recipes should reflect these observations.
Think It Over Answers may vary. A typical answer might suggest that soil is a mixture of different substances, including sand, clay, rock particles, and material derived from living things.

Soil Formation

Using the Visuals: Figure 4

To emphasize the connection between weathering and soil formation, have students make a flowchart that shows how bedrock changes to become soil embedded in the crack of a rock.
learning modality: verbal

Soil Composition

Using the Visuals: Figure 5

After students have examined the circle graph, ask: **How is the large percentage of air and water related to the amount of humus in loam?** (*Humus helps create spaces for air and water.*) **If the percentage of clay greatly increased, say to 35 percent, how would that probably change the percentages of other materials? How would that affect the soil's quality for growth of plants?** (*Increasing the clay percentage would likely increase the water percentage, because clay soils hold water. The percentages of sand, silt, and air would probably, therefore, decrease. More water and less air would make the soil's quality for plant growth poorer.*)
learning modality: logical/ mathematical

Sharpen your Skills

Predicting

Time 5 minutes
Expected Outcome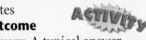
Answers may vary. A typical answer might suggest that adding compost would change the composition of the soil, increasing its percentage of organic matter and decreasing its percentage of other materials. The addition of compost will help the sandy soil hold more water and air and will make it more fertile.
Extend Ask: **Which soil horizon is the soil most like before the compost is added, and which is it like after compost is added?** (*It is like the B horizon before and the A horizon after.*) **learning modality: logical/mathematical**

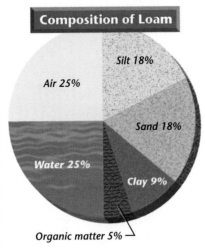

Composition of Loam

- Silt 18%
- Air 25%
- Sand 18%
- Water 25%
- Clay 9%
- Organic matter 5%

Figure 5 Loam, a type of soil, is made up of air, water, and organic matter as well as materials from weathered rock.
Interpreting Graphs What two materials make up the major portion of this soil?

Soil Composition

Soil is more than just particles of weathered bedrock. **Soil is a mixture of rock particles, minerals, decayed organic material, air, and water.**

The type of rock particles and minerals in any given soil depends on two factors: the bedrock that was weathered to form the soil and the type of weathering. Together, sand, silt, and clay make up the portion of soil that comes from weathered rock.

The decayed organic material in soil is humus. **Humus** (HYOO mus) is a dark-colored substance that forms as plant and animal remains decay. Humus helps create spaces in soil for the air and water that plants must have. Humus is also rich in the nitrogen, sulfur, phosphorus, and potassium that plants need to grow.

Soil Texture

Sand feels coarse and grainy, but clay feels smooth and silky. These differences are differences in texture. Soil texture depends on the size of individual soil particles.

The particles of rock in soil are classified by size. As you can see in Figure 6, the largest soil particles are gravel. Small pebbles and even large boulders are considered gravel. Next in size are particles of sand, followed by silt particles, which are smaller than sand. The smallest soil particles are clay. Clay particles are smaller than the period at the end of this sentence.

Soil texture is important for plant growth. Soil that is mostly clay has a dense, heavy texture. Some clay soils hold a lot of water, so plants grown in them may "drown" for lack of air. In contrast, sandy soil has a coarse texture. Water quickly drains through it, so plants may die for lack of water.

Soil that is made up of about equal parts of clay, sand, and silt is called **loam.** It has a crumbly texture that holds both air and water. Loam is best for growing most types of plants.

Figure 6 Soil particles range in size from gravel to clay particles too small to be seen by the unaided eye. The sand, silt, and clay shown here have been enlarged.

Gravel	Sand	Silt	Clay
2 mm and larger	less than 2 mm	less than $\frac{1}{16}$ mm	less than $\frac{1}{256}$ mm

Background

Facts and Figures The air in soil is important not only for plants but also for the microorganisms and animals in the soil. Without the air, the plants and other living things would not have the oxygen and carbon dioxide they need to carry out their life processes. The problem with too much water in soil is not the water itself but the resulting lack of air for the soil organisms.

Soil color is another characteristic scientists use to classify soils. A black or brown color usually indicates a high level of humus. A red or yellow color usually indicates the presence of iron compounds. A light gray or white color means different things depending on the climate. In wetter climates, it means the soil is low in iron; in drier areas, it means the soil is high in salts.

Soil Horizons

Soil formation continues over a long period of time. Gradually, soil develops layers called horizons. A **soil horizon** is a layer of soil that differs in color and texture from the layers above or below it.

If you dug a hole in the ground about half a meter deep, you would see the different soil horizons. Figure 7 shows how soil scientists classify the soil into three horizons. The A horizon is made up of **topsoil**, a crumbly, dark brown soil that is a mixture of humus, clay, and other minerals. The B horizon, often called **subsoil**, usually consists of clay and other particles washed down from the A horizon, but little humus. The C horizon contains only partly weathered rock.

☑ *Checkpoint* *What are soil horizons?*

The Rate of Soil Formation

The rate at which soil forms depends on the climate and type of rock. Remember that weathering occurs most rapidly in areas with a warm, rainy climate. As a result, soil develops more quickly in these areas. In contrast, weathering and soil formation take place slowly in areas where the climate is cold and dry.

Some types of rock weather and form soil faster than others. For example, limestone weathers faster than granite. Thus, soil forms more quickly from limestone than from granite.

Figure 7 Soil horizons form in three steps.

1. The C horizon forms as bedrock weathers and rock breaks up into soil particles.

2. The A horizon develops from the C horizon when plant roots weather the rock mechanically and chemically. Plants also add organic material to the soil.

3. The B horizon develops as rainwater washes clay and minerals from the A horizon to the B horizon.

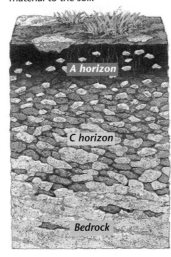

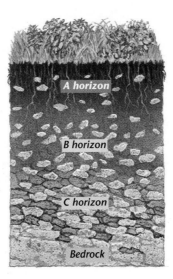

Sharpen your Skills

Predicting ACTIVITY

Gardeners often improve soil by adding materials to it. These added materials change the soil's composition. They make the soil more fertile or improve its ability to hold water. For example, a gardener might add compost (partly decayed leaves) to sandy soil. How would the compost change the sandy soil?

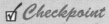

Answers to Self-Assessment

Caption Question

Figure 5 Air and water make up the major portion of loam.

☑ *Checkpoint*

A soil horizon is a layer of soil that differs in color and texture from the layers above or below it.

Soil Texture

Building Inquiry Skills: Comparing and Contrasting

Materials *hand lens, toothpick, white paper, samples of soil with different textures, including loam, sandy soil, clay soil, silty soil* ACTIVITY

Time 15 minutes

Obtain commercially classified soil samples. Then have pairs of students examine a sample of each. Encourage students to separate the gravel, sand, silt, clay, and humus in each sample and estimate the proportions. **learning modality: kinesthetic**

Soil Horizons

Using the Visuals: Figure 7

Materials *soil samples from different levels of a roadcut, white paper, toothpick, hand lens* ACTIVITY

Time 15 minutes

Collect soil samples from different levels of a local roadcut or similar vertical exposure of soil horizons. Then have small groups of students compare and contrast samples from each level, identifying the sample that most likely is from the A horizon, B horizon, and C horizon. **learning modality: visual**

The Rate of Soil Formation

Including All Students

To support students who need more help in making a connection between weathering and soil formation, ask: **What factors determine the rate of weathering?** *(Type of rock and climate)* **What factors determine the rate of soil formation?** *(Type of rock and climate)* Emphasize that weathering and soil formation are essentially parts of the same process, determined by the same factors. **learning modality: verbal**

Ongoing Assessment

Drawing Have students make a drawing of the A, B, and C horizons, writing a brief description of each.

Life in Soil

EXPLORING
Living Organisms in Soil

Give students a few minutes to examine the feature. Then elicit their experiences in observing these organisms. Ask: **What do decomposers make in soil as they break down plant and animal remains?** *(humus)* Emphasize that without humus in soil, most plants could not grow. **learning modality: verbal**

Integrating Life Science

Materials *plastic bag, soil sample, petri dish with agar and cover, incubator*

ACTIVITY

Time 5 minutes for setup; 5 minutes the next day for observation

To demonstrate the presence of bacteria in soil, place a soil sample in a plastic bag. Then, as students watch, sprinkle a tiny amount of the soil on nutrient agar in a petri dish. Cover the dish and incubate for 24 hours. Have students observe the results. They should see colonies of bacteria growing on the surface of the nutrient. (Follow the guidelines for disposing of bacteria cultures in Appendix A, Teacher's Edition. Make sure you follow all local and state guidelines for disposing of such cultures.) **learning modality: visual**

Including All Students

Materials *earthworms, large plastic container, plastic trash bag, shredded newspapers, fallen leaves*

ACTIVITY

Time 30 minutes

Encourage students who need additional challenges to find out how to build a worm compost bin in which plant materials can be added to make fertile soil for gardens. A typical bin is simply a large container with drainage holes in the bottom. To prepare the bin for worms, fill it halfway with strips of newspaper and fallen leaves. Then add worms and cover the container with plastic. The worms will digest most food scraps except meat and dairy products. **learning modality: kinesthetic**

Life in Soil

INTEGRATING LIFE SCIENCE Soil is more than just bits of rock. If you look closely at some soil, you can see that it is teeming with living things. **Some soil organisms mix the soil and make spaces in it for air and water. Other soil organisms make humus, the material that makes soil fertile.** Fertile soil is rich in nutrients that plants need, such as nitrogen and phosphorus.

Plants contribute most of the organic remains that form humus. As plants shed leaves, they form a loose layer called **litter.**

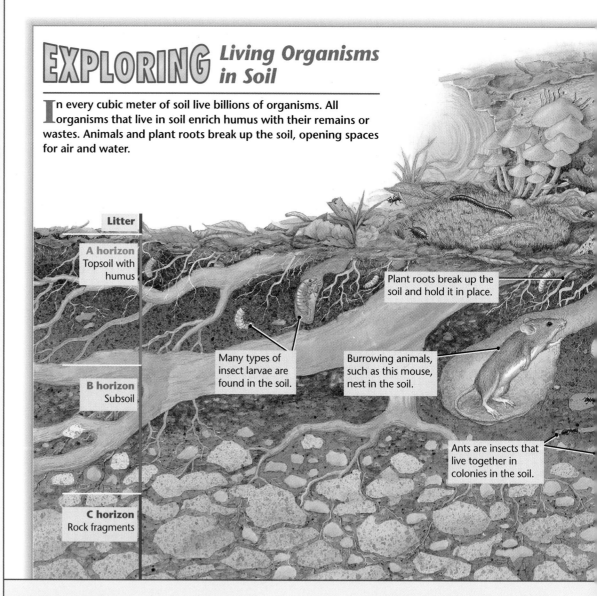

EXPLORING Living Organisms in Soil

In every cubic meter of soil live billions of organisms. All organisms that live in soil enrich humus with their remains or wastes. Animals and plant roots break up the soil, opening spaces for air and water.

Litter

A horizon Topsoil with humus

B horizon Subsoil

C horizon Rock fragments

Plant roots break up the soil and hold it in place.

Many types of insect larvae are found in the soil.

Burrowing animals, such as this mouse, nest in the soil.

Ants are insects that live together in colonies in the soil.

Background

History of Science In the 1940s at Rutgers University, microbiologist Selman Waksman began searching for soil organisms that produced chemicals that killed bacteria. He discovered a moldlike type of bacteria in the genus *Streptomyces* that was very effective. From that bacteria, the medicine streptomycin was made. It was Waksman who coined the term *antibiotic*. Further research discovered other soil microorganisms from which antibiotics were derived, including the tetracyclines.

Integrating Science Fresh soil owes its distinctive smell in part to chemicals produced by *Streptomyces* bacteria. Commercial potting soil does not have this smell because it has been sterilized. Once plants are added to the soil, the "fresh" smell becomes evident because bacteria arrives on plant roots.

When plants die, their remains fall to the ground and become part of the litter. Plant roots also die and begin to decay underground. Although plant remains are full of stored nutrients, they are not yet humus.

Humus forms in a process called decomposition. As decomposition occurs, organisms that live in soil turn dead organic material into humus. These organisms are called decomposers. **Decomposers** are the organisms that break the remains of dead organisms into smaller pieces and digest them with chemicals.

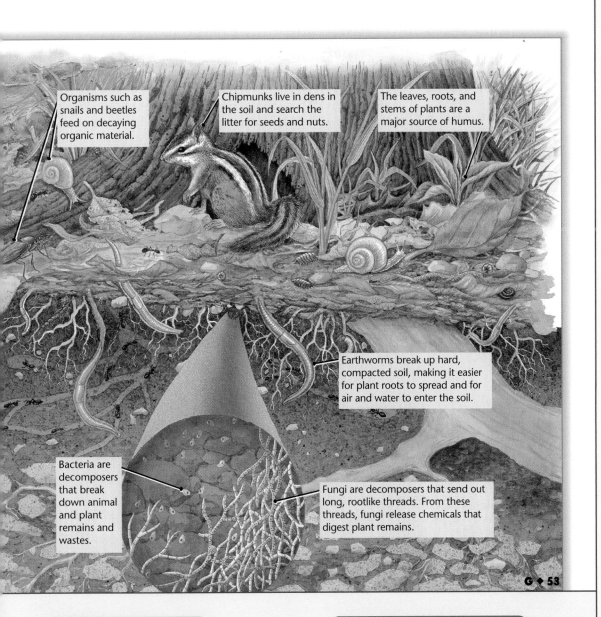

Organisms such as snails and beetles feed on decaying organic material.

Chipmunks live in dens in the soil and search the litter for seeds and nuts.

The leaves, roots, and stems of plants are a major source of humus.

Earthworms break up hard, compacted soil, making it easier for plant roots to spread and for air and water to enter the soil.

Bacteria are decomposers that break down animal and plant remains and wastes.

Fungi are decomposers that send out long, rootlike threads. From these threads, fungi release chemicals that digest plant remains.

G ◆ 53

Building Inquiry Skills: Calculating

Materials *soil sample, 2 measuring cups, trowel, water*

Time 15 minutes

Point out that many of the living things in soil need oxygen from air to carry out their life processes. Then challenge small groups of students to determine the amount of air in a soil sample by adding a measured volume of soil to a measuring cup and then pouring an equal volume of water into the cup. The water will fill the air spaces in the soil, and as a result, the amount of soil and water in the cup will be less than the two volumes added together. Students can find the volume of air in the original volume of soil by subtracting the final volume in the cup from the sum of the original volumes of soil and water. **learning modality: logical/mathematical**

Inquiry Challenge

Divide the class into small groups, and have each group develop a hypothesis about how well plants will grow in soil that contains no living organisms. After groups have written a hypothesis, challenge them to design an experiment that can test their hypothesis. A typical experiment might involve eliminating living things from a soil sample by removing worms and other animals and using a microwave oven to kill fungi and bacteria. (You might need to suggest this part of the procedure to students.) Then seeds can be planted in the sterile soil. Growth of these plants can be compared with a control—plants growing in normal soil. Have students discuss their groups' designs, modify them as needed, and then carry out their revised designs. **cooperative learning**

Ongoing Assessment

Oral Presentation Call on students at random to explain how each different kind of soil organism contributes to soil formation.

G ◆ 53

Life in Soil, continued

Skills Focus drawing conclusions

Materials *metric ruler, string, stakes, trowel, hand lens*

Time 30 minutes

Tips Students can carry out this investigation on the school grounds or on a private, vacant lot. For either option, permission should be obtained in advance. Choose areas that are not completely sod-covered, and advise students not to remove plants from their sites. Encourage students to keep notes of their observations as they go along. To help students observe the materials in the soil, give each student a piece of white table paper on which they can spread out their diggings. The light background will make it easier for students to observe the makeup of the soil.

Expected Outcome Students should find a variety of materials in their square area, including rocks, sand, silt, clay, insects, worms, plants, and even human-made objects. Students can draw conclusions about the soil's fertility based on its composition, particularly the amount of humus in it, and on the kinds of plants growing in the area.

Extend Encourage interested students to examine a second plot of ground in a very different location. For example, if the first was in a field, the second might be in a forest or along a stream. Students can compare and contrast what they observe in the two different places.

learning modality: kinesthetic

Soil Types in the United States

Real-Life Learning

Obtain a soil profile of the local soil. Your public library may have soil profiles of your county. If not, contact either a federal farm agency or an office of the state department of natural resources or agriculture in your area. Give small groups copies of the profile, and challenge them to interpret its information. Then review their findings in a whole-class discussion. **learning modality: verbal**

A Square Meter of Soil

1. Outdoors, measure an area of one square meter. Mark your square with string.
2. Observe the color and texture of the surface soil. Is it dry or moist? Does it contain sand, clay, or gravel? Are there plants, animals, or humus?
3. Use a trowel to dig down several centimeters into the soil. What is the soil's color and texture there?
4. When you finish, leave the soil as you found it. Wash your hands.

Drawing Conclusions What can you conclude about the soil's fertility? What evidence supports your conclusions?

Figure 8 Earthworms break up the soil, allowing in air and water. An earthworm eats its own weight in soil every day.

Fungi, protists, bacteria, and worms are the main soil decomposers. Fungi are organisms such as molds and mushrooms. Fungi grow on, and digest, plant remains. Bacteria are microscopic decomposers that cause decay. Bacteria attack dead organisms and their wastes in soil. Other very small animals, such as mites and worms, also decompose dead organic material and mix it with the soil.

Earthworms do most of the work of mixing humus with other materials in soil. As earthworms eat their way through the soil, they carry humus down to the subsoil and subsoil up to the surface. Earthworms also pass out the soil they eat as waste. The waste soil is enriched with substances that plants need to grow, such as nitrogen.

Many burrowing mammals such as mice, moles, prairie dogs, and gophers break up hard, compacted soil and mix humus through it. These animals also add nitrogen to the soil when they excrete waste. They add organic material when they die and decay.

Earthworms and burrowing animals also help to aerate, or mix air into, the soil. Plant roots need the oxygen that this process adds to the soil.

☑ *Checkpoint* How do decomposers contribute to the formation of soil?

Soil Types in the United States

If you were traveling across the hills of north-central Georgia, you would see soils that seem to be made of red clay. In other parts of the country, soils can be black, brown, yellow, or gray. In the United States alone, differences in climate and local bedrock have led to the formation of thousands of different types of soil.

Background

Integrating Science The amount of living organic matter in soil varies greatly. In typical topsoil found in the eastern United States, living organisms make up about 0.2 percent of the top 15 cm of soil. In 1 hectare (which is over twice the size of an acre), there are about 2,000 kg of living roots, about 700 kg of animals (mostly worms), about 500 kg of bacteria, and about 400 kg of fungi.

Facts and Figures In classifying soils, scientists consider the physical and chemical properties of the soil, much as geologists consider similar properties in classifying rocks. Climate is also a major factor in classification because it is so important in soil formation. Among other things, climate determines temperature, precipitation, vegetation, and kind and amount of soil organisms.

Soils of North America

☐	**Tundra soils**	Form where it is cold year-round; thin soil with little humus.
☐	**Northern forest soils**	Form in cool, wet climates; range from thick and fertile to thin with little humus.
☐	**Prairie soils**	Form in cool, dry climates of grasslands; topsoil thick and rich in humus.
☐	**Mountain soils**	Topsoil often thin because cold temperatures slow chemical weathering and erosion causes soil loss.
☐	**Southern forest soils**	Form in warm, wet climates; may be low in humus.
☐	**Desert soils**	Form in dry areas with few plants and little chemical weathering; often sandy, thin soil that is low in humus.
☐	**Tropical soils**	Form in wet, tropical climates; often low in humus and minerals.

Scientists classify the different types of soil into groups. These groups are based partly on the climate in a region. The most common plants found in a region are also used to help classify the soil. In addition, scientists classify soil by its composition—whether it is rocky, sandy, or rich in clay. Major soil types found in North America include forest, prairie, desert, mountain, tundra, and tropical soils. Look at Figure 9 to see where each of the major soil types is found. Which soil type is found in your part of the country?

Figure 9 An area's climate and plant life help to determine what type of soil forms from bedrock. *Interpreting Maps Recall that soil forms more rapidly in warm, wet areas than in cold, dry areas. Which types of soil on the map would you expect to form most slowly?*

Section 2 Review

1. What role does weathering play in the formation of soil?
2. What are the different materials that make up soil?
3. How do plants and animals affect the formation and composition of soil?
4. How do forest soils differ from prairie soils?
5. **Thinking Critically Relating Cause and Effect** Earthworms breathe by absorbing air in the soil through their skin. Why do you think earthworms crawl to the surface when it rains? Explain.

Check Your Progress
CHAPTER PROJECT 2

Obtain samples of the soil and growing materials you will use to grow your bean seeds. Choices include sand, vermiculite, gravel, potting soil, and local topsoil. **CAUTION:** *Avoid collecting soil near animal droppings. Wash your hands after handling the soil.* Make notes describing each sample. Predict which soil or mixture will be best for the growth of bean seeds. Design a method for recording the growth of your bean plants. Plant the bean seeds in the growing materials.

Chapter 2 **G ◆ 55**

Program Resources

◆ **Teaching Resources** 2-2 Review and Reinforce, p. 47; 2-2 Enrich, p. 48

Media and Technology

 Transparencies "Soils of North America," Transparency 8

Answers to Self-Assessment

Caption Question

Figure 9 Tundra soils and desert soils would probably form most slowly.

☑ *Checkpoint*

Decomposers turn dead organic material into humus.

Using the Visuals: Figure 9

Ask students: **What are the two main variables that determine a region's climate?** (*Average temperature and average rainfall*) Then guide students to understand that those variables also determine the common plants as well as the kind and rate of weathering of the bedrock of the region. Since soil is a mixture of rock and organic materials, climate greatly determines soil type.
learning modality: verbal

3 Assess

Section 2 Review Answers

1. Soil forms as rock is broken down by weathering and mixes with other materials on the surface.
2. Rock particles, minerals, decayed organic material, air, and water
3. Some soil organisms mix the soil and make spaces in it for air and water. Other soil organisms make humus, the material that makes soil fertile.
4. Prairie soils have topsoil that is thick and rich in humus, while northern and southern forest soils may be low in humus.
5. When the soil becomes full of water, there are no spaces for air in the soil. Worms must crawl to the surface to find air.

Check Your Progress
CHAPTER PROJECT 2

Make sure groups have chosen the soils they will use and planted the bean seeds. Each student should write a description of each soil and make a prediction about which soil will prove best for plant growth. Demonstrate how to plant the seeds in soil. Provide places for groups to place their growing plants.

Performance Assessment

Writing Challenge students to design and write a two-page pamphlet, such as a local park might hand out, that explains the formation and composition of the local soil. This pamphlet should be complete with drawings of soil horizons and any other relevant visual aids.

G ◆ 55

Careers in Science

Getting to Know the Soil

Preparing for Inquiry

Key Concept Scientists classify soil by its composition.

Skills Objectives Students will be able to:
◆ observe a soil sample to determine its composition;
◆ infer the type of environment from which the soil came;
◆ pose questions to help determine the soil's fertility.

Time 40 minutes

Advance Planning Collect soil at least a day in advance, and make sure the soil is relatively dry. Use a balance to prepare individual samples of 20–30 grams each.

Guiding Inquiry

Introducing the Procedure
Ask students: **What materials do you expect to find in a soil sample?** *(Rock fragments, sand, silt, clay, organic material)* **How do you predict that each of these materials will be affected by water?** *(The rocks and sand will look wet; the silt and clay will cloud the water; organic material will probably float.)*

Troubleshooting the Experiment
◆ Students can observe both the wet and dry soil under the stereomicroscope. Advise students to leave the wet soil in the petri dish.

Expected Outcome
Specific outcomes will depend on the composition of the soil samples used. All students should be able to observe various characteristics of their sample.

Analyze and Conclude
1. Students should notice various characteristics, including color and texture.
2. From observations of particle size, texture, and how water changed the sample, students should be able to estimate what proportions of the sample are sand, clay, silt, and organic material. Students may be most surprised by the kinds of organic material in the sample.

3. Answers will vary. Students should support their inferences with evidence from their observations.
4. Questions will vary. *Sample questions:* What percentage of the soil is composed of humus? What is the texture of the soil?

Extending the Inquiry
More to Explore Have soil samples from different locations available. They should find that samples from different locations have different characteristics.

Careers in Science

Getting to Know the Soil

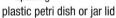

Soil scientists observe soil to determine its composition and how well it holds water. Farmers use this information in growing their crops.

Problem
What are the characteristics of a sample of soil?

Skills Focus
observing, inferring, posing questions

Materials
20–30 grams of soil
plastic spoon
plastic dropper
toothpick
water
stereomicroscope
graph paper ruled with 1- or 2-mm spacing
plastic petri dish or jar lid

Procedure

1. Your teacher will give you a dry sample of soil. As you observe the sample, record your observations in your lab notebook.
2. Spread half of the sample on the graph paper. Spread the soil thinly so that you can see the lines on the paper through the soil. Using the graph paper as a background, estimate the sizes of the particles that make up the soil.
3. Place the rest of the sample in the palm of your hand, rub it between your fingers, and squeeze it. Is it soft or gritty? Does it clump together or crumble when you squeeze it?
4. Place about half the sample in a plastic petri dish. Using the dropper, add water one drop at a time. Watch how the sample changes. Does any material in the sample float? As the sample gets wet, do you notice any odor?
5. Look at some of the soil under the stereomicroscope. (*Hint:* Use the toothpick to examine the particles in the soil.) Sketch what you see. Label the particles, such as gravel, organic matter, or strangely shaped grains.
6. Clean up and dispose of your soil sample as directed by your teacher. **CAUTION:** *Wash your hands when you finish handling the soil.*

Analyze and Conclude
1. What did you notice about the appearance of the soil sample when you first obtained it?
2. What can you infer about the composition of the soil from the different sizes of its particles? From your observations of its texture? From how the sample changed when water was added? What surprised you the most about the composition of your sample?
3. Based on the composition of your soil sample, can you determine the type of environment from which it was taken?
4. **Apply** List several questions that a soil scientist would need to answer to determine whether a soil sample was good for growing flowers or vegetables. Did your observations answer these questions for your soil sample?

More to Explore
Repeat the procedure using a soil sample from a different location. How does it compare with the first soil sample you tested?

Program Resources
◆ **Teaching Resources** Real-World Lab blackline masters, pp. 56–57

Media and Technology
Lab Activity Videotape
Earth's Changing Surface, 4

SECTION 3 Soil Conservation

INTEGRATING ENVIRONMENTAL SCIENCE

SECTION 3 Soil Conservation

DISCOVER ·ACTIVITY· · · · ·

How Can You Keep Soil From Washing Away?

1.  Pour about 500 mL of soil into a pie plate, forming a pile.

2. Devise a way to keep the soil from washing away when water is poured over it. To protect the pile of soil, you may use craft sticks, paper clips, pebbles, modeling clay, strips of paper, or other materials approved by your teacher.

3. After arranging your materials to protect the soil, hold a container containing 200 mL of water about 20 cm above the center of the soil. Slowly pour the water in a stream onto the pile of soil.

4. Compare your pan of soil with those of your classmates.

Think It Over

Observing Based on your observations, what do you think is the best way to prevent soil on a slope from washing away?

Suppose you were a settler traveling west in the early 1800s. Much of your journey would have been through vast, open grasslands called prairies. After the forests and mountains of the East, the prairies were an amazing sight. Grass taller than a person rippled and flowed in the wind like a sea of green.

The prairie soil was very fertile. It was rich with humus because of the tall grass. The **sod**—the thick mass of tough roots at the surface of the soil—kept the soil in place and held onto moisture.

The prairies covered a vast area. They included the eastern parts of Kansas, Nebraska, North and South Dakota, as well as Iowa and Illinois. Today, farms growing crops such as corn, soybeans, and wheat have replaced the prairies. But the prairie soils are still among the most fertile in the world.

GUIDE FOR READING

◆ Why is soil one of Earth's most valuable resources?

◆ What caused the Dust Bowl?

◆ What are some ways that soil can be conserved?

Reading Tip As you read, make a list of human activities that can harm the soil and a list of activities that can help save the soil.

The Value of Soil

Soil is one of Earth's most valuable resources because everything that lives on land depends directly or indirectly on soil. Plants depend directly on the soil to live and grow. Animals depend on plants—or on other animals that depend on plants—for food. Soil is a renewable resource that can be found wherever weathering occurs. But soil formation takes a long time. It can take hundreds of years for just a few centimeters of soil to form. The thick, fertile soil of the prairies took many thousands of years to develop.

Prairie grasses and wildflowers ▶

G ◆ 57

Program Resources

◆ **Teaching Resources** 2-3 Lesson Plan, p. 49; 2-3 Section Summary, p. 50

Safety

Caution students to wear their goggles when handling the soil sample and to wash their hands thoroughly when finished. Review the safety guidelines in Appendix A.

READING STRATEGIES

Reading Tip Harmful activities mentioned in the section include exhausting the soil and poor farming practices, including overgrazing. Beneficial activities include contour plowing and conservation plowing. Encourage students to add to their lists any practices that arise during class discussions or as a result of activities and research they do about soil conservation.

INTEGRATING ENVIRONMENTAL SCIENCE

SECTION 3 Soil Conservation

Objectives

After completing the lesson, students will be able to

◆ explain why soil is a valuable resource;

◆ list ways that soil can be lost or destroyed;

◆ identify some ways that soil can be conserved.

Key Terms sod, Dust Bowl, soil conservation, contour plowing, conservation plowing

1 Engage/Explore

Activating Prior Knowledge

Recall for students a place in town that is a wide area of dirt, such as a construction site or a vacant lot used for parking. Ask: **What happens when it rains?** (*The area becomes a sea of mud.*) **What is the water like that runs off the area?** (*It is dirty, full of mud.*) **Is there anything that could be done to prevent this erosion of soil?** (*Answers will vary. Some students might suggest barriers. Others might suggest planting grass or some other ground cover.*)

· · · · · · · · DISCOVER · · · · · · · · ·

Focus observing
Materials *soil, pie plate, water, container, craft sticks, paper clips, pebbles, modeling clay, paper*
Time 15 minutes
Tips Provide students with soil in measured amounts, or prepare each pie plate with 500 mL of soil before class. Encourage students to be creative in their arrangements.
Expected Outcome Students should discover a variety of ways to prevent the soil from washing away.
Think It Over Answers may vary. A typical answer might suggest that a barrier of clay or clay mixed with other materials best prevents soil from washing away.

2 Facilitate

The Value of Soil

Using the Visuals: Figure 10

After students have examined the map and read the caption, ask: **What does it mean for soil to be "fertile"?** *(Rich in materials needed for plants to grow.)* **What substance must be in soil for it to be fertile?** *(humus)* Have students re-examine the table of soils in Figure 9. Which type of soil is rich in humus? *(prairie soils)* Point out that most of the farming areas in the world are where these rich soils are found. **learning modality: verbal**

Real-Life Learning

Have student volunteers call several local garden stores and greenhouses to find out how much it would cost to have a truckload of topsoil delivered to a site near the school. Suggest that they price enough to cover a garden of 10 m² at a thickness of about 10 cm. Have these students report their findings to the class. **learning modality: verbal**

Soil Damage and Loss

Inquiry Challenge

Materials *soil, sod, water, 2 painter's pans* **ACTIVITY**
Time 20 minutes

Ask: **How can plants help reduce loss of soil?** Challenge small groups to form a hypothesis that addresses that question and then design an experiment that can test their hypothesis. A typical experiment might entail comparing the difference in the amount of soil in runoff when water is poured on a slope of bare soil and on a slope of soil covered by sod. Review groups' plans, and then encourage students to carry out their experiments. **cooperative learning**

Earth's Food-Growing Regions

KEY
Major farming region
Livestock-raising region

Figure 10 The world's best soils for farming often are found in river valleys or interior and coastal plains. Areas too dry, too mountainous, or not fertile enough for farming may be used for grazing cattle, sheep, or other livestock.

Figure 11 George Washington Carver (1864–1943) taught new methods of soil conservation to farmers in the South.

Fertile soil is valuable because there is a limited supply. Less than one eighth of the land on Earth has soils that are well suited for farming. Figure 10 shows where these regions are located. In many areas, farming is difficult and little food is produced. The reasons for this include low soil fertility, lack of water, steep slopes, or a short growing season.

☑ *Checkpoint* *Why is soil valuable?*

Soil Damage and Loss

Soil is one of Earth's most important resources. But soil can be lost or damaged. For example, soil can become exhausted, or lose its fertility. This occurred in large parts of the South in the late 1800s. Soils in which only cotton had been grown were exhausted. Many farmers abandoned their farms. Early in the 1900s in Alabama, a scientist named George Washington Carver developed new crops and farming methods that helped to restore soil fertility in the South. Peanuts were one crop that helped make the soil fertile again.

Soil can be lost to erosion by water and wind. Water erosion can occur wherever soil is not protected by plant cover. Plants break the force of falling rain, and plant roots hold the soil together. Wind erosion is another cause of soil loss. Wind erosion, combined with farming methods that were not suited to dry conditions, caused the Dust Bowl on the Great Plains.

Background

History of Science George Washington Carver was born a slave in Missouri at the end of the Civil War, shortly before slavery was abolished. An orphan, Carver was raised by a family that provided for his education. He ultimately received degrees from Iowa State Agricultural College, along with many awards and honors for his work.

Carver spent most of his adult life as director of the Department of Agricultural Research at the Tuskegee Institute in Tuskegee, Alabama. He helped the South enormously by showing farmers how to enrich soil that was infertile due to growing only cotton and tobacco. To accomplish this, Carver used muck from swamps and composted organic matter. He also advised the planting of peanuts and sweet potatoes, crops that enrich the soil.

The Dust Bowl

Toward the end of the 1800s, farmers had settled most of the prairies. New settlers moved on to the Great Plains farther west. This region sweeps eastward from the base of the Rocky Mountains across the western parts of North and South Dakota, Nebraska, Kansas, Oklahoma, and Texas.

The soil of the Great Plains is fertile. But there is an important difference between the Great Plains and the prairie. Rainfall decreases steadily from east to west across the Great Plains. The tall grass gives way to shorter, thinner grass needing less moisture. **Plowing removed the grass from the Great Plains and exposed the soil. In times of drought, the topsoil quickly dried out, turned to dust, and blew away.**

By 1930, almost all of the Great Plains had been turned into farms or ranches. Then, several very dry years in a row turned the soil on parts of the Great Plains to dust. The wind blew the soil east in great, black clouds. The clouds turned the sky dark as far away as Chicago and even New York City. Eventually the soil blew out over the Atlantic Ocean, where it was lost forever.

The problem was most serious in the southern Plains states. There, the drought and topsoil loss lasted until 1938. This area, shown in Figure 12, was called the **Dust Bowl.** Many people in the Dust Bowl states abandoned their farms and moved away.

Language Arts CONNECTION

Woody Guthrie wrote and sang folk songs. Guthrie lived in Oklahoma and Texas at the time of the Dust Bowl and wrote a series of songs called "Dust Bowl Ballads." (A ballad is a song that tells a story.) One of the ballads describes how

> We saw outside our window
> Where wheat fields they had grown
> Was now a rippling ocean
> Of dust the wind had blown.

In Your Journal

Write the words for a ballad that tells the story of a problem in your community and how you think the problem should be solved.

Figure 12 The Dust Bowl included western Oklahoma and parts of the surrounding states. Wind blew dry particles of soil into great clouds of dust that traveled thousands of kilometers.

KEY
- Dust Bowl
- Other areas affected by dust storms

MONTANA · NORTH DAKOTA · WYOMING · SOUTH DAKOTA · NEBRASKA · IOWA · ROCKY MOUNTAINS · COLORADO · KANSAS · MISSOURI · NEW MEXICO · OKLAHOMA · TEXAS · Mississippi River

G ◆ 59

The Dust Bowl

Using the Visuals: Figure 12

To tie concepts together, have students compare the map in this figure with the map of soil types in Figure 9, as well as the map of landform regions in Figure 3 in Chapter 1. Ask: **In what landform region did the Dust Bowl occur?** *(In the Great Plains landform region)* **What soil types are found in that region?** *(Prairie soils and desert soils)* Point out that there is no exact boundary between the two. Instead, prairie soils gradually become desert soils as you go west. **Why would plowing and drought greatly affect desert soils?** *(They are sandy and thin, with little humus.)* **learning modality: visual**

Language Arts CONNECTION

Woody Guthrie (1912–1967) first became famous as a chronicler of the "Dust Bowl refugees" or "Okies," who fled the devastation of the Dust Bowl for California and other Western states in the 1930s. Many libraries have recordings of his "Dust Bowl Ballads." They include songs of many verses that describe living through dust storms and other hardships. Perhaps the most famous in the collection is "So Long, It's Been Good to Know You." Guthrie's most noted song, "This Land Is Your Land," was written later in his life.

In Your Journal

A folk ballad often has four-line verses, with rhymes of the last words of every other line. Encourage students to write two or three verses. Guthrie and other folk balladeers often wrote new words to tunes of popular songs. To give students a structure on which to write their verses, they could write new words to a song they know. **learning modality: verbal**

Ongoing Assessment

Skills Check Have students make a flowchart that shows what caused people to leave the Great Plains in the 1930s.

Answers to Self-Assessment

Checkpoint

Soil is valuable because everything that lives on land depends directly or indirectly on soil.

Soil Conservation

3 Assess

Figure 13 Contour plowing (above) and conservation plowing (below) help prevent soil erosion. *Predicting How might conservation plowing affect the amount of humus in the soil?*

Soil Conservation

The Dust Bowl helped people appreciate the value of soil. In the 1930s, with government support, farmers in the Great Plains and throughout the country began to take better care of their land. They adopted methods of farming that helped save the soil. Some of the methods were new. Others had been practiced for hundreds of years.

Farmers in the United States adopted modern methods of soil conservation. **Soil conservation** is the management of soil to prevent its destruction. **Two ways that soil can be conserved include contour plowing and conservation plowing.**

Contour plowing is the practice of plowing fields along the curves of a slope. This helps slow the runoff of excess rainfall and prevents it from washing the soil away.

Conservation plowing disturbs the soil and its plant cover as little as possible. Dead weeds and stalks of the previous year's crop are left in the ground to help return soil nutrients, retain moisture, and hold soil in place. This method is also called low-till or no-till plowing.

In grasslands such as the Great Plains, grazing livestock is an important use of the land. But if too many cattle graze on the grass during dry periods, the grass cover protecting the soil may be damaged. This exposes the soil to both wind and water erosion. To prevent damage to the soil, ranchers must limit the size of their herds.

Section 3 Review

1. Explain the importance of soil as one of Earth's resources.
2. How did settlers on the Great Plains help create the Dust Bowl?
3. What are some techniques that farmers use to conserve soil?
4. **Thinking Critically** **Problem Solving** If you had to plant corn on a steep hillside, how would you do it so that rain would not wash the soil away?

Check Your Progress · CHAPTER PROJECT 2

Check your bean seeds daily and water them as needed. Count and record the number of seeds that sprout. You can also measure the height of each plant, count the number of leaves, and note the leaf color. After about 14 days, you should be able to make comparisons. What differences did you observe in the bean plants grown in the different materials? When did these differences appear? Based on your data, what conclusions can you draw about which material is best for growing bean plants?

SECTION 1 Rocks and Weathering

Key Ideas
- Rock weathers, or wears down, when it is exposed to air, water, weather, and living things at Earth's surface.
- Mechanical weathering breaks rock into smaller pieces. The agents of mechanical weathering include freezing and thawing, release of pressure, growth of plants, actions of animals, and abrasion.
- Chemical weathering changes the mineral content of rock. The agents of chemical weathering are water, oxygen, carbon dioxide, living organisms, and acid rain.
- Climate and rock type determine how fast weathering occurs.

Key Terms

weathering	ice wedging
erosion	chemical weathering
mechanical weathering	permeable
abrasion	

SECTION 2 Soil Formation and Composition

Key Ideas
- Soil is made of small particles of rock mixed with the decaying remains of organisms.
- Soil forms in layers called horizons as bedrock weathers and organic materials build up.
- The three soil horizons are the A horizon, the B horizon, and the C horizon. The A horizon is made up of topsoil, which is rich in humus. The B horizon consists of clay and other particles washed down from the A horizon, but little humus. The C horizon is made up of partly weathered rock without clay or humus.
- Plants and animals break up and mix the soil, and also add the organic materials that form humus.

Key Terms

soil	loam	subsoil
bedrock	soil horizon	litter
humus	topsoil	decomposers

SECTION 3 Soil Conservation

INTEGRATING ENVIRONMENTAL SCIENCE

Key Ideas
- Soil is a valuable resource because life on land depends on it, yet it forms very slowly.
- Soil can be eroded away and its fertility can be decreased by improper farming practices.
- Soil can be conserved and its fertility can be maintained by using various methods of soil conservation.

Key Terms

sod	contour plowing
Dust Bowl	conservation plowing
soil conservation	

Organizing Information

Concept Map Copy the concept map about soil horizons onto a piece of paper. Then complete it and add a title. (For more on concept maps, see the Skills Handbook.)

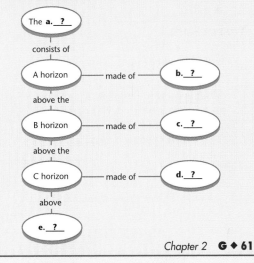

Organizing Information

Concept Map Sample Title: *Soil Horizons* **a.** soil **b.** topsoil **c.** subsoil **d.** partly weathered rock **e.** bedrock

Media and Technology

Interactive Student Tutorial CD-ROM G-2

Computer Test Bank *Earth's Changing Surface*, Chapter 2 Test

Program Resources

- **Teaching Resources** Chapter 2 Project Scoring Rubric, p. 40; Chapter 2 Performance Assessment, pp. 145–147; Chapter 2 Test, pp. 148–151

Reviewing Content

Multiple Choice

1. b **2.** b **3.** a **4.** d **5.** c

True or False

6. Erosion **7.** true **8.** humus **9.** true
10. true

Checking Concepts

11. Rapid mechanical weathering is more likely where the temperature shifts back and forth because each time water expands and contracts, ice wedging would widen and deepen cracks in rocks.

12. Soil forms as rock is broken down by weathering and mixes with other materials on the surface.

13. Topsoil contains more humus than subsoil.

14. Plants act as an agent of mechanical weathering when their roots pry apart cracks in rocks and as an agent of chemical weathering when their roots produce a weak acid that slowly dissolves rocks.

15. Grass kept the soil in place and held onto moisture.

16. Conservation plowing disturbs the soil and plant cover as little as possible, thus keeping the soil in place, retaining moisture, and conserving soil nutrients.

17. A typical answer should mention how earthworms break up hard, compacted soil, decompose organic material in soil, mix humus with other materials, enrich soil with their wastes, and aerate the soil.

Thinking Critically

18. Breaking rocks into pieces increases the rate at which the rock will weather chemically because breaking the rock exposes more surface area to weathering agents.

19. A. mechanical weathering
B. chemical weathering **C.** chemical weathering

20. Answers may vary. A typical hypothesis should suggest that weathering would be much slower on the moon because water and air are important agents of both mechanical and chemical weathering.

21. Answers may vary. A typical answer may mention that type of rock and climate determine the rate at which the rock weathers and soil forms. Thus, one

---

Reviewing Content

 For more review of key concepts, see the Interactive Student Tutorial CD-ROM.

Multiple Choice
Choose the letter of the best answer.

1. The most important force of mechanical weathering in cool climates is
a. oxidation.
b. freezing and thawing.
c. animal activity.
d. abrasion.

2. Most chemical weathering is caused by
a. acid rain.
b. water.
c. oxygen.
d. carbon dioxide.

3. The B horizon consists of
a. subsoil.
b. topsoil.
c. rock particles.
d. bedrock.

4. One of the best types of soil for farming is
a. forest soil.
b. mountain soil.
c. tropical soil.
d. prairie soil.

5. Most of the work of mixing humus into the soil is done by
a. fungi.
b. bacteria.
c. earthworms.
d. mites.

True or False
If the statement is true, write true. If it is false, change the underlined word or words to make the statement true.

6. <u>Mechanical weathering</u> is the movement of rock particles by wind, water, or ice.

7. Weathering occurs faster in a <u>wet</u> climate.

8. The decayed organic material in soil is called <u>loam</u>.

9. <u>Fungi</u> produce chemicals that digest plant remains.

10. Scientists classify types of soil based partly on a region's <u>climate</u>.

Checking Concepts

11. Where is mechanical weathering likely to occur more quickly: where the winter temperature usually stays below freezing, or where it more often shifts back and forth around the freezing point? Explain.

12. Briefly describe how soil is formed.

13. Which contains more humus, topsoil or subsoil?

14. Explain how plants can act as agents of both mechanical and chemical weathering.

15. What role did grass play in conserving the soil of the prairies?

16. How does conservation plowing contribute to soil conservation?

17. Writing to Learn Write a description of your life as an earthworm. What would it be like to live in the soil? What would you see? What would you eat? How would you move through the soil? How would you change it?

Thinking Critically

18. Predicting Suppose mechanical weathering breaks a rock into pieces. How would this affect the rate at which the rock weathers chemically?

19. Classifying Classify the following examples as either mechanical weathering or chemical weathering:
A. Cracks appear in a sidewalk next to a large tree.
B. A piece of limestone develops holes like Swiss cheese.
C. A rock exposed at the surface slowly turns reddish brown.

20. Developing Hypotheses On the moon there is no air or water. Develop a hypothesis about how fast rocks would weather on the moon compared with their rate of weathering on Earth. Explain.

21. Relating Cause and Effect Two rocks, each in a different location, have been weathering for the same amount of time. Mature soil has formed from one rock but only immature soil from the other. What factors might have caused this difference in rate of soil formation?

---

or both of those factors may have caused the difference in rate at the two locations.

Applying Skills

22. The sandy soil would lose water more quickly because there is space between the larger, jagged sand particles for water to run through, while clay particles can hold a lot of water.

23. Answers will vary. A typical design might include the following: use two identical flower pots with drain holes; place gravel at the bottom of each pot and cover with equal amounts of the sample soils; suspend the pots over two catch basins and pour equal amounts of water into the pots. Compare the amount of water that passes through the pots.

24. Answers may vary. *Sample questions:* In what kind of soil do soybeans grow best? What needs to be added to either type of soil to make it suitable for growing soybeans?

Applying Skills

Use the following information to answer Questions 22–24. You have two samples of soil. One is mostly sand and one is mostly clay.

22. Developing Hypotheses Which soil sample do you think would lose water more quickly? Why?

23. Designing Experiments Design an experiment to test how quickly water passes through each soil sample.

24. Posing Questions Suppose you are a farmer who wants to grow soybeans in one of these two soils. What questions would you need to answer before choosing where to plant your soybeans?

Performance — CHAPTER PROJECT 2 — Assessment

Project Wrap Up You are ready to present your conclusions about what type of material is best for growing bean plants. Decide how to display the data you collected on the different materials. How did your group's results compare with those of the other groups in your class?

Reflect and Record In your journal, describe how well the results of your experiment matched your predictions. What have you learned from this project about soil characteristics that help plants to grow? What improvements could you make to your experiment?

Performance — CHAPTER PROJECT 2 — Assessment

Project Wrap Up As each group presents its results to the class, assess how well students explain the experiment they carried out, including their descriptions of the types of soils used, explanations of the data they collected, and conclusions they have drawn from their data. Also assess the way in which they present their findings, including any visual aids or graphs they use.

Reflect and Record In assessing their work in this project, students should compare the data and conclusions of their group both with their predictions and with the data and conclusions of other groups. Each student should also explain what lessons can be drawn from the project and how the project could have been carried out in a better way.

Test Preparation

25. d **26.** a **27.** b **28.** c **29.** d

Test Preparation

Use these questions to prepare for standardized tests.

Use the diagram of soil horizons to answer Questions 25–29.

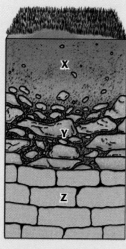

25. Layer X in the diagram consists of a mixture of humus, clay, and other minerals called
  a. litter.   **b.** gravel.
  c. subsoil.   **d.** topsoil.

26. Layer Y is made up of partly weathered rock called the
  a. C horizon.
  b. B horizon.
  c. A horizon.
  d. humus horizon.

27. One soil horizon, made up of clay and other particles but little humus, has not yet developed in this soil. The missing soil horizon is the
  a. A horizon.
  b. B horizon.
  c. C horizon.
  d. bedrock horizon.

28. The missing soil horizon will develop
  a. above layer X.
  b. below layer Z.
  c. between layers X and Y.
  d. between layers Y and Z.

29. In which layer or layers would you expect to find the most plant roots, insects, and other soil organisms?
  a. layers Y and Z   **b.** layer Z
  c. layer Y   **d.** layer X

Program Resources

◆ **Inquiry Skills Activity Book** Provides teaching and review of all inquiry skills
◆ **Standardized Test Preparation Book** Provides standardized test practice
◆ **Reading in the Content Area** Provides strategies to improve science reading skills
◆ **Teacher's ELL Handbook** Provides multiple strategies for English language learners

CHAPTER 3 Erosion and Deposition

Sections	Time	Student Edition Activities	Other Activities
CHAPTER PROJECT 3 **Changes in the Land** p. G65	Ongoing (3 weeks)	Check Your Progress, pp. G88, G93, G97 Project Wrap Up, p. G103	
1 Changing Earth's Surface pp. G66–71 ◆ 3.1.1 Describe the processes that wear down and build up Earth's surface. ◆ 3.1.2 Identify the force that pulls rock and soil down slopes.	2–3 periods/ 1–1½ blocks	**Discover** How Does Gravity Affect Materials on a Slope?, p. G66 **Sharpen Your Skills** Observing, p. G69 **Science at Home,** p. G69 **Skills Lab: Developing Hypotheses** Sand Hills, pp. G70–71	TE Demonstration, p. G73
2 Water Erosion pp. G72–84 ◆ 3.2.1 Explain how water erosion is mainly responsible for shaping Earth's land surface. ◆ 3.2.2 Describe land features formed by water erosion. ◆ 3.2.3 Describe land features formed when rivers and streams deposit sediment. ◆ 3.2.4 Describe the features of a river system.	4–5 periods/ 2–2½ blocks	**Discover** How Does Moving Water Wear Away Rocks?, p. G72 **Try This** Raindrops Falling, p. G74 **Science at Home,** p. G81 **Real-World Lab: You and Your Environment** Streams in Action, pp. G82–83	TE Real-Life Learning, pp. G73, G76, G79 TE Including All Students, pp. G74, G79 TE Inquiry Challenge, pp. G75, G76, G80 TE Using the Visuals: Figure 9, p. G75; Figure 12, p. G77 TE Integrating Chemistry, p. G80
3 **INTEGRATING PHYSICS** **The Force of Moving Water** pp. G85–88 ◆ 3.3.1 Describe how water is able to do work. ◆ 3.3.2 Explain how sediment enters rivers and streams. ◆ 3.3.3 List the factors that affect a river's ability to erode and carry sediment.	1–2 periods/ ½–1 block	**Discover** How Are Sediments Deposited?, p. G85 **Sharpen Your Skills** Developing Hypotheses, p. G87	TE Inquiry Challenge, p. G87 ISLM G-3, "The Daily Grind"
4 Glaciers pp. G89–93 ◆ 3.4.1 Name and describe two kinds of glaciers. ◆ 3.4.2 Describe processes by which glaciers erode land. ◆ 3.4.3 Explain how glaciers deposit sediments, and the role of the ice ages in glacial erosion.	1–2 periods/ ½–1 block	**Discover** How Do Glaciers Change the Land?, p. G89	TE Building Inquiry Skills: Designing Experiments, p. G90 TE Building Inquiry Skills: Observing, p. G91 TE Demonstration, p. G92
5 Waves pp. G94–97 ◆ 3.5.1 Identify what gives ocean waves their energy. ◆ 3.5.2 Describe how waves shape a coast and create landforms.	1–2 periods/ ½–1 block	**Discover** What Can Be Learned From Beach Sand?, p. G94 **Sharpen Your Skills** Calculating, p. G95	TE Inquiry Challenge, p. G96
6 Wind pp. G98–100 ◆ 3.6.1 Describe the process by which wind causes erosion. ◆ 3.6.2 Identify the features resulting from deposition by wind.	1–2 periods/ ½–1 block	**Discover** How Does Moving Air Affect Sediment?, p. G98 **Science at Home,** p. G100	TE Inquiry Challenge, p. G99 TE Demonstration, p. G99
Study Guide/Assessment pp. G101–103	1 period/ ½ block		ISAB Provides teaching and review of all inquiry skills

For Standard or Block Schedule The Resource Pro® CD-ROM gives you maximum flexibility for planning your instruction for any type of schedule. Resource Pro® contains Planning Express®, an advanced scheduling program, as well as the entire contents of the Teaching Resources and the Computer Test Bank.

Key: **SE** Student Edition
PLM Probeware Lab Manual
ISAB Inquiry Skills Activity Book

CHAPTER PLANNING GUIDE

Program Resources	Assessment Strategies	Media and Technology
TR Chapter 3 Project Teacher Notes, pp. G58–59 **TR** Chapter 3 Project Overview and Worksheets, pp. G60–63	**TE** Performance Assessment: Chapter 3 Project Wrap Up, p. G103 **TE** Check Your Progress, pp. G88, G93, G97 **TR** Chapter 3 Project Scoring Rubric, p. G64	Science Explorer Internet Site Audio CDs and Audiotapes, English-Spanish Section Summaries
TR 3-1 Lesson Plan, p. G65 **TR** 3-1 Section Summary, p. G66 **TR** 3-1 Enrich, p. G68 **TR** Skills Lab blackline masters, pp. G89–90	**SE** Section 1 Review, p. G69 **SE** Analyze and Conclude, p. G71 **TE** Ongoing Assessment, p. G67 **TE** Performance Assessment, p. G69	Exploring Earth Science Videodisc, Unit 2 Side 2, "Flying Over America" Transparency 9, "Landslide, Slump, and Creep" Lab Activity Videotape, *Earth's Changing Surface,* 5
TR 3-2 Lesson Plan, p. G69 **TR** 3-2 Section Summary, p. G70 **TR** 3-2 Review and Reinforce, p. G71 **TR** 3-2 Enrich, p. G72 **TR** Real-World Lab blackline masters, pp. G91–93 **SES** Book H, *Earth's Waters,* Chapter 2	**SE** Section 2 Review, p. G81 **SE** Analyze and Conclude, p. G83 **TE** Ongoing Assessment, pp. G73, G75, G77, G79 **TE** Performance Assessment, p. G81	Transparency 10, "Exploring the Course of a River" Lab Activity Videotape, *Earth's Changing Surface,* 6
TR 3-3 Lesson Plan, p. G73 **TR** 3-3 Section Summary, p. G74 **TR** 3-3 Review and Reinforce, p.G75 **TR** 3-3 Enrich, p. G76 **SES** Book M, *Motion, Forces, and Energy,* Chapters 2 and 5 **SES** Book L, *Chemical Interactions,* Chapter 3	**SE** Section 3 Review, p. G88 **TE** Ongoing Assessment, p. G87 **TE** Performance Assessment, p. G88	Transparency 11, "Water Erosion, Deposition, and Movement of Sediment"
TR 3-4 Lesson Plan, p. G77 **TR** 3-4 Section Summary, p. G78 **TR** 3-4 Review and Reinforce, p. G79 **TR** 3-4 Enrich, p. G80 **SES** Book H, *Earth's Waters,* Chapter 2	**SE** Section 4 Review, p. G93 **TE** Ongoing Assessment, p. G91 **TE** Performance Assessment, p. G93	Transparency 12, "Exploring Glacial Landforms"
TR 3-5 Lesson Plan, p. G81 **TR** 3-5 Section Summary, p. G82 **TR** 3-5 Review and Reinforce, p. G83 **TR** 3-5 Enrich, p. G84	**SE** Section 5 Review, p. G97 **TE** Ongoing Assessment, p. G95 **TE** Performance Assessment, p. G97	Exploring Earth Science Videodisc, Unit 2 Side 2, "The Wave" Transparency 13, "Wave Erosion and Wind Erosion"
TR 3-6 Lesson Plan, p. G85 **TR** 3-6 Section Summary, p. G86 **TR** 3-6 Enrich, p. G88	**SE** Section 6 Review, p. G100 **TE** Ongoing Assessment, p. G99 **TE** Performance Assessment, p. G100 **TR** 3-6 Review and Reinforce, p. G87	Transparency 13, "Wave Erosion and Wind Erosion"
GSW Provides worksheets to promote student comprehension of content **RCA** Provides strategies to improve science reading skills **ELL** Provides multiple strategies for English language learners	**SE** Study Guide/Assessment, pp. G101–103 **TR** Performance Assessment, pp. G152–154 **TR** Chapter 3 Test, pp. G155–158 **CTB** *Earth's Changing Surface,* Chapter 3 **STP** Provides standardized test practice	Interactive Student Tutorial CD-ROM, G-3 Computer Test Bank, *Earth's Changing Surface,* Chapter 3

TE Teacher's Edition   **TR** Teaching Resources   **CTB** Computerized Test Bank
RCA Reading in the Content Area   **ISLM** Integrated Science Laboratory Manual   **STP** Standardized Test Preparation Book
GSW Guided Study Workbook   **ELL** Teacher's ELL Handbook   **SES** Science Explorer Series Text

Meeting the National Science Education Standards and AAAS Benchmarks

National Science Education Standards	Benchmarks for Science Literacy	Unifying Themes
Science As Inquiry (Content Standard A) ◆ **Develop descriptions, explanations, predictions, and models using evidence** Students make models to show how erosion and deposition can change a landscape. Students investigate the relationship between the height and width of a hill. Students use a stream table to model how rivers erode the land. (*Chapter Project; Skills Lab; Real-World Lab*) **Physical Science** (Content Standard B) ◆ **Transfer of energy** As gravity pulls water down a slope, the water's potential energy changes to kinetic energy. The energy in waves comes from wind that blows across the water's surface. (*Sections 3, 5*) **Earth and Space Science** (Content Standard D) ◆ **Structure of the Earth system** Weathering, erosion, and deposition act together in a cycle that wears down and builds up Earth's surface. The forces that cause erosion and deposition are gravity, running water, glaciers, waves, and wind. (*Chapter Project; Skills Lab; Real-World Lab*) **Science in Personal and Social Perspectives** (Content Standard F) ◆ **Risks and benefits** Students examine the issue of protecting homes in flood plains. (*Science and Society*)	**1B Scientific Inquiry** Students make models to show how erosion and deposition can change a landscape over time. Students investigate the relationship between the height and width of a hill using a model. Students use a stream table to model how rivers erode the land. (*Chapter Project; Skills Lab; Real-World Lab*) **4B The Earth** Gravity pulls everything toward the center of Earth. (*Section 1*) **4C Processes That Shape the Earth** Weathering, erosion, and deposition act together in a cycle that wears down and builds up Earth's surface. The forces that cause erosion and deposition are gravity, running water, glaciers, waves, and wind. (*Chapter Project; Sections 1, 2, 3, 4, 5, 6; Skills Lab; Real-World Lab*) **4E Energy Transformation** As gravity pulls water down a slope, the water's potential energy changes to kinetic energy that can do work. The energy in waves comes from wind that blows across the water's surface. (*Sections 3, 5*) **7D Social Trade-Offs** Students examine the issue of protecting homes in flood plains. (*Science and Society*)	◆ **Energy** Gravity is the force that pulls rocks and soil down slopes. Moving water is the major agent of erosion. Energy is the ability to do work or cause change. Gravity pulls glaciers downhill. The energy in waves comes from wind that blows across the water's surface. Deflation is the process by which wind removes surface materials. (*Sections 1, 2, 3, 4, 5, 6; Skills Lab; Real-World Lab*) ◆ **Modeling** Students model forces of erosion and deposition. (*Chapter Project; Skills Lab; Real-World Lab*) ◆ **Patterns of Change** Weathering, erosion, and deposition act together in a cycle that wears down and builds up Earth's surface. (*Chapter Project; Sections 1, 2, 3, 4, 5, 6; Skills Lab; Real-World Lab*) ◆ **Scale and Structure** Students investigate the relationship between the height and width of a hill. A drainage basin is the land area from which a river and its tributaries collect their water. (*Skills Lab; Section 2*) ◆ **Stability** Erosion and deposition are at work everywhere on Earth. (*Sections 1, 2, 3, 4, 5, 6*) ◆ **Systems and Interactions** Gravity, running water, glaciers, waves, and wind are the forces that cause erosion and deposition. (*Chapter Project; Sections 1, 2, 3, 4, 5, 6; Skills Lab; Real-World Lab*)

Take It to the Net

 Interactive text at www.phschool.com

Science Explorer comes alive with iText.

- **Complete student text** is accessible from any computer with a browser.

- **Animations, simulations, and videos** enhance student understanding and retention of concepts.

- **Self-tests and online study tools** assess student understanding.

- **Teacher management tools** help you make the most of this valuable resource.

STAY CURRENT with **SCIENCE NEWS**®

Find out the latest research and information about Earth's surface at:
www.phschool.com

Go to **www.phschool.com** and click on the Science icon.
Then click on Science Explorer under PH@school.

ACTIVITY	Time (minutes)	Materials Quantities for one work group	Skills
Section 1			
Discover, p. 66	10	**Nonconsumable** small board, marble, block of wood, sandpaper	Developing Hypotheses
Sharpen Your Skills, p. 69	10	No special materials are required.	Observing
Science at Home, p. 69	Home	**Nonconsumable** camera (optional)	Observing
Skills Lab, pp. 70–71	40	**Consumable** cardboard toilet paper tube, several sheets of white paper, masking tape **Nonconsumable** 500 mL of dry sand, tray (about 15 × 45 × 60 cm), wooden barbecue skewer, spoon, ruler, pencil or crayon	Developing Hypotheses, Designing Experiments, Creating Data Tables, Graphing, Predicting
Section 2			
Discover, p. 72	15	**Consumable** 2 bars of soap **Nonconsumable** cold-water faucet, watch or clock with second hand	Predicting
Try This, p. 74	15	**Consumable** fine-textured soil, newspaper, water **Nonconsumable** petri dish, plastic dropper, meter stick	Drawing Conclusions
Science at Home, p. 81	Home	**Consumable** 27 sugar cubes, paper towel, water **Nonconsumable** small dish	Comparing and Contrasting
Real-World Lab, pp. 82–83	40	**Consumable** blue food coloring, water, 13–15 cm of 20-gauge wire, 10–12 cm plastic stirrers with two small holes each, plastic foam cup, liquid detergent **Nonconsumable** plastic tub (27 × 40 × 10 cm), diatomaceous earth, spray bottle, watch or clock, metal spoon, scissors, 2 wood blocks about 2.5 cm thick, 2–3 L bucket, plastic measuring cup, hand lens	Making Models, Observing, Predicting
Section 3			
Discover, p. 85	15	**Consumable** fine and coarse sand, soil, clay, small pebbles, water **Nonconsumable** clear plastic jar or bottle with top, plastic beaker	Inferring
Sharpen Your Skills, p. 87	5	No special materials are required.	Developing Hypotheses
Section 4			
Discover, p. 89	5; 10	**Consumable** sand, water, paper towel, bar of soap **Nonconsumable** small plastic container, freezer	Inferring
Section 5			
Discover, p. 94	15	**Nonconsumable** sand from 2 beaches, hand lens	Posing Questions
Sharpen Your Skills, p. 95	10	**Nonconsumable** calculator (optional)	Calculating
Section 6			
Discover, p. 98	10	**Consumable** cornmeal, plastic straw **Nonconsumable** shallow pan	Observing
Science at Home, p. 100	Home	**Consumable** flour **Nonconsumable** 1-cm deep pan, plastic straw, several coins	Making Models

A list of all materials required for the Student Edition activities can be found beginning on page T15. You can obtain information about ordering materials by calling 1-800-848-9500 or by accessing the Science Explorer Internet site at: **www.phschool.com**

Most people think of the land as static—what is here today will be here tomorrow and forever. In the context of a human lifetime, that notion makes some sense. But in the context of the history of Earth, that notion is not valid, since Earth's surface is constantly changing.

Purpose In the Chapter 3 Project, students will make models to show how erosion and deposition change Earth's surface over time. By doing this project, students will gain a better understanding of the processes that change the land and the kinds of landforms that result.

Skills Focus Students will be able to:
- ◆ make models of a landscape—an initial basic landscape, and then a second model of the landscape as changed by water erosion and wave erosion;
- ◆ predict how the first landscape will be changed by erosion;
- ◆ relate cause and effect in making changes to the initial landscape due to erosion;
- ◆ communicate the results of the project in a presentation to the class.

Project Time Line The entire project will require about three weeks. Depending on how much time students spend working on the project each day, two or three days will be required for each of the following phases.
- ◆ Make a drawing of a landscape that will be changed by erosion.
- ◆ Collect and prepare materials for making the model.
- ◆ Make a three-dimensional model of the landscape using the drawing as a guide.
- ◆ Make a second drawing that predicts the effects of gravity, water erosion, and glacial erosion on the landscape.
- ◆ Make a second model using the second sketch as a guide.
- ◆ Add the effects of wave erosion to the second model.
- ◆ Make a presentation of the two models to the class.

For more detailed information on planning and supervising this project, see Chapter 3 Project Teacher Notes, pages 58–59 in Teaching Resources.

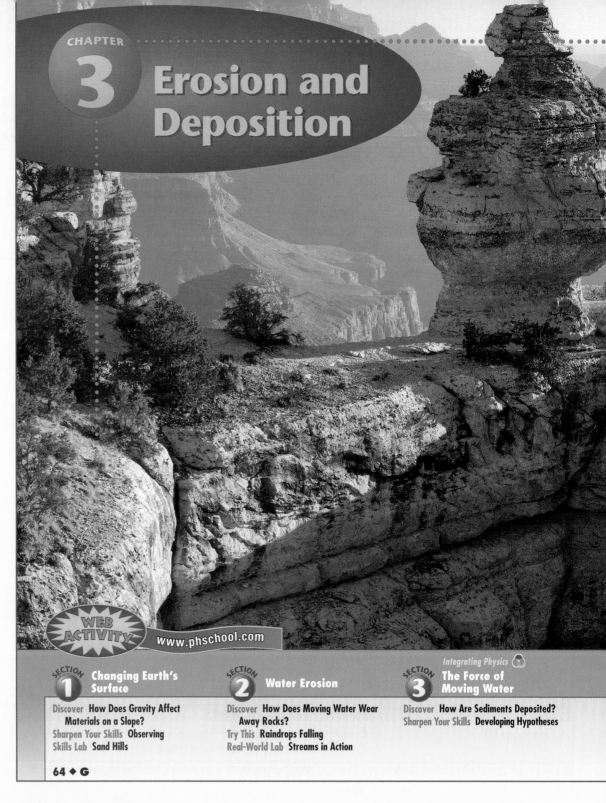

CHAPTER

3 Erosion and Deposition

WEB ACTIVITY www.phschool.com

SECTION 1 Changing Earth's Surface

Discover How Does Gravity Affect Materials on a Slope?
Sharpen Your Skills Observing
Skills Lab Sand Hills

SECTION 2 Water Erosion

Discover How Does Moving Water Wear Away Rocks?
Try This Raindrops Falling
Real-World Lab Streams in Action

SECTION 3 *Integrating Physics* The Force of Moving Water

Discover How Are Sediments Deposited?
Sharpen Your Skills Developing Hypotheses

64 ◆ G

Suggested Shortcuts
- ◆ You may wish to divide the class into small groups to carry out the project.
- ◆ You can make this project shorter and less involved by having students make the initial drawing of an uneroded landscape but forego making the first model. After each section, students can make new drawings that reflect changes from erosion. Then, about the time students learn about wave erosion, they could begin making a model that reflects all types of erosion. In the presentation, students could show their series of drawings and then present their model.
- ◆ For a class project, build one large model on a board covering a large table. Small groups can be in charge of making different sections of the model.

Possible Materials The suggested basic material for making such a model is a mixture of white glue and sand. For each small model, students will need about 20 mL of white glue, 700 mL of sand, and 60 mL of water. This can

Changes In the Land

The view from the South Rim of the Grand Canyon in Arizona is one of Earth's most memorable sights.

The walls of the Grand Canyon reveal the colorful rock layers that make up the Colorado Plateau. What force shaped such a vast canyon? For about 6 million years the Colorado River has been cutting and grinding through the plateau. The river also carries away the broken particles of rock.

In this chapter you will explore the forces that change Earth's surface. Flowing water, frozen glaciers, waves, and wind all wear down and build up landforms. Throughout the chapter, you will build models showing how erosion shapes a landscape.

Your Goal To make three-dimensional models that show how the forces of erosion and deposition can change a landscape over millions of years.

To complete this project, you must
- ◆ make a three-dimensional model of a landscape
- ◆ predict how the model would be affected by erosion
- ◆ construct a second model showing how your landscape might look after erosion has continued for millions of years

Get Started Begin now by sketching a mountainous or hilly landscape. Include sharp peaks, deep valleys, a river or stream, and a coastline.

Check Your Progress You will be working on this project as you study this chapter. To keep your project on track, look for Check Your Progress boxes at the following points.
Section 3 Review, page 88: Draw and make your first model.
Section 4 Review, page 93: Begin to make your second model, showing how water and glaciers cause erosion.
Section 5 Review, page 97: Add the effects of wave erosion to the model.

Wrap Up At the end of the chapter (page 103), you will present your models to the class. In your presentation, you will explain how the landscape changed and predict how it might change in the future.

be mixed in a 4-L plastic bucket. Wear plastic gloves when preparing the mixture. For a base, use either a plastic-coated paper plate, a piece of wood, or a small tray. Students can add any other materials to make their models attractive and realistic. Alternatives to the glue-sand mixture include modeling clay, salt dough, and papier mâché.

Launching the Project To introduce the project, describe the region in which students live, mentioning prominent rivers and landforms. Then ask: **If you could go back a few million years, would this region look the same?** (*Most students will say that changes have occurred in the last million years, though they may lack specifics.*) **What if you could go forward a few million years? What changes in the land would you expect to see?** (*Answers will vary. Students may speculate about added mountains or rivers.*) Explain that in Chapter 3 they will learn about how erosion and deposition make changes in the land, and in the Chapter 3 Project, they will make models that dramatically show such changes. To help students get started, pass out Chapter 3 Project Overview and Worksheets, pages 60–63 in Teaching Resources. You may also wish to pass out the Chapter 3 Project Scoring Rubric, page 64, at this time.

 SECTION 4 Glaciers

Discover **How Do Glaciers Change the Land?**

 SECTION 5 Waves

Discover **What Can Be Learned From Beach Sand?**
Sharpen Your Skills **Calculating**

 SECTION 6 Wind

Discover **How Does Moving Air Affect Sediment?**

G ◆ 65

Program Resources

◆ **Teaching Resources** Chapter 3 Project Teacher Notes, pp. 58–59; Project Overview and Worksheets, pp. 60–63; Project Scoring Rubric, p. 64

Media and Technology

 Audio CDs and **Audiotapes**
English-Spanish Section Summaries

 **WEB ACTIVITY** www.phschool.com

You will find an Internet activity, chapter self-tests for students, and links to other chapter topics at this site.

Performance Assessment

Use the Chapter 3 Project Scoring Rubric to assess students' work. Students will be assessed on
- ◆ how well they make their initial drawings and first model;
- ◆ how effectively and comprehensively they represent the different kinds of erosion in their second model;
- ◆ how well-constructed and attractive their models are;
- ◆ how effectively they present their models and related concepts to the class.

Objectives

After completing the lesson, students will be able to
◆ describe the processes that wear down and build up Earth's surface;
◆ identify the force that pulls rock and soil down slopes.

Key Terms erosion, sediment, deposition, mass movement

1 Engage/Explore

Activating Prior Knowledge

Encourage students to relate their experiences on a steep path up a hill or mountain. Ask: **What happens when you step on loose rock or dirt?** (*You will slip, and the rock and dirt falls downhill.*) **What could naturally cause a similar movement of sediment downhill?** (*Students might suggest a heavy storm or earthquake.*)

DISCOVER

Skills Focus developing hypotheses
Materials *small board, marble, block of wood, sandpaper*
Time 10 minutes
Tips Precut sandpaper to sizes that can be wrapped around the board and the block of wood. The block of wood should be completely wrapped in sandpaper; the board does not have to be completely wrapped if there is enough overlap.
Think It Over Upon tipping the board, the marble will immediately roll down the slope, while the block of wood will move down when the board is tipped higher. When sandpaper covers the board and the block, the block or wood may move only when the board is tipped up almost to vertical. Hypotheses will vary. A typical hypothesis might suggest that movement downward depends both on the angle of the board and on the type of material on the board.

DISCOVER • ACTIVITY

How Does Gravity Affect Materials on a Slope?

1. Place a small board flat on your desk. Place a marble on the board and slowly tip the board up slightly at one end. Observe what happens.

2. Place a block of wood on the board. Slowly lift one end of the board and observe the result.

3. Next, cover the board and the wood block with sandpaper and repeat Step 2.

Think It Over
Developing Hypotheses How do the results of each step compare? Develop a hypothesis to explain the differences in your observations.

GUIDE FOR READING

◆ What processes wear down and build up Earth's surface?

◆ What force pulls rock and soil down slopes?

◆ What are the different types of mass movement?

Reading Tip As you read, make a list of main ideas and supporting details about erosion, deposition, and mass movement.

Madison River Canyon is a quiet wilderness area in the Rocky Mountains of Montana. In 1959, something happened to change the canyon forever. When a strong earthquake jolted nearby Yellowstone National Park, a mountainside along the canyon gave way. In a few seconds, nearly 30 million cubic meters of rock, soil, and trees slid into the canyon. If this much material were in the shape of a cube, then each side of the cube would be three times longer than a football field. Rock and soil from the landslide dammed the Madison River, forming a new lake.

Figure 1 During a landslide, loose rock and soil on the side of a mountain suddenly slide away from underlying bedrock. This landslide in Madison River Canyon, Montana, buried a highway and campground.

READING STRATEGIES

Reading Tip Students should make three lists, one of ideas about erosion, another of ideas about deposition, and a third of ideas about mass movement. Students can use the subheadings as organizers for the third list, listing details about each type of mass movement under the subheadings. Suggest that they use their lists as a study guide for the section.

Vocabulary In this and following sections, the term *slope* is used to indicate a natural incline. In common speech, a *slope* means the side of a hill or mountain or any sloping surface. In a more technical sense, the term is also used to indicate the amount or degree of an incline, as in the "angle of slope is 45 degrees." In this chapter, that sense of the word is implied in such uses as "land that is steeply sloped" or "a river's slope."

Wearing Down and Building Up

A landslide like the one in Madison River Canyon is a spectacular example of erosion. **Erosion** is the process by which natural forces move weathered rock and soil from one place to another. A landslide is a very rapid type of erosion. Other types of erosion move soil and rock more slowly. Gravity, running water, glaciers, waves, and wind can all cause erosion. You may have seen water carrying soil and gravel down a driveway after it rains. That's an example of erosion. Erosion also caused the damage to the road in Figure 2.

The material moved by erosion is **sediment.** Both weathering and erosion produce sediment. **Deposition** occurs where the agents of erosion lay down sediment. Deposition changes the shape of the land. You may have watched a playing child who picked up several toys and then carried them across a room and put them down. This child was acting something like an agent of erosion and deposition.

Weathering, erosion, and deposition act together in a cycle that wears down and builds up Earth's surface. Erosion and deposition are at work everywhere on Earth. Sometimes they work slowly. At other times, they work more quickly, such as during a thunderstorm. Then, heavy rain soaks into rock and soil. These water-soaked materials may then come loose suddenly and slide down a mountain. But as a mountain wears down in one place, new landforms build up in other places. Erosion and deposition are never-ending.

☑ *Checkpoint* *What happens to sediment as a result of erosion and deposition?*

Mass Movement

Imagine that you are sitting on a bicycle at the top of a hill. With only a slight push, you can coast down the hill. If the slope of the hill is very steep, you will reach a high speed before reaching the bottom. The force that pulls you and your bicycle downward is gravity. Gravity pulls everything toward the center of Earth.

Gravity is the force that moves rock and other materials downhill. Gravity causes **mass movement,** any one of several processes that move sediment downhill. Mass movement can be rapid or slow. **The different types of mass movement include landslides, mudslides, slump, and creep.**

Figure 2 Heavy winter rains washed out this California highway. *Relating Cause and Effect What caused the erosion that you can see in the photograph?*

Program Resources

◆ **Teaching Resources** 3-1 Lesson Plan, p. 65; 3-1 Section Summary, p. 66
◆ **Guided Study Workbook** Section 3-1

Media and Technology

 Transparencies "Landslide, Slump, and Creep," Transparency 9

Answers to Self-Assessment

Caption Question

Figure 2 Heavy rain caused the erosion in the photograph.

☑ *Checkpoint*

Erosion moves sediment from one place to another. Deposition lays down sediment in new locations, building new landforms.

Wearing Down and Building Up

Including All Students

To help students who have limited English proficiency better understand the concept of a cycle, ask: **Can you name other natural cycles?** *(Cycle of day and night, water cycle, rock cycle, oxygen–carbon dioxide cycle)* Emphasize that a cycle has no beginning and no end and that it is continually occurring everywhere on Earth. Ask: **What part of this cycle wears down Earth's surface?** *(weathering)* **What part builds up Earth's surface?** *(deposition)* Point out that erosion acts as a bridge between those two processes. **limited English proficiency**

Mass Movement

Using the Visuals: Figure 1

After students have examined the figure and read the caption, ask: **Have you ever seen a pile of rocks at the bottom of a cliff?** *(Students may mention such sights at roadcuts or at the bottom of cliffs in parks.)* **What type of landform is necessary for such a landslide to occur?** *(A steep slope)* Then have students speculate on what could cause a landslide. Guide them to an understanding that any disturbance can begin one rock rolling, and that rock can cause another to move, and so on until a whole mass moves together down a slope. Ask: **How could mechanical or chemical weathering result in a landslide?** *(A block of rock could break apart due to weathering and then move down a slope because of gravity.)* **learning modality: visual**

Ongoing Assessment

Writing Have students use the key terms *erosion, deposition,* and *mass movement* in sentences.

Mass Movement,
continued

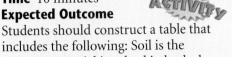

Observing

Time 10 minutes
Expected Outcome

Students should construct a table that includes the following: Soil is the primary material involved in both slump and creep. Slump occurs on a steep slope, while creep occurs on a gentle slope. Slump occurs quickly, while creep occurs slowly.
Extend Have students complete their tables by including similar information about landslides and mudflows.
learning modality: visual

Demonstration

Materials *soil, sand, gravel, large plastic tray, water, watering can*
Time 10 minutes

Build a model mountain on the plastic tray using soil, sand, and gravel. Then, as students observe, shake the tray. Ask: **What does the shaking model?** *(An earthquake)* **What does the model earthquake cause?** *(A landslide)* Rebuild the mountain, and then use the watering can to "rain" on the model. Continue this until some movement occurs. Ask: **What did the "rainfall" cause?** *(A mudslide or slump)* **What did the water do to the mountain that caused mass movement to occur?** *(The water added weight to the material. It also caused the soil to become mud, which can flow.)* Students might infer that for a time the added water actually held the "mountain" together, because the addition of water causes cementation. But once a certain amount is reached, the added weight and change to mud causes a downward movement. Ask: **What force is responsible for all these types of mass movement?** *(Gravity)*
learning modality: visual

Figure 3 A mudflow caused by heavy rains raced through the streets of this town in Italy. *Relating Cause and Effect What characteristic of soil can contribute to a mudflow?*

Landslides The most destructive kind of mass movement is a landslide, which occurs when rock and soil slide quickly down a steep slope. Some landslides may contain huge masses of rock. But many landslides contain only a small amount of rock and soil. Such mass movement is common where road builders have cut highways through hills or mountains.

Mudflows A mudflow is the rapid downhill movement of a mixture of water, rock, and soil. The amount of water in a mudflow can be as high as 60 percent. Mudflows often occur after heavy rains in a normally dry area. In clay soils with a high water content, mudflows may occur even on very gentle slopes. Under certain conditions, clay soils suddenly turn to liquid and begin to flow. For example, an earthquake can trigger both mudflows and landslides. Mudflows like the one in Figure 3 can be very dangerous.

Slump If you slump your shoulders, the entire upper part of your body drops down. In the type of mass movement known as slump, a mass of rock and soil suddenly slips down a slope. Unlike a landslide, the material in slump moves down in one large mass. It looks as if someone pulled the bottom out from under part of the slope. Figure 4 shows an example of slump. Slump often occurs when water soaks the base of a mass of soil that is rich in clay.

Figure 4 Slump can look as if a giant spoon has started to scoop a mass of soil out from a hillside.

Facts and Figures Gravity is the force that causes mass movement, but water almost always plays a major role, even in landslides of rock fragments. Water reduces friction, so that during a wet season rocks that previously were stable may suddenly slide over other rocks. In sand or clay, some water may add to stability, just as wet beach sand is used to make a sand castle. But too much water causes flow.

Landslides and mudflows result in 25–50 deaths per year in the United States and an average of 600 deaths per year throughout the world. They are also responsible for huge monetary losses, including more than $1.5 billion a year in the United States. In earthquakes, damage from mass movement can be more significant than that from the quake itself.

Creep Landscapes affected by creep may have the eerie, out-of-kilter look of a funhouse in an amusement park. Creep is the very slow downhill movement of rock and soil. It can even occur on gentle slopes. Like the movement of an hour hand on a clock, creep is so slow you can barely notice it. But you can see the effects of creep in objects such as telephone poles, gravestones, and fenceposts. Creep may tilt these objects at spooky angles. Creep often results from the freezing and thawing of water in cracked layers of rock beneath the soil. How have the trees in Figure 5 been affected by creep?

Figure 5 Creep has slowly tilted these trees downhill, causing their trunks to grow in a curve. *Predicting If creep continues, how might it affect the road, the fence, and the electric power lines?*

Sharpen your Skills

Observing ACTIVITY

Compare the examples of mass movement in Figures 4 and 5. Based on your observations, construct a table comparing slump and creep. Include the Earth materials involved, the type of slope, and the speed for each type of mass movement.

Section 1 Review

1. Explain the difference between erosion and deposition.
2. What force causes erosion?
3. What are four types of mass movement?
4. **Thinking Critically Relating Cause and Effect** Why would a landslide be more likely on a steep mountain than on a gently sloping hill?

Science at Home

After a rainstorm, take a walk with an adult family member around your neighborhood. Look for evidence of erosion. Try to find areas where there is loose soil, sand, gravel, or rock. (**CAUTION:** *Stay away from any large pile of loose sand or soil—it may slide without warning.*) Which areas have the most erosion? The least erosion? How does the slope of the ground affect the amount of erosion? Sketch or take photographs of the areas showing evidence of erosion.

Media and Technology

 Exploring Earth Science Videodisc
Unit 2, Side 2, "Flying Over America"

Chapter 7

Program Resources

◆ **Teaching Resources** 3-1 Review and Reinforce, p. 67; 3-1 Enrich, p. 68

Answers to Self-Assessment

Caption Questions

Figure 3 Clay soils with high water content can suddenly turn to liquid.
Figure 5 Students may predict that the road will buckle or even break and the fence and poles will tilt and perhaps fall over.

3 Assess

Section 1 Review Answers

1. Erosion moves sediment from one place to another, while deposition lays down sediment in new locations.
2. The force of gravity and the forces exerted by running water, glaciers, waves, and wind cause erosion.
3. The four types of mass movement are landslides, mudflows, slump, and creep.
4. On a gently sloping hill, the force of gravity cannot pull down rock and soil quickly because of the friction between the hill and the rock and soil. On a steep mountain, though, the force of gravity can much more easily overcome the force of friction.

Science at Home

Tips Encourage students to make this erosion ACTIVITY survey around their neighborhood. They should especially look for evidence of mass movement, such as piles of rock at the bottom of a hill or cliff as well as landscapes affected by creep. Also have students anticipate what they will learn in the next section by looking for evidence of water erosion, especially in places that lack vegetation. Students can bring their drawings and/or photos to class and present interesting examples. Use the best examples to make a bulletin board that focuses on mass movement and water erosion.

Performance Assessment

Drawing Have students make drawings of each of the four types of mass movement, using the block illustrations in Figures 1, 4, and 5 for models of landslide, slump, and creep, respectively. For mudslide, they will have to create their own illustration to represent that type in a similar way. Display the best illustrations on a bulletin board.

Portfolio Students can keep their drawings in their portfolios.

Sand Hills

Preparing for Inquiry

Key Concept Gravity causes mass movement, a process that moves sediment downhill.

Skills Objectives Students will be able to:
◆ develop a hypothesis about how the height and width of a sand hill will change as more sand is added;
◆ design an experiment to test the hypothesis;
◆ create a data table and use the data to make a graph;
◆ predict what would happen if the experiment was continued.

Time 40 minutes

Advance Planning For the trays, collect either cardboard box tops or plastic trays. Make sure the sand is very dry.

Alternative Materials A fine aquarium gravel could be used in place of the sand. Butcher-block paper cut to fit the tray bottom could be used instead of taping smaller sheets together. If barbecue skewers are unavailable, cut stiff wire to about the same length as a skewer.

Guiding Inquiry

Invitation Focus on the primary skill of the lab—developing hypotheses—by asking: **What is a hypothesis?** (*A hypothesis is a proposed explanation or answer to a question.*) **What do scientists do to support or disprove a hypothesis?** (*They test the hypothesis through an experiment.*) **Why is it better to formulate a hypothesis with specifics rather than generalities?** (*Specifics can be tested with experiments and either confirmed or proved wrong. Generalities are hard to test experimentally.*)

Introducing the Procedure

◆ Give students time to read through the whole procedure, and then ask: **What sort of mass movement is involved in this lab? Explain.** (*Landslides, because the material pulled down the slope slides quickly and doesn't involve water.*)
◆ **What is the force that moves material down a slope?** (*Gravity*)

Sand Hills

In this lab, you will develop and test a hypothesis about how mass movement affects the size and shape of a sand hill.

Problem

What is the relationship between the height and width of a sand hill?

Materials

Dry sand, 500 mL
Cardboard tube
Tray (about 15 cm × 45 cm × 60 cm)
Wooden barbecue skewer   Masking tape
Spoon   Ruler   Pencil or crayon
Several sheets of white paper

Procedure

1. Begin by observing how gravity causes mass movement in sand. To start, place the cardboard tube vertically in the center of the tray.
2. Using the spoon, fill the cardboard tube with the dry sand. Take care not to spill the sand around the outside of the tube.
3. Carefully lift the sand-filled tube straight up so that all the sand flows out. As you lift the tube, observe the sand's movement.
4. Develop a hypothesis explaining how you think the width of the sand pile is related to its height for different amounts of sand.
5. Empty the sand in the tray back into a container. Then set up your system for measuring the sand hill.
6. Copy the data table into your lab notebook.
7. Following Steps 1 through 3, make a new sand hill.

How to Measure a Sand Hill

1. Cover the bottom of the tray with unlined white paper and tape it firmly in place.
2. Mark off points 0.5 cm apart along one side of the paper in the tray.
3. Carefully draw the sand hill's outline on the paper. The line should go completely around the base of the hill.
4. Now measure the width of the hill against the marks you made along the edge of the paper.
5. Measure the sand hill's height by inserting a barbecue skewer through its center. Make a mark on the skewer at the top of the hill.
6. Remove the skewer and use the ruler to measure how much of the skewer was buried in the hill. Try not to disturb the sand.

Troubleshooting the Experiment

◆ Guide students in developing a specific hypothesis that can be tested. A testable hypothesis might be: "As sand is added to the sandhill, the hill's height increases half as much as its width." Allow students to test any reasonable hypothesis.
◆ Tell students to fill the cardboard tube carefully so that they don't spill sand outside the tube onto the hill. In filling the tube, one student can hold it while another student pours in the sand.

◆ The rate of raising the tube will affect how fast the sand flows out, and thus affect how much sand moves down the hill. Students should raise the tube at about the same rate each time.
◆ Demonstrate how to use the skewer to measure the height of the hill. Caution students to be as gentle as possible when inserting the skewer into the hill so as not to cause mass movement because of the skewer.

DATA TABLE

Test	1	2	3	4	5
Width					
Height					

8. Measure and record the sand hill's height and width for Test 1. (See the instructions on the bottom of the previous page to help you accurately measure the height and width.)

9. Now test what happens when you add more sand to the sand hill. Place your cardboard tube vertically at the center of the sand hill. Be careful not to push the tube down into the sand hill! Using the spoon, fill the tube with sand as before.

10. Carefully raise the tube and observe the results of the sand's movement.

11. Measure and record the sand hill's height and width for Test 2.

12. Repeat Steps 9 through 11 at least three more times. After each test, record your results. Be sure to number each test.

Analyze and Conclude

1. Make a graph showing how the sand hill's height and width changed with each test. (*Hint:* Use the *x*-axis of the graph for height. Use the *y*-axis of the graph for width.)

2. What does your graph show about the relationship between the sand hill's height and width?

3. Does your graph support your hypothesis about the sand hill's height and width? Why or why not?

4. How would you revise your original hypothesis after examining your data? Give reasons for your answer.

5. **Think About It** Predict what would happen if you continued the experiment for five more tests. Extend your graph with a dashed line to show your prediction. How could you test your prediction?

Design an Experiment

Do you think the use of different materials, such as wet sand or gravel, would produce different results from dry sand? Make a new hypothesis about the relationship between slope and width in hills made of materials other than dry sand. Design an experiment in which you test how these different materials form hills. Obtain your teacher's approval before you try the experiment.

Program Resources

◆ **Teaching Resources** Skills Lab blackline masters, pp. 89–90

Media and Technology

 Lab Activity Videotape
Earth's Changing Surface, 5

Safety

Students should wear their goggles when working with sand, since dry sand could become lodged in an eye and cause damage. Also, advise students to be careful when handling the skewer, for it could penetrate skin or harm the eyes. Review the safety guidelines in Appendix A.

Expected Outcome

Results may vary depending on several factors, including the type and dryness of the sand, the diameter of the cardboard tube, and the way in which students add sand to the hill. In tests 2 through 5, both height and width will increase, though width will probably increase more. Repeated tests show that the relationship between the sand hill's height and width remains constant (*i.e.,* the points fall approximately along a straight line on the graph). The amount by which the hill's height and width increase depends on the amount of sand added in relation to the total amount of sand in the pile.

Analyze and Conclude

1. Graphs will vary. A typical graph should show a line rising from left to right.

2. Answers will vary. A typical response may suggest that as the height of the sand hill increases, the hill's width increases more.

3. Answers will vary depending on students' hypotheses. Students should compare their original hypothesis with the data collected to determine whether the hypothesis was supported or not.

4. Answers will vary depending on the original hypotheses. Students whose hypotheses were not supported should develop a new hypothesis that would be supported by the data collected.

5. Answers will vary depending on the graphs made from the data of the five tests. Most students should infer from the graph that width will continue to increase more rapidly than height.

Extending the Inquiry

Design an Experiment Hypotheses will vary. Using wet sand would probably increase the height of the hill at the expense of the width; using wet gravel might produce the opposite effect. Encourage students to make a hypothesis about one of the materials and design an experiment. Allow students to carry out the best designs and report their findings to the class.

Objectives

After completing the lesson, students will be able to

◆ explain how water erosion is mainly responsible for shaping Earth's land surface;

◆ describe some of the land features formed by water erosion;

◆ describe land features formed when rivers and streams deposit sediment;

◆ describe the features of a river system.

Key Terms runoff, rill, gully, stream, river, tributary, drainage basin, divide, flood plain, meander, oxbow lake, alluvial fan, delta, groundwater, stalactite, stalagmite, karst topography

1 Engage/Explore

Activating Prior Knowledge

Elicit students' descriptions of a major river in their region. Then ask: **Where does the river get its water?** *(From smaller rivers and streams)* Keep backtracking until students describe something like a rill or gully.

DISCOVER

Skills Focus predicting
Materials *2 bars of soap, cold-water faucet, watch or clock with second hand*
Time 15 minutes
Tips Before students carry out the experiment, have them read the procedure and identify the variable tested (dripping water) and the control (the bar in the dry place). For Step 2, students should record the number of drops in one minute; for Step 3, they should record a prediction.
Expected Outcome The dripping water will wear a depression in the bar of soap.
Think It Over Predictions may vary. Typical predictions may suggest that the depression will grow larger in another 10 minutes and larger still after an hour. Increasing the flow would speed up the process; decreasing the flow would slow it down.

DISCOVER ••••••••••••••••••••••••••••••••••• ACTIVITY

How Does Moving Water Wear Away Rocks?

1. Obtain two bars of soap that are the same size and brand.

2. Open a faucet just enough to let the water drip out very slowly. How many drops of water does the faucet release per minute?

3. Place one bar of soap in a dry place. Place the other bar of soap under the faucet. Predict the effect of the dripping water droplets on the soap.

4. Let the faucet drip for 10 minutes.

5. Turn off the faucet and observe both bars of soap. What difference do you observe between them?

Think It Over
Predicting What would the bar of soap under the dripping faucet look like if you left it there for another 10 minutes? For an hour? How could you speed up the process? Slow it down?

GUIDE FOR READING

◆ What process is mainly responsible for shaping Earth's land surface?

◆ What features are formed by water erosion?

◆ What features are formed when rivers and streams deposit sediment?

Reading Tip Before you read, use the headings to make an outline on water erosion and deposition.

Walking in the woods in summer, you can hear the racing water of a stream before you see the stream itself. The water roars as it foams over rock ledges and boulders. When you reach the stream, you see water rushing by. Sand and pebbles tumble along the bottom of the stream. As it swirls downstream, it also carries twigs, leaves, and bits of soil. In sheltered pools, insects such as water striders silently skim the water's calm surface. Beneath the surface, you see a rainbow trout hovering in the clear water.

If you visit the stream at other times of year, it will be very different. In winter, the stream freezes. Chunks of ice scrape and grind away at the stream's bed and banks. In spring, the stream floods. Then the flow of water may be strong enough to move large rocks. But throughout the year, the stream continues to erode its small part of Earth's surface.

A woodland stream ▼

READING STRATEGIES

Reading Tip If necessary, review with students how to make an outline. Then encourage them to read the section once before beginning their outlines. Suggest students use the subheadings under each main heading for the first two levels of the outline. For example, the next level under "Runoff and Erosion" should include "Rills and Gullies," "Streams and Rivers," and "Amount of Runoff."

Vocabulary Call student's attention to the highlighted sentence on page 73, in which moving water is said to be an "agent" of erosion. Students have learned about "agents" of chemical weathering, and now they study "agents" of erosion. An *agent* in this sense is not a representative, such as in "insurance agent," or a spy, such as in "secret agent." Rather, here *agent* means a "force or substance that causes change."

Figure 6 A falling raindrop starts the process of erosion. Water flowing across the surface runs together in small rills. Rills combine to form larger gullies. *Predicting What will happen to the land between the gully and the side gully as the two gullies grow wider?*

Gully

Side gully

Rills

Stream

Runoff and Erosion

Running water creates many landforms. **Moving water is the major agent of the erosion that has shaped Earth's land surface.**

Erosion by water begins with the splash of rain, as you can see in Figure 6. Some rainfall sinks into the ground. Some evaporates or is taken up by plants. The force of a falling raindrop can loosen and pick up soil particles. As water moves over the land, it carries these particles with it. This moving water is called runoff. **Runoff** is all the remaining water that moves over Earth's surface. When runoff flows in a thin layer over the land, it may cause a type of erosion called sheet erosion.

Rills and Gullies Because of gravity, runoff and the material it contains move downhill. As runoff travels, it forms tiny grooves in the soil called **rills.** As the rills flow into one another, they grow larger, forming gullies. A **gully** is a large groove, or channel, in the soil that carries runoff after a rainstorm. As water flows through gullies, it moves soil and rocks with it, thus enlarging the gullies through erosion. Gullies flow only after it rains.

Program Resources

◆ **Teaching Resources** 3-2 Lesson Plan, p. 69; 3-2 Section Summary, p. 70
◆ **Guided Study Workbook** Section 3-2
  Science Explorer Series *Earth's Waters,* Chapter 2, can provide more information on streams and rivers.

Answers to Self-Assessment

Caption Question

Figure 6 The land between will erode until the gullies run together, lengthening the stream.

2 Facilitate

Runoff and Erosion

Real-Life Learning

Time 15 minutes

ACTIVITY

Most schools have a baseball field on the grounds or nearby. After a rain, take students out to the field and direct their attention to the base paths around the infield, which are usually made of easily eroded sandy soil. There, challenge students to find rills, and rills that converge to form gullies. **learning modality: visual**

Building Inquiry Skills: Comparing and Contrasting

Materials *clear plastic or glass jars, samples of runoff from different locations, marker, masking tape*

ACTIVITY

Time 10 minutes

On the day of a heavy rain, encourage students to collect a sample of runoff. They can do this after school, in a location near where they live. To collect a sample, they can dip a jar into a stream of runoff water. Students should use tape and a marker to label the jar as to where the runoff was collected. Then in school the next day, have students examine each sample and note how much sediment it contains. Challenge students to draw conclusions about the locations in which runoff picks up the most sediment particles. **learning modality: kinesthetic**

Ongoing Assessment

Writing Have students explain how rills and gullies become streams.

Runoff and Erosion,
continued

Skills Focus drawing conclusions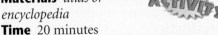

Materials *petri dish, fine-textured soil, newspaper, plastic dropper, water, meter stick*

Time 15 minutes

Tips To drop water from a height of 2 m, many students will have to climb onto a table or chair. Make sure they can accomplish this safely. An alternative would be to cut the distances in half, dropping water from 0.5 m in the first trials and then 1 m in the second trials.

Expected Outcome Students should observe that the drops from 2 m caused splashes that traveled farther than the splashes from the 1-m drops. Since the drops picked up sediment when they hit the soil, the 2-m drops also caused more erosion. Students should draw the conclusion that the 2-m drops had more force because the water fell a greater distance.

Extend Encourage students to try the same procedure with different materials in the dish, including sand, clayey soil, and gravel, and then compare results.

learning modality: kinesthetic

River Systems

Including All Students

Materials *atlas or encyclopedia*

Time 20 minutes

Pair students with different abilities and assign each pair one of the major rivers of North America, including the Colorado, the Columbia, the Hudson, the Mackenzie, the Mississippi, the Ohio, the Rio Grande, the Sacramento, and the Yukon. Then have students make a labeled map that includes the assigned river and its important tributaries. On this map, students should also show and label states, major cities, and the body of water into which the river flows.

learning modality: visual

74 ◆ G

Figure 7 As water erodes gullies, soil can be lost.

Raindrops Falling

Find out how the force of falling raindrops affects soil.

1. Fill a petri dish with fine-textured soil to a depth of about 1 cm. Make sure the soil has a smooth flat surface, but do not pack it firmly in the dish.

2. Place the dish in the center of a newspaper.

3. Fill a dropper with water. Squeeze a large water drop from a height of 1 m onto the surface of the soil. Repeat 4 times.

4. Use a meter stick to measure the distance the soil splashed from the dish. Record your observations.

5. Repeat Steps 1 through 4, this time from a height of 2 m. Which traveled further, the splash from 1 m or the splash from 2 m?

Drawing Conclusions Which test produced the greater amount of erosion? Why?

74 ◆ G

Streams and Rivers Gullies join together to form a larger channel called a stream. A **stream** is a channel along which water is continually flowing down a slope. Unlike gullies, streams rarely dry up. Small streams are also called creeks or brooks. As streams flow together, they form larger and larger bodies of flowing water. A large stream is often called a **river.**

Amount of Runoff The amount of runoff in an area depends on five main factors. The first factor is the amount of rain an area receives. A second factor is vegetation. Grasses, shrubs, and trees reduce runoff by absorbing water and holding soil in place. A third factor is the type of soil. Some types of soils absorb more water than others. A fourth factor is the shape of the land. Land that is steeply sloped has more runoff than flatter land. Finally, a fifth factor is how people use the land. For instance, a paved parking lot absorbs no water, so all the rain that falls on it becomes runoff. Runoff also increases when a farmer cuts down crops, since this removes vegetation from the land.

Generally, more runoff means more erosion. In contrast, things that reduce runoff, such as plant leaves and roots, will reduce erosion. Even though deserts have little rainfall, they often have high runoff and erosion. This is because deserts usually have few plants. In wet areas, runoff and erosion may be low because there are more plants to protect the soil.

✓ *Checkpoint* *What factors affect the amount of runoff in a region?*

River Systems

A stream grows into a larger stream or river by receiving water from tributaries. A **tributary** is a stream that flows into a larger stream. A small creek that flows into a large river is a tributary to that river. So too is a large river that adds its water to another large river. For instance, the Missouri River becomes a tributary of the Mississippi River near the city of St. Louis, even though both rivers are about the same size there.

Background

Facts and Figures Urbanization makes a tremendous difference in amount of runoff. When precipitation occurs in a natural area, 80–100% of the water that doesn't evaporate filters through the surface to become groundwater and 0–20% flows as runoff. In an urban area—because of roads, parking lots, and buildings—only 0–10% of water filters into the ground while 90–100% flows as surface runoff.

The Ohio River begins in Pittsburgh, Pennsylvania, at the confluence of the Allegheny and Monongahela rivers and flows 1,579 km before emptying into the Mississippi. The Ohio's drainage basin is about 528,400 km^2, about 16% of the Mississippi River's drainage basin of 3,222,000 km^2. Tributaries other than those shown in Figure 8 include the Kanawha, Scioto, Great Miami, and Green rivers.

Look at Figure 8. Notice all the tributaries to the Ohio River. Together, all these streams—from tiny rills to great rivers—form a system that drains a large part of eastern North America. A **drainage basin** is the land area from which a river and its tributaries collect their water.

If you were to follow a river upstream all the way to its source, you would finally reach a divide. A **divide** is the high ground between two drainage basins. The most famous divide within the United States is the Continental Divide, which follows the high ground of the Rocky Mountains. The Continental Divide separates streams that flow into the Gulf of Mexico from streams that flow into the Great Basin or the Pacific Ocean.

Erosion by Rivers

Scientists classify rivers by identifying certain features that form as a result of erosion. **Through erosion, a river creates valleys, waterfalls, flood plains, meanders, and oxbow lakes.**

Rivers often form on steep mountain slopes. Near its source, a river is often fast-flowing and generally follows a straight, narrow course. The steep slopes along the river erode rapidly. The result is a deep, V-shaped valley.

Waterfalls may occur where a river meets an area of rock that is very hard and erodes slowly. The river flows over this rock and then flows over softer rock downstream. The softer rock wears away faster than the harder rock. Eventually a waterfall develops where the softer rock was removed. This process formed Niagara Falls, shown in Figure 9. Areas of rough water called rapids also occur where a river tumbles over hard rock.

Ohio River Drainage Basin

Figure 8 The drainage basin of the Ohio River drains much of eastern North America. *Interpreting Maps What are the tributaries of the Ohio River? Could a tributary come from outside the drainage basin?*

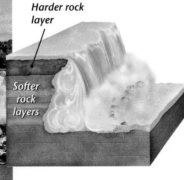

Figure 9 Niagara Falls formed on the Niagara River, which connects Lake Erie and Lake Ontario. A flat layer of tough rock lies over a layer of softer rock that erodes easily. When the softer rock erodes, pieces of the harder rock above break off, creating the waterfall's sharp drop.

Harder rock layer

Softer rock layers

Chapter 3 **G ◆ 75**

Answers to Self-Assessment

☑ Checkpoint

The amount of rain, the vegetation, type of soil, shape of the land, and how people use the land

Caption Question

Figure 8 The Allegheny, Monongahela, Wabash, Kentucky, and Tennessee rivers. A tributary could not come from outside the drainage basin.

Inquiry Challenge

Materials *shallow pan (2 cm deep, 10 cm wide, and at least 50 cm long), 2 buckets, rubber tubing (2-cm diameter), screw clamp, bricks, sand, water*
Time 30 minutes for setup

Challenge groups of students to design and build a stream table to study stream erosion and deposition. A typical design using the materials listed above would entail placing the pan on a table, with one end raised by several bricks. A bucket for adding water is then placed on a higher stack of bricks on the high side of the pan. Water is added to the pan by siphoning through rubber tubing and into the pan; a screw clamp on the tubing regulates the flow. The second bucket acts as an overflow reservoir at the low end of the pan. Help students make a notch in the pan to facilitate overflow. Once the stream table is made, groups can investigate whether a drainage basin forms when several small streams are begun at the high end of the table. **cooperative learning**

Erosion by Rivers

Using the Visuals: Figure 9

Materials *stream table, eraser, sand, water*
Time 20 minutes

After students examine the figure and read the caption, ask: **What is necessary for a waterfall to form on a stream?** (*An area of rock that is very hard and erodes much more slowly than the softer rock downstream.*) Then challenge small groups to create a model of the formation of a waterfall in a stream table. Students can use any hard material to model the hard-to-erode rock layer. An eraser, for example, could be placed across the stream in the stream table, stuck into the sand as a barrier. As water flows over the ruler, a "waterfall" will form as the soil downstream erodes. **learning modality: kinesthetic**

Ongoing Assessment

Oral Presentation Call on students to explain how the Ohio River can have its own drainage basin but also be a tributary to the Mississippi River.

Erosion by Rivers,
continued

Real-Life Learning

Materials *topographic map*

Time 15 minutes

Provide students with copies of a topographic map that shows a river in their city or region. Then challenge students to use the map to measure and describe the boundaries of the flood plain of that river. Because interpretations will vary, invite selected students to explain to the class what they have found, and help students come to a consensus about the extent of the flood plain. For a definitive statement, have students contact the office of the county engineer. Because counties have rules about building on flood plains, the county engineer usually can give details about the width of the plain. **learning modality: logical/mathematical**

Using the Visuals: Figure 10

Draw students' attention to the photo of meanders. Have each student trace the river onto a clean sheet of paper. Then challenge students to use their tracings to make a labeled diagram of one or more illustrations that shows how an oxbow lake forms. A typical diagram should illustrate the processes of flooding, the river finding a new channel between two meanders, and the isolation of the oxbow lake. **learning modality: visual**

Inquiry Challenge

Materials *stream table, sand, water*

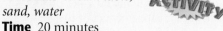

Time 20 minutes

Point out that meanders occur on wide, relatively flat plains rather than in mountainous areas. Challenge groups to form a hypothesis about how steepness of slope is related to development of meanders. After discussing each group's hypothesis, encourage students to test their hypotheses by designing and carrying out an experiment.
cooperative learning

Figure 10 The oxbow lake (above) was formerly a part of the channel of the Kasanak River in Alaska. These meanders (right) were formed by a river in Australia.

Lower down on its course, a river usually flows over more gently sloping land. The river spreads out and erodes the land, forming a wide river valley. The flat, wide area of land along a river is a **flood plain.** A river often covers its flood plain when it overflows its banks during floods. On a wide flood plain, the valley walls may be kilometers away from the river itself.

A river often develops meanders where it flows through easily eroded rock or sediment. A **meander** is a looplike bend in the course of a river. As the river widens from side to side, it tends to erode the outer bank and deposit sediment on the inner bank of a bend. Over time, the bend—or meander—becomes more and more curved.

When the gently sloping part of a river flows through an area of sediment or soft rock, it can erode a very wide flood plain. Along this part of a river's course, its channel is deep and wide. Meanders are common along this part of a river. The southern stretch of the Mississippi River is one example of a river that meanders on a wide, gently sloping flood plain.

Sometimes a meandering river forms a feature called an oxbow lake. An **oxbow lake** is a meander that has been cut off from the river. An oxbow lake may form when a river floods. During the flood, high water finds a straighter route downstream. As the flood waters fall, sediments dam up the ends of a meander. The meander has become an oxbow lake.

✓ *Checkpoint* *How does an oxbow lake form?*

Background

History of Science The term *delta* as used to describe the landform at the mouth of a river was coined by the ancient Greek historian Herodotus in the fifth century B.C. He noticed that the shape of the area where the Nile River flowed into the Mediterranean Sea was roughly triangular, the same shape as the Greek letter delta.

Facts and Figures The Mississippi Delta is actually a combination of seven lobes, or

subdeltas. The river created each subdelta one after another over 5,000 years as it shifted its course six times. The reason for each shift is that deposition fills in a channel over time. When the channel becomes too shallow, the river shifts course by breaking through a natural levee back upstream. Studies show that the Mississippi has flowed through its present course for 500 years.

Deposits by Rivers

As water moves, it carries sediments with it. Any time moving water slows down, it drops, or deposits, some of the sediment. As the water slows down, fine particles fall to the river's bed. Larger stones quit rolling and sliding. **Deposition creates landforms such as alluvial fans and deltas. It can also add soil to a river's flood plain.** In *Exploring the Course of a River* on pages 78–79, you can see these and other features shaped by rivers and streams.

Alluvial Fans Where a stream flows out of a steep, narrow mountain valley, the stream suddenly becomes wider and shallower. The water slows down. Here sediments are deposited in an alluvial fan. An **alluvial fan** is a wide, sloping deposit of sediment formed where a stream leaves a mountain range. As its name suggests, this deposit is shaped like a fan.

Deltas A river ends its journey when it flows into a still body of water, such as an ocean or a lake. Because the river water is no longer flowing downhill, the water slows down. At this point, the sediment in the water drops to the bottom. Sediment deposited where a river flows into an ocean or lake builds up a landform called a **delta**. Deltas can be a variety of shapes: some are arc-shaped, others are triangle-shaped. The delta of the Mississippi River is an example of a type of delta called a "bird's foot" delta.

Soil on Flood Plains Deposition also occurs during floods.

 INTEGRATING LIFE SCIENCE Then heavy rains or melting snow cause a river to rise above its banks and spread out over its flood plain. When the flood water finally retreats, it deposits sediment as new soil. Deposition of new soil over a flood plain is what makes a river valley fertile. Dense forests can grow in the rich soil of a flood plain. The soil is also perfect for growing crops.

Figure 11 This alluvial fan in Death Valley, California, was formed from deposits by streams from the mountains.

Figure 12 This satellite image shows part of the Mississippi River delta, which is always growing and changing. *Observing What happens to the Mississippi River as it flows through its delta? Can you find the river's main channel?*

Answers to Self-Assessment

Caption Question

Figure 12 The river's main channel flows almost to the tip of the delta, where it divides into two or three large channels and many smaller ones.

☑ *Checkpoint*

An oxbow lake forms when a meander is cut off from the river, such as after flood waters fall.

Deposits by Rivers

Using the Visuals: Figure 12

Materials *world atlas or encyclopedia*
Time 15 minutes

Have pairs of students find maps in an atlas or encyclopedia that show the deltas of these major world rivers: Nile River (Egypt), Niger River (Nigeria), Ganges River (Bangladesh), Mekong River (Vietnam), Mississippi River (Louisiana), Columbia River (Oregon/Washington). Have students make drawings and write descriptions of each delta. In a class discussion, call on students to compare and contrast the deltas. Then ask: **Why do you think the Columbia River has no delta at its end?** (*Some students should infer that the currents of the Pacific Ocean move the sediments away, preventing development of a delta.*) **learning modality: visual**

Integrating Life Science

Refer students back to their study of soil composition in Chapter 2. Ask: **What kind of soil composition is good for plant growth?** (*Loam is best, in which sand, silt, and clay are in balance and there is adequate humus content.*) Point out that flooding causes deposits that enrich the soil of a flood plain. Ask: **How could deposits from a river enrich soil?** (*The sediment carried by the river must include the materials that make up good soil, including organic material.*) Explain that this new soil has never held crops or other vegetation and so it contains a lot of nutrients. **learning modality: logical/mathematical**

Ongoing Assessment

Skills Check Have students make two flowcharts, one for the process that results in an alluvial fan and the other for the process that results in a delta.

Deposits by Rivers, continued

EXPLORING
the Course of a River

After students have examined the feature, display a large map of the United States where all students can see. Then call on students to read the feature's annotations. Begin with the river's beginnings, in the mountains. On the map, point to the source of the Missouri River in the Rocky Mountains of southwestern Montana. Ask: **Why would a river in the mountains have rapids, waterfalls, and a V-shaped valley?** (*In mountains, the slopes are steep and the land is not easily eroded. The river cuts down rather than spreads out.*) Continue examining the course of the river, questioning students about the process that creates each characteristic. Also, keep referring to the map of the Missouri River and the river into which it flows, the Mississippi. Explain that many scientists speak of the Missouri-Mississippi system as one river. On the map, point out meanders, oxbow lakes, and the Mississippi Delta. **limited English proficiency**

Building Inquiry Skills: Predicting

Challenge students to write a prediction about what they would see if they could use a time machine to examine the landscape in *Exploring the Course of a River* a million years from today. (*Predictions will vary. Students might predict that the mountains will be worn down by the river, the meanders will be wider, and the delta will be larger. Students who have an understanding of other Earth processes, such as plate tectonics, may predict more profound changes.*) Have student volunteers read their predictions to the class. Then invite analysis from other students. **learning modality: logical/mathematical**

EXPLORING the Course of a River

The slope and size of a river, as well as the land through which it flows, determine how a river shapes the land.

Tributary A river receives water and sediment from a tributary—a smaller river or stream that flows into it.

Oxbow lakes An oxbow lake is a meander cut off from a river by deposition of sediment.

Valley widening As a river approaches sea level, it may meander more and develop a wider valley and a broader flood plain.

Delta Where a river flows into the ocean, the river deposits sediment, forming a delta.

Background

Facts and Figures A river begins at its *headwaters*, or *head*. This is often in a mountainous region, but not always. The head of the Mississippi River is in the lake region of Minnesota. A river ends at its *mouth*. A delta often forms at a river's mouth, but not always. The Columbia River in the Northwest has no delta because of the strong ocean currents near its mouth at the Pacific Ocean.

The flood plain of the southern stretch of the Mississippi River extends over 1,000 km, from Cairo, Illinois, to its mouth at the Gulf of Mexico. At some places, this flood plain is more than 200 km wide. Throughout, the river meanders back and forth, ever widening its flood plain. Between 1765 and 1932, the river cut off 19 meanders, forming oxbow lakes. Since that time, dams and artificial levees have somewhat stabilized the course.

Waterfalls and rapids Waterfalls and rapids are common where the river passes over harder rock.

V-shaped valley Near its source, a river often flows through a deep, V-shaped valley. As the river flows, it cuts a deeper valley.

Meanders Where a river flows across easily eroded sediment, its channel bends from side to side in a series of meanders.

Oxbow lake

Flood plain A flood plain forms when a river's power of erosion widens its valley rather than deepening it.

Beaches Sand carried downstream by rivers spreads along the coast to form beaches.

G ◆ 79

Cultural Diversity

Have students use an encyclopedia, library books, or videos to find out about life along a river, using the Missouri-Mississippi rivers as an example. Ask students to write a description of what it would be like to live near the river in Montana, in Missouri, and in the delta region of Louisiana. After students have completed, ask: **If a friend told you she once lived near a river, would you automatically know what her life had been like?** *(No, because life varies along the course of a river.)* Encourage students to share their descriptions and compare life in the three different regions. **learning modality: verbal**

Real-Life Learning

Materials *state map*
Time 15 minutes

Provide maps of your state for students to examine. Then challenge students to plan a canoe or rafting trip along one of the state's major rivers, writing a description of what they could see. Some students might even wish to create a travel-type brochure. Encourage students to share their plans in a class discussion. **learning modality: visual**

Including All Students

Materials *poster board, colored pencils, markers*
Time 30 minutes

Have students who need additional challenges make a bulletin board that shows the course of a river. They can make drawings of river features and add labels with definitions and descriptions of processes. **learning modality: visual**

Ongoing Assessment

Drawing Have students make their own drawing of the course of a river. In their drawing, students could add the river's origin where two or more streams run together, as well as an alluvial fan as the river leaves the mountains.

 Students can keep their drawings in their portfolio.

G ◆ 79

Groundwater Erosion and Deposition

Addressing Naive Conceptions

Many students may believe that all or most of the groundwater consists of rivers or lakes beneath Earth's surface. Point out that underground caves do sometimes contains streams and lakes, but this is the exception rather than the rule. Groundwater can be found everywhere beneath the surface—even under dry deserts. **learning modality: verbal**

Integrating Chemistry

Materials *small pieces of limestone, corrugated cardboard, plastic wrap, books, piece of clear plastic, plastic dropper, vinegar*

Time 10 minutes

Have students observe a model of the weathering of limestone by groundwater. Make a trough of corrugated cardboard, line it with plastic wrap, and elevate one end on a stack of books. Under the low end, place a piece of clear plastic. Spread the limestone pieces along the inside of the trough, and then add drops of vinegar—a weak acid—to the top of the trough. Students will see the water trickling through the limestone pieces. The drops will trickle down to the piece of plastic. Allow the liquid to dry, and have students observe the resulting deposition. **learning modality: visual**

Inquiry Challenge

Materials *aluminum cake pan, plaster of Paris, bowl, washcloth, ringstand*

Time 20 minutes a day for 2-3 days

Challenge small groups of students to use the materials above, or other materials of their choosing, to model the formation of stalagmites on a cave floor. A typical setup might involve mixing plaster of Paris in a bowl, saturating a washcloth, hanging the saturated washcloth from a ringstand, and then allowing the washcloth to drip into a cake pan. Students will have to periodically resaturate the washcloth. After 2–3 days, "stalagmites" will have formed in the pan. **learning modality: kinesthetic**

Groundwater Erosion and Deposition

When rain falls and snow melts, not all of the water evaporates or becomes runoff. Some water soaks into the ground. There it fills the openings in the soil and trickles into cracks and spaces in layers of rock. **Groundwater** is the term geologists use for this underground water. Like running water on the surface, groundwater affects the shape of the land.

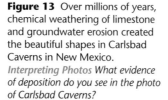 Groundwater can cause erosion through a process of chemical weathering. When water sinks into the ground, it combines with carbon dioxide to form a weak acid, called carbonic acid. Carbonic acid can break down limestone. Groundwater containing carbonic acid flows into cracks in the limestone. Then some of the limestone changes chemically and is carried away in a solution of water. This gradually hollows out pockets in the rock. Over time, these pockets develop into large holes underground, called caves or caverns.

The action of carbonic acid on limestone can also result in deposition. Inside limestone caves, deposits called stalactites and stalagmites often form. Water containing carbonic acid and calcium from limestone drips from a cave's roof. As the water

Figure 13 Over millions of years, chemical weathering of limestone and groundwater erosion created the beautiful shapes in Carlsbad Caverns in New Mexico. *Interpreting Photos What evidence of deposition do you see in the photo of Carlsbad Caverns?*

Background

Facts and Figures Carlsbad Caverns, a national park, is located in southeastern New Mexico. These caverns formed 60–70 million years ago when plate movements created cracks in the limestone of the area, allowing groundwater to move into the rock and hollow out the caverns. The largest chamber of the caverns is the Big Room, which is 550 m long, 335 m wide, and 78 m high at its highest.

Mammoth Cave in central Kentucky is also part of the national park system. This cave, created through chemical weathering of limestone, is part of the Flint Ridge cave system. About 550 km of interconnected passageways have been explored in this system, more than anywhere else in the world. Mammoth Cave contains lakes, waterfalls, and rivers, including Echo River, which is as much as 18 m wide.

Figure 14 A sinkhole, such as this one in Florida, is a characteristic feature of karst topography. Sinkholes can pose a hazard for people who live in a karst region.

evaporates, a deposit of calcite forms. A deposit that hangs like an icicle from the roof of a cave is called a **stalactite** (stuh LAK tyt). Slow dripping builds up a cone-shaped **stalagmite** (stuh LAG myt) from the cave floor.

In rainy regions where there is a layer of limestone near the surface, groundwater erosion can significantly change the shape of the land. Streams are rare, because water sinks easily down into the weathered limestone. Deep valleys and caverns are common. If the roof of a cave collapses because of the erosion of the underlying limestone, the result is a depression called a sinkhole. This type of landscape is called **karst topography** after a region in Eastern Europe. In the United States, there are regions of karst topography in Florida, Kentucky, and Indiana.

Section 2 Review

1. What is the major cause of erosion on Earth's surface?
2. Briefly describe five features formed by rivers and streams as they erode the land.
3. What are the results of deposition along the course of a stream or river?
4. How can groundwater contribute to erosion?
5. **Thinking Critically Comparing and Contrasting** How is an alluvial fan similar to a delta? How is it different?

Science at Home

In a small dish, build a cube out of 27 small sugar cubes. Your cube should be three sugar cubes on a side. Fold a square piece of paper towel to fit the top of the cube. Wet the paper towel, place it on the cube, and let it stand for 15 or 20 minutes. Every few minutes, sprinkle a few drops of water on the paper towel to keep it wet. Then remove the paper towel. What happened to your cube? How is the effect of water on a sugar cube similar to groundwater eroding limestone? How is it different?

Program Resources

◆ **Teaching Resources** 3-2 Review and Reinforce, p. 71; 3-2 Enrich, p. 72

Answers to Self-Assessment

Caption Question

Figure 13 The photo shows both stalactites and stalagmites, which are evidence of deposition.

---

3 Assess

Section 2 Review Answers

1. Moving water is the major cause of erosion on Earth's surface.
2. Students' descriptions should reflect the section's discussion of valleys, waterfalls, flood plains, meanders, and oxbow lakes.
3. Deposition results in the creation of alluvial fans and deltas, as well as new soil over flood plains.
4. Groundwater can cause erosion through a process of chemical weathering. Carbonic acid in the water breaks down limestone, which is carried away by the water in solution.
5. An alluvial fan is similar to a delta in that both are deposits of sediment that occur when a stream slows down. An alluvial fan is a wide, sloping deposit formed where a stream leaves a mountain range, while a delta is a deposit when a stream flows into an ocean or lake.

Science at Home

Materials *small dish, 27 small sugar cubes, paper towel, water*

Tips Encourage students to carry out this activity and write answers to the questions about what occurred. Students should find that some of the sugar of the large cube will dissolve in the water of the paper towel, and the paper towel will absorb that solution, leaving the cube smaller and misshapen. The purpose of building a large cube with smaller ones is to provide more surface area for water to seep through. The result is analogous to water seeping through cracks in limestone, eroding the rock with carbonic acid, and then carrying the limestone away in solution.

Performance Assessment

Skills Check Have students make a table that compares and contrasts the features created by water erosion and water deposition.

You and Your Environment

Streams in Action

Preparing for Inquiry

Key Concept As water moves over land, it moves soil and rock with it, forming a channel through erosion.

Skills Objectives Students will be able to:
- make a model of a stream;
- observe differences in how time and angle of slope affect how a stream erodes the land;
- predict how increasing the angle of slope will affect how a stream erodes the land.

Time 40 minutes

Advance Planning Diatomaceous earth is a silica material that works well in stream tables. In dry form, though, its dust can cause lung damage and eye irritation. The dust will not be a problem if the material is kept moist.

Wear goggles and plastic gloves when preparing the stream tables. First, place about 1 kg of diatomaceous earth into each tub. Pour water into the tub and allow it to soak through the diatomaceous earth. Agitate the tub slightly to expose all the diatomaceous earth to the water. Drain off any excess water. Then, wearing gloves, form a hill at one end of the tub, sloping the diatomaceous earth from high on one side to the bottom of the tub, leaving about a third of the tub free of the material.

Use plastic stirrers with two holes; straws with only one hole will not work as well. Experiment with making the dripper before the lab so that you can advise students about the procedure.

Alternative Materials The advantage of using diatomaceous earth is that after it dries it can be used again. But local topsoil or commercial soil or sand could be used instead.

Guiding Inquiry

Invitation Help students focus on the key concept by asking: **What is the major agent of erosion that shapes Earth's surface?** (*Moving water*) **How**

Streams in Action

Erosion can form gullies, wash away topsoil, and pollute rivers with sediment. You can observe the effects of erosion using a stream table.

Problem

How do rivers and streams erode the land?

Skills Focus

making models, observing, predicting

Materials

plastic tub at least 27 cm × 40 cm × 10 cm
diatomaceous earth   plastic measuring cup
spray bottle   hand lens
watch or clock   water
1 metal spoon   plastic foam cup
blue food coloring   liquid detergent
scissors
2 wood blocks about 2.5 cm thick
bucket to hold 2–3 L of water or a source of tap water
plastic stirrers, 10–12 cm long, with two small holes each
wire 13–15 cm long, 20 gauge

Procedure

Part A Creating Streams Over Time

1. Your teacher will give you a plastic tub containing diatomaceous earth that has been soaked with water. Place the tub on a level surface. **CAUTION:** *Dry diatomaceous earth produces dust that may be irritating if inhaled. To keep the diatomaceous earth from drying out, spray it lightly with water.*

Making the Dripper

1. Insert the wire into one of the two holes in a plastic stirrer. The ends of the wire should protrude from the stirrer.
2. Gently bend the stirrer into a U shape. Be careful not to make any sharp bends. This is the dripper.
3. With scissors, carefully cut two small notches on opposite sides of the top of the foam cup.
4. Fill the cup to just below the notches with water colored with two drops of blue food coloring. Add more food coloring later as you add more water to the cup.
5. Add one drop of detergent to keep air bubbles out of the dripper and increase flow.
6. To start the dripper, fill it with water. Then quickly tip it and place it in one of the notches in the cup, as shown above.
7. Adjust the flow rate of the dripper to about 2 drips per 1 second. (*Hint:* Bend the dripper into more of a U shape to increase flow. Lessen the curve to reduce flow.)

2. One end of the tub will contain more diatomaceous earth. Use the block of wood to raise this end of the tub 2.5 cm.
3. Place the cup at the upper end of the slope with the notches pointing to the left and right.
4. Press the cup firmly down into the earth to secure its position.
5. Start the dripper (see Step 6 in the box above). Allow the water to drip to the right onto the diatomaceous earth.

---

does water cause erosion? (*The force of moving water picks up soil and rock particles and carries them with it as it moves downhill.*) **What factors affect how much sediment a river can erode?** (*Factors include a river's slope, volume of flow, and shape of its streambed.*)

Introducing the Procedure

- Give students time to read through the whole procedure, and then ask: **What factor are you investigating in Part A?** (*How the amount of runoff affects the amount of*

erosion.) **What factor are you investigating in Part B?** (*How the slope of a stream affects its power to erode.*)

Troubleshooting the Experiment

- When starting the dripper, students should see a stream of water forming as the drops accumulate on the diatomaceous earth. If not, the dripper needs to be adjusted to increase the flow.
- Have each group select a time keeper who will keep track of drip time.

6. Allow the dripper to drip for 5 minutes. (*Hint:* When you need to add more water, be careful not to disturb the dripper.)
7. Observe the flow of water and the changes it makes. Use the hand lens to look closely at the stream bed.
8. After 5 minutes, remove the dripper.
9. In your lab notebook, draw a picture of the resulting stream and label it "5 minutes."
10. Now switch the dripper to the left side of the cup. Restart the dripper and allow it to drip for 10 minutes. Then remove the dripper.
11. Draw a picture and label it "10 minutes."

Part B Changing the Angle of Slope
1. Remove the cup from the stream table.
2. Save the stream bed on the right side of the tub. Using the bowl of the spoon, smooth out the diatomaceous earth on the left side.
3. To increase the angle of slope of your stream table, raise the end of the tub another 2.5 cm.

4. In your lab notebook, predict the effects of increasing the angle of slope.
5. Replace the cup and restart the dripper, placing it in the notch on the left side of the cup. Allow the dripper to drip for 5 minutes. Notice any changes in the new stream bed.
6. At the end of 5 minutes, remove the dripper.
7. Draw a picture of the new stream bed in your lab notebook. Label it "Increased Angle."
8. Follow your teacher's instructions for clean-up after this activity. Wash your hands when you have finished.

Analyze and Conclude

1. Compare the 5-minute stream with the 10-minute stream. How did the length of time that the water flowed affect erosion along the stream bed?
2. Were your predictions about the effects of increasing the angle of slope correct? Explain your answer.
3. What eventually happened to the eroded material that was carried downstream?
4. What other variables besides time and angle of slope might affect the way rivers and streams erode the land?
5. **Apply** Have you ever seen water flowing down a hillside or street after a heavy rain? If so, how much did the land slope in that area? Did you notice anything about the color of the water? Explain.

Design an Experiment

Design a stream table experiment to measure how the amount of sediment carried by a river changes as the volume of flow of the river increases. Obtain your teacher's approval before you try the experiment.

◆ Advise students to have their lab notebooks handy to make their drawings and write their predictions.

Expected Outcome
In Part A, students should observe that the dripping water erodes the diatomaceous earth, moving some of the material from the high end to the low end. The dripping water will form a channel; the 10-minute drip will form a deeper channel than the 5-minute drip. In Part B, increasing the angle of slope will produce a deeper channel and more erosion.

Analyze and Conclude
1. Students should observe that the 10-minute stream produced a deeper channel than the 5-minute stream. Likewise, the 10-minute stream moved more material down the slope.
2. Answers may vary. Most students will have predicted that increasing the angle of slope would result in a deeper channel and more erosion, and their results should have confirmed that prediction.
3. Students should observe that the eroded material moves down the slope and is deposited at the open end of the stream table.
4. Answers may vary. A typical answer might suggest that the volume of flow and the speed of the water affect the way rivers and streams erode the land. Some students might also mention that the kind of material over which the water flows also affects erosion.
5. Answers will vary. A typical answer might mention water flowing down a steeply sloping hillside or street, with the water being cloudy or dirty from eroded soil.

Extending the Inquiry

Design an Experiment Designs will vary. A typical design might investigate volume of flow. Students could suggest pouring water onto opposite sides of the slope from two sizes of plastic straws and comparing the erosion caused by each stream. After reviewing the designs, encourage students to carry out their experiments.

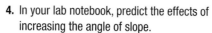
Safety

Caution students to wear their goggles at all times when working with diatomaceous earth, since any dust in their eyes could be harmful. Also advise students to wear lab aprons and be careful when using the scissors and wire. Review the safety guidelines in Appendix A.

Protecting Homes in Flood Plains

Purpose

Students will learn about a difficult societal issue related to flooding and water erosion.

Role-Play

Time 40 minutes

◆ In this activity, students will role-play a town meeting after a major flood has destroyed homes and businesses within a river's flood plain. If there is a major river in your area, students could predict what would be damaged if it flooded and then use those projections in the role-play. You could also develop a flood scenario for any river and give students copies.

◆ Divide the class into three main groups. Students in one group of four or five will role-play public officials, including a mayor, a Congressperson, the head of a federal agency for flood relief, and so on. This group will run the town meeting. Students in a second group will role-play people affected by the flood. Students in a third group will role-play citizens who oppose public moneys for rebuilding in the flood plain. Give each group 10–15 minutes to discuss within the group positions and arguments to take in the town meeting. Then hold the town meeting, with rules set by the "officials" group. Encourage students to assert their positions respectfully but passionately.

Extend Encourage students to find out what happened in Grand Forks after the 1997 Red River flood. With real data, students can realistically assess positions taken during the role-play.

You Decide

Have students write their speeches after participating in the role-play. A good speech should include a clear description of the problems the flood caused, a list of options, and an argument for one option.

Protecting Homes in Flood Plains

At least ten million American households are located in flood plains. Living near a river is tempting. Riverside land is often flat and easy to build on. Because so many people now live in flood plains, the cost of flood damage has been growing. Communities along rivers want to limit the cost of flooding. They want to know how they can protect the people and buildings already in flood plains. They also want to know how to discourage more people from moving into flood plains.

The Issues

Should the Government Insure People Against Flood Damage? The United States government offers insurance to households in flood plains. The insurance pays part of the cost of repairs after a flood. Insurance helps people, but it is very expensive. Only 17 percent of people who live in flood plains buy the government insurance. Government flood insurance is available only in places that take steps to reduce flood damage. Cities must allow new building only on high ground. The insurance will not pay to rebuild homes that are badly damaged by floodwater. Instead, these people must use the money to find a home somewhere else.

Critics say that insurance just encourages people to move back into areas that flood. Supporters say it rewards towns and cities that make rules to control building on flood plains.

How Much of the Flood Plain Should Be Protected? Government flood insurance is available only in areas where scientists expect flooding about once in 100 years, or once in 500 years. Such figures are just estimates. Three floods occurred in only 12 years in a government flood-insurance area near Sacramento, California.

Should the Government Tell People Where They Can Live? Some programs of flood control forbid all new building. Other programs may also encourage people to move to safer areas. The 1997 flood on the Red River in Grand Forks, North Dakota, is one example. After the flood, the city of Grand Forks offered to buy all the damaged buildings near the river. The city wants to build high walls of earth to protect the rest of the town.

The Grand Forks plan might prevent future damage, but is it fair? Supporters say that since the government has to pay for flood damage, it has the right to make people leave flood plains. Critics of such plans say that people should be free to live where they want, even in risky areas.

Who should decide in which neighborhood no new houses can be built? Who decides which people should be asked to move away from a flood plain? Experts disagree over whether local, state, or United States government officials should decide which areas to include. Some believe scientists should make the decision.

You Decide

1. Identify the Problem
In your own words, describe the controversy surrounding flood plains and housing.

2. Analyze the Options
List several steps that could be taken to reduce the damage done to buildings in flood plains. For each step, include who would benefit from the step, and who would pay the costs.

3. Find a Solution
Your town has to decide what to do about a neighborhood damaged by the worst flood in 50 years. Write a speech that argues for your solution.

Background

Facts and Figures A flood plain might be thought of as a natural safety valve for times when a river's channel can't hold all the runoff. Because the flooding of any particular river is relatively rare, builders often don't take this natural feature into consideration. Geologists try to predict major floods by using the past to calculate a probability. A "50-year flood," for instance, is one that occurs only once every 50 years, *on average.* The problem is that such a flood *can* occur in any year, and even two years in a row.

The 1997 Red River flood was a 500-year flood caused by an ice block to the north that prevented runoff from heavy snows and rains from flowing downstream (north into Canada). Flood waters spread out over the 64-km-wide flood plain, causing catastrophic damage.

SECTION 3 The Force of Moving Water

ACTIVITY

How Are Sediments Deposited?

1. Put on your goggles.

2. Obtain a clear plastic jar or bottle with a top. Fill the jar about two-thirds full with water.

3. Fill a plastic beaker with 200 mL of fine and coarse sand, soil, clay, and small pebbles.

4. Pour the mixture into the jar of water. Screw on the top tightly and shake for two minutes. Be sure to hold onto the jar firmly.

5. Set the jar down and observe it for 10 to 15 minutes.

Think It Over

Inferring In what order are the sediments in the jar deposited? What do you think causes this pattern?

The Merrimack River in New Hampshire and Massachusetts is only 180 kilometers long. But the Merrimack does a great deal of work as it runs from the mountains to the sea. The river's waters fall 82 meters through many rapids and waterfalls. During the 1800s, people harnessed this falling water to run machines. These machines could spin thread and weave cloth very quickly and cheaply. Thanks to water power, the towns along the river grew quickly into cities.

Work and Energy

The waters of the Merrimack River could drive machines because a river's water has energy. **Energy** is the ability to do work or cause change. There are two kinds of energy. **Potential energy** is energy that is stored and waiting to be used later. The Merrimack's waters begin with potential energy due to their position above sea level. **Kinetic energy** is the energy an object has due to its motion. **As gravity pulls water down a slope, the water's potential energy changes to kinetic energy that can do work.**

GUIDE FOR READING

◆ What enables water to do work?

◆ How does sediment enter rivers and streams?

◆ What factors affect a river's ability to erode and carry sediment?

Reading Tip Before you read, rewrite the headings of the section as *how, why,* or *what* questions. As you read, look for answers to these questions.

Figure 15 Dams like this one on the Merrimack River in Lowell, Massachusetts, help to harness the power of flowing water.

G ◆ 85

SECTION 3 The Force of Moving Water

Objectives

After completing the lesson, students will be able to

◆ describe how water is able to do work;

◆ explain how sediment enters rivers and streams;

◆ list the factors that affect a river's ability to erode and carry sediment.

Key Terms energy, potential energy, kinetic energy, abrasion, load, friction, turbulence

1 Engage/Explore

Activating Prior Knowledge

Encourage students to describe different rivers they've seen in terms of size and speed. Then ask: **The water in which river moves faster, a narrow river moving down from a steep mountain valley or a large river moving over a wide coastal plain?** *(Most students will say the narrow mountain river moves faster.)* Suggest that they may have to revise their opinions after reading the section.

Skills Focus inferring
Materials *clear plastic jar or bottle with top, water, plastic beaker, fine and coarse sand, soil, clay, small pebbles*

ACTIVITY

Time 15 minutes
Tips To simplify the activity, make the sediment mixtures in advance.
Expected Outcome Students will observe the slow settling of the sediments, with the larger particles settling first and the smaller sizes settling in succession. After 10–15 minutes, most particles will have settled, though the water will remain cloudy due to the suspension of fine particles.
Think It Over The particles are deposited by size, with the largest on the bottom and the smallest on top. Gravity acting on the different weights of the sediment particles causes the pattern.

Work and Energy

Social Studies CONNECTION

Throughout the nineteenth century, Lowell was noted for its textile mills, as were other towns in New England. Today, part of the old central city of Lowell is a national historical park, designated as a birthplace of the American industrial revolution. In the twentieth century, the textile industry largely abandoned the Northeast for the South, and then relocated much of its production overseas.

In Your Journal Challenge students to find library books that explore a mill worker's life in the nineteenth century. Books on American life in the 1800s contain such material. Typically, women workers worked over 10 hours a day, six days a week. **learning modality: verbal**

How Water Erodes and Carries Sediment

Using the Visuals: Figure 16

Ask: **What are three main ways that a stream carries sediment?** (*A stream carries sediment in solution, suspended in the water, and by moving it along its bed.*) Explain that scientists divide a stream's load into three parts, called the dissolved load, the suspended load, and the bed load. Ask: **Does a stream move all sediment particles on the bed the same way?** (*No. The way in which sediment moves along the bed depends on the particle size. Smaller particles bounce, while larger particles roll.*) Explain that the bed load is responsible for most of the erosive power of a stream—the cutting down through rock that streams and rivers do. The movement of sand and gravel on the bed wears away the bottom and sides of the channel by abrasion. **learning modality: visual**

Social Studies CONNECTION

The cotton mills in Lowell, Massachusetts, were built in the 1820s. The mills employed young women from the farms and small towns of New England. At that time, it was unusual for women to work outside the home. The hours of work at a mill were long and pay was low. But mill work helped these women to earn and save their own money. Most later returned to their hometowns.

In Your Journal

Use library references to find out more about the daily life of the mill workers. Write a diary entry describing a worker's typical day.

Figure 16 Rivers and streams carry sediment in several ways. *Predicting What will eventually happen to a boulder on the bottom of a river?*

When energy does work, the energy is transferred from one object to another. At the textile mills along the Merrimack River, the kinetic energy of the moving water was transferred to the spinning machines. It became mechanical energy harnessed for a human purpose—making cloth. But all along a river, kinetic energy does other work. A river is always moving sediment from the mountains to the sea. At the same time, a river is also eroding its banks and valley.

☑ *Checkpoint* **What are potential energy and kinetic energy?**

How Water Erodes and Carries Sediment

Gravity causes the movement of water across Earth's land surface. But how does water cause erosion? In the process of water erosion, water picks up and moves sediment. Sediment includes soil, rock, clay, and sand. Sediment can enter rivers and streams in a number of ways. **Most sediment washes or falls into the river as a result of mass movement and runoff. Other sediment erodes from the bottom or sides of the river.** Wind may also drop sediment into the water.

Abrasion is another process by which a river obtains sediment. **Abrasion** is the wearing away of rock by a grinding action. Abrasion occurs when particles of sediment in flowing water bump into the streambed again and again. Abrasion grinds down sediment particles. For example, boulders become smaller as they are moved down a streambed. Sediments also grind and chip away at the rock of the streambed, deepening and widening the stream's channel.

The amount of sediment that a river carries is its **load.** Gravity and the force of the moving water cause the sediment load to move downstream. Most large sediment falls to the bottom and moves by rolling and sliding. Fast-moving water actually lifts sand and other, smaller, sediment and carries it downstream. Water dissolves some sediment completely. The river carries these dissolved sediments in solution. If you look at Figure 16, you can observe the different ways in which water can carry sediment. Notice for example, how grains of sand or small stones can move by bouncing.

Dissolved sediment

Direction of flow

Suspended sediment

Larger particles pushed or rolled along stream bed

Smaller particles move by bouncing

Background

Facts and Figures A typical river transports most sediment in suspension, a lesser amount in solution, and the least amount along its bed. The Mississippi River has a sediment load of about 450 million metric tons of sediment per year.

The bouncing movement of sand particles along the river bed is called saltation. This occurs when a swift-flowing stream becomes turbulent, picking up sand grains and moving them a short distance. When a grain falls back to the bed, it strikes another grain, causing it to jump up into the current.

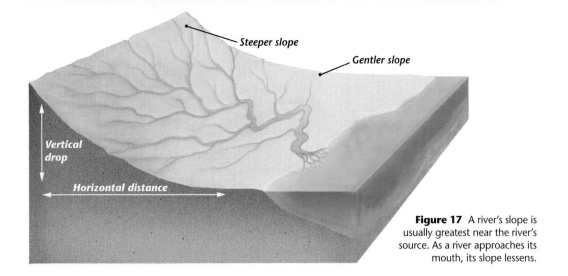

Steeper slope

Gentler slope

Vertical drop

Horizontal distance

Figure 17 A river's slope is usually greatest near the river's source. As a river approaches its mouth, its slope lessens.

Erosion and Sediment Load

The power of a river to cause erosion and carry sediment depends on several factors. **A river's slope, volume of flow, and the shape of its streambed all affect how fast the river flows and how much sediment it can erode.**

A fast-flowing river carries more and larger particles of sediment. When a river slows down, its sediment load is deposited. The larger particles of sediment are deposited first.

Slope Generally, if a river's slope increases, the water's speed also increases. A river's slope is the amount the river drops toward sea level over a given distance. If a river's speed increases, its sediment load and power to erode may increase. But other factors are also important in determining how much sediment the river erodes and carries.

Volume of Flow A river's flow is the volume of water that moves past a point on the river in a given time. As more water flows through a river, its speed increases. During a flood, the increased volume of water helps the river to cut more deeply into its banks and bed. A flooding river may have hundreds of times more eroding power than the river has at other times. A flooding river can carry huge amounts of sand, soil, and other sediments. It may move giant boulders as if they were pebbles.

Streambed Shape A streambed's shape affects the amount of friction between the water and the streambed. **Friction** is the force that opposes the motion of one surface as it moves across another surface. Friction, in turn, affects a river's speed. Where a river is deep, less water comes in contact with the streambed. This reduces

Developing Hypotheses

A geologist is comparing alluvial fans. One alluvial fan is composed of gravel and small boulders. The other fan is composed of sand and silt. Propose a hypothesis to explain the difference in the size of the particles in the two fans. (*Hint*: Think of the characteristics of the streams that formed each alluvial fan.)

Sharpen your Skills

Developing Hypotheses

Time 5 minutes
Tips Suggest that students reread the description in Section 2 of how an alluvial fan forms and examine the accompanying photo in Figure 11.
Expected Outcome Hypotheses may vary. A typical hypothesis might suggest that the river that produced the gravel-boulder alluvial fan had a greater slope and volume of flow than the river that produced the sand-silt fan, because the heavier sediment could have been carried only by a fast-flowing river.
Extend Challenge students to design an experiment to test their hypotheses using a stream table. After reviewing designs, encourage students to test their hypotheses. **learning modality: logical/mathematical**

Inquiry Challenge

Materials *stream table, sand or diatomaceous earth, water*
Time 30 minutes

Challenge small groups to develop a hypothesis from one of the concepts related to erosion and sediment load. Examples: A river's sediment load increases as the river's speed increases. An increase in a river's volume of flow causes its speed to increase. Have students design an experiment to test their hypothesis, designating the variable to be tested. Review groups' designs, and then have each group carry out its design using a stream table. If more than one group does the same experiment, have groups compare results at the end. **cooperative learning**

Program Resources

Science Explorer Series *Chemical Interactions*, Chapter 3, has information about solutions.

Media and Technology

Transparencies "Water Erosion, Deposition, and Movement of Sediment", Transparency 11

Answers to Self-Assessment

Caption Question

Figure 16 The boulder will become smaller as it is moved down the streambed due to abrasion.

☑ Checkpoint

Potential energy is energy that is stored and waiting to be used later. Kinetic energy is the energy an object has due to its motion.

Ongoing Assessment

Oral Presentation Call on students at random to explain how a river deepens and widens its channel and how slope and volume of flow affect sediment load.

G ◆ 87

Using the Visuals: Figure 18

Ask: Where does the river erode its bank, at point A or B? (*At B, on the outside of the curve*) **As this process of erosion and deposition continues, what river feature will this curve develop into?** (*A meander*) Emphasize that this is how meanders develop. **learning modality: visual**

3 Assess

Section 3 Review Answers

1. As gravity pulls water down a slope, the water's potential energy changes to kinetic energy that can do work.

2. Most sediment washes or falls into a river as a result of mass movement and runoff. Other sediment erodes from the bottom or sides of a river.

3. Slope, volume of flow, and streambed shape

4. Large sediment moves by rolling or sliding along the streambed. Smaller sediment moves when water lifts it up and carries it downstream. Some sediment is also carried as dissolved sediment in solution.

5. As slope increases, so does a river's speed. And as a river's speed increases, so does its sediment load.

Check Your Progress
CHAPTER PROJECT 3

Students may have trouble with the scale of their first drawing. Explain that they need to think in terms of a large area, such as a whole state or region. Suggest that they refer back to Chapter 1, in which they learned about landforms and how to represent areas on a map. Supply the materials students will need to make their first model.

Performance Assessment

Writing Have students explain the difference in erosive power between a mountain stream and a river with a wide flood plain.

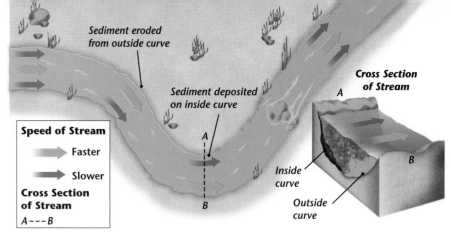

Figure 18 A river erodes sediment from its banks on the outside curve and deposits its sediment on the inside curve.
Relating Cause and Effect Why does a river deposit sediment on the inside of a curve?

friction and allows the river to flow faster. In a shallow river, much of the water comes in contact with the streambed. Therefore friction increases, reducing the river's speed.

A streambed is often full of boulders and other obstacles. This roughness prevents the water from flowing smoothly. Roughness thus increases friction and reduces the river's speed. Instead of moving downstream, the water moves every which way in a type of movement called **turbulence.** For example, a stream on a steep slope may flow at a lower speed than a large river on a gentle slope. Friction and turbulence slow the stream's flow. But a turbulent stream or river may have great power to erode.

The shape of a river affects the way it deposits sediment. Where a river flows in a straight line, the water flows faster near the center of the river than along its sides. Deposition occurs along the sides of the river, where the water moves more slowly.

If a river curves, the water moves fastest along the outside of the curve. There, the river tends to cut into its bank. Sediment is deposited on the inside curve, where the water speed is slowest. You can see this process in Figure 18.

Section 3 Review

1. How can moving water on Earth's surface do work?
2. How does a river collect sediment?
3. What are three factors that affect a river's sediment load?
4. Describe three ways that sediment moves in a river.
5. **Thinking Critically** **Relating Cause and Effect** What effect does increased slope have on a river's speed and sediment load? Explain.

Check Your Progress
CHAPTER PROJECT 3

Make a drawing of the landscape that you plan to model. This landscape will show the land before erosion. What kinds of landforms will you show in the model? Be sure to include a high mountain and a coastline. Make a list of materials that you will use to build your model. Once your teacher has approved your drawing and your list of materials, you may build your first model.

Answers to Self-Assessment

Caption Question

Figure 18 A river deposits sediment on the inside of a curve because the water speed is slowest there.

Program Resources

◆ **Teaching Resources** 3-3 Review and Reinforce, p. 75; 3-3 Enrich, p. 76
◆ **Integrated Science Laboratory Manual** G-3, "The Daily Grind"
  Science Explorer Series *Motion, Forces, and Energy,* Chapter 2, has more information on friction and gravity.

DISCOVER

How Do Glaciers Change the Land?

1. Put some sand in a small plastic container.

2. Fill the container with water and place the container in a freezer until the water turns to ice.

3. Remove the block of ice from the container.

4. Holding the ice with paper towels, rub the ice, sand side down, over a bar of soap. Observe what happens to the surface of the soap.

Think It Over

Inferring Based on your observations, how do you think moving ice could change the surface of the land?

You are on a boat trip near the coast of Alaska. You sail by vast evergreen forests and snow-capped mountains. Then, as your boat rounds a point of land, you see an amazing sight. A great mass of ice winds like a river between rows of mountains. Suddenly you hear a noise like thunder. Where the ice meets the sea, a giant chunk of ice breaks off and plunges into the water. Carefully, you pilot your boat around the iceberg and toward the mass of ice. It towers over your boat. You see that it is made up of solid ice that is deep blue and green as well as white. What is this river of ice?

GUIDE FOR READING

◆ What are the two kinds of glaciers?

◆ How do glaciers cause erosion and deposition?

Reading Tip Before you read, preview the headings and key terms in the section. Make a list of predictions about the characteristics of glaciers.

Kinds of Glaciers

Geologists define a **glacier** as any large mass of ice that moves slowly over land. **There are two kinds of glaciers—valley glaciers and continental glaciers.**

A **valley glacier** is a long, narrow glacier that forms when snow and ice build up high in a mountain valley. The sides of mountains keep these glaciers from spreading out in all directions. Instead, they usually move down valleys that have already been cut by rivers. Valley glaciers are found on many high mountains.

A **continental glacier** is a glacier that covers much of a continent or large island. Continental glaciers are much larger than

Figure 19 The Mendenhall Glacier in Alaska winds downhill between high mountains.

G ◆ 89

SECTION
4 Glaciers

Objectives

After completing the lesson, students will be able to

◆ name and describe two kinds of glaciers;

◆ describe the two processes by which glaciers erode the land;

◆ explain how glaciers deposit sediments, and the role of the ice ages in glacial erosion.

Key Terms glacier, valley glacier, continental glacier, ice age, plucking, till, moraine, kettle

1 Engage/Explore

Activating Prior Knowledge

Encourage students to recall their experiences with packed snow. Ask: **Is there a difference between the snow on top of a mound of snow and the snow on the bottom?** (*The snow is fluffier on top, while it's chunky like ice on the bottom.*) **What causes this difference?** (*The weight of the snow on top compresses the snow on the bottom.*) Explain that huge glaciers form by the same process.

DISCOVER

Skills Focus inferring
Materials *sand, small plastic container, water, freezer, paper towel, bar of soap*
Time 5 minutes for setup; 10 minutes the next day
Tips Make sure the containers are kept in the freezer long enough for the water to freeze solid.
Expected Outcome The sand should have frozen to the bottom of the ice. Rubbing the sand-side of the ice over soap will produce gouges and scratches by abrasion.
Think It Over Answers may vary. A typical answer might suggest that the sediment in ice changes the surface by abrasion, causing scratches and gouges in rock and soil.

2 Facilitate

Kinds of Glaciers

Including All Students

To help students unfamiliar with world geography, use a globe or large world map to point out Antarctica and Greenland. Then ask: **Where would valley glaciers be found?** (*In mountain ranges such as the Rockies, Alps, and Himalayas*) **Do all mountain ranges contain glaciers?** (*No*) Explain that glaciers occur only in mountain ranges where more snow falls than melts each year. For instance, there are no glaciers in the Appalachian Mountains. **learning modality: verbal**

Ice Ages

Using the Visuals: Figure 20

After students have examined the figure, ask: **What could have started and ended the last ice age?** (*A change in climate*) Explain that Earth's climate has changed many times in the past and may change again. Tell students they will learn more about Earth's past in Chapter 4. **learning modality: logical/ mathematical**

How Glaciers Form and Move

Building Inquiry Skills: Designing Experiments

Ask: **Since huge glaciers move only very short distances every day, how could you measure the movement of a valley glacier?** Then divide students into small groups and challenge each to design an experiment that would test the hypothesis that valley glaciers move several centimeters to a few meters daily. One way would be to drive stakes into a glacier, record their positions in relation to surrounding landforms, and then check those positions periodically over many years. **learning modality: logical/mathematical**

The Ice Age in North America

KEY
☐ Area covered by continental glacier

Figure 20 The continental glacier of the last ice age covered most of Canada and Alaska as well as much of the northern United States. The ice age lasted about 70,000 years and ended about 10,000 years ago.

valley glaciers. They spread out over large areas of the land. Today, continental glaciers cover about 10 percent of Earth's land. They cover Antarctica and most of Greenland. The glacier covering Antarctica spreads out over 14 million square kilometers and is over 2 kilometers thick.

Ice Ages

Many times in the past, continental glaciers have covered large parts of Earth's surface. These times are known as **ice ages.** For example, about 9 million years ago, continental glaciers began to form in North America, Europe, and Asia. These glaciers slowly grew and advanced southward. By about 2.5 million years ago, they covered about a third of Earth's land. The glaciers advanced and retreated, or melted back, several times. Figure 20 shows how far south the glaciers came on the North American continent during the most recent ice age. They finally retreated about 10,000 years ago.

How Glaciers Form and Move

Glaciers can form only in an area where more snow falls than melts. High in mountain valleys, temperatures seldom rise above freezing. Snow builds up year after year. The pressure of the weight of more and more snow compacts the snow at the bottom into ice. Once the depth of snow and ice reaches more than 30 to 40 meters, gravity begins to pull the glacier downhill.

Valley glaciers flow at a rate of a few centimeters to a few meters per day. But sometimes a valley glacier slides down more quickly in what is called a surge. A surging glacier can flow as much as 6 kilometers a year. Unlike valley glaciers, continental glaciers can flow in all directions. Continental glaciers spread out much as pancake batter spreads out in a frying pan.

☑ *Checkpoint* How do glaciers form?

Glacial Erosion

The movement of a glacier changes the land beneath it. Although glaciers work slowly, they are a major force of erosion. **The two processes by which glaciers erode the land are plucking and abrasion.**

As a glacier flows over the land, it picks up rocks in a process called **plucking.** Beneath a glacier, the weight of the ice can break rocks apart. These rock fragments freeze to the bottom of the

---

Background

History of Science To the northeast of Juneau, Alaska, is Glacier Bay National Park and Preserve, which includes numerous glaciers. In 1794, the British explorer George Vancouver described an "immense body" of ice that extended from shore to shore. Now, more than two centuries later, the glaciers that composed that ice have retreated 135 km, leaving behind many fiords, including Glacier Bay.

In the last 1 billion years, Earth has had several major ice ages, each lasting generally for millions of years. The last one is often called the Pleistocene Ice Age, or simply the Ice Age. Fluctuations in Earth's climate cause the advance and retreat of glaciers over continents. During the Pleistocene Ice Age, glaciers actually advanced over North America and then melted back several times over periods of about 60,000 years.

glacier. When the glacier moves, it carries the rocks with it. Figure 21 shows plucking by a glacier. Plucking can move even huge boulders.

Many rocks remain on the bottom of the glacier, and the glacier drags them across the land. This process, called abrasion, gouges and scratches the bedrock. You can see the results of erosion by glaciers in *Exploring Glacial Landforms* on pages 92–93.

Glacial Deposition

A glacier gathers a huge amount of rock and soil as it erodes the land in its path. **When a glacier melts, it deposits the sediment it eroded from the land, creating various landforms.** These landforms remain for thousands of years after the glacier has melted.

The mixture of sediments that a glacier deposits directly on the surface is called **till.** Till is made up of particles of many different sizes. Clay, silt, sand, gravel, and boulders can all be found in till.

The till deposited at the edges of a glacier forms a ridge called a **moraine.** A terminal moraine is the ridge of till at the farthest point reached by a glacier. Long Island in New York is a terminal moraine from the continental glaciers of the last ice age.

 INTEGRATING LIFE SCIENCE Other features left in glacial sediments are prairie potholes. These potholes are shallow depressions in till that were formed by flowing water as the continental glacier melted. Today, prairie potholes contain water for only part of the year. Each prairie pothole is a small oasis for living things. Grasses and moisture-loving plants grow thickly in and around the potholes. In the spring, the potholes brim with water from melting snow or rain. Thousands of migrating ducks and other birds stop off at the potholes to feed and rest on their way north. Some stay to build nests and raise their young.

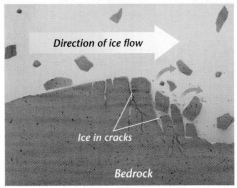

Direction of ice flow

Ice in cracks

Bedrock

Figure 21 As a glacier moves downhill, the ice plucks pieces of bedrock from the ground. *Predicting What evidence of plucking might you find after a glacier melts?*

Figure 22 This prairie pothole in Wisconsin is surrounded by farmland. Prairie potholes were left in till deposited by glaciers.

Program Resources

 **Science Explorer Series** *Earth's Waters,* Chapter 2, provides more information on glaciers and icebergs.

Answers to Self-Assessment

Caption Question

Figure 21 Evidence includes rocky knobs that are rounded on one side, but steep on the other side, where the glacier plucked away pieces of rock.

✓ *Checkpoint*

Glaciers form where more snow falls than melts. As snow builds up, its weight compacts the snow beneath into ice.

Glacial Erosion

Using the Visuals: Figure 21

After students have examined the figure, ask: **Why does the rock beneath a glacier crack?** (*The weight of the glacier causes the rock to crack.*) **Is this erosion or weathering?** (*The cracking itself weathers the rock. Erosion occurs when the rock fragments attach to the glacier by freezing and are carried away.*) **How do the rock fragments shown in the figure cause further weathering?** (*They scratch and gouge the land as the glacier moves.*) **learning modality: visual**

Building Inquiry Skills: Observing

Materials *ice cube, modeling compound, sand, cardboard*

ACTIVITY

Time 10 minutes; observe 1 hour later

Have students make a model landscape by spreading clay over a sheet of cardboard and rubbing sand over the clay. Then invite students to slide an ice cube slowly over the sand. Finally, have them leave the ice cube to melt at the end of the path. Students should sketch and write a description of the model glacial landforms they have made, including till, moraines, and a glacial lake. **learning modality: kinesthetic**

Glacial Deposition

Integrating Life Science

Have students turn back to the map of landform regions in Figure 3 of Chapter 1. Have students compare that map with the ice age map in Figure 20. Ask: **What type of glacier created prairie potholes in Wisconsin?** (*Most of Wisconsin is in the Central Lowlands and was covered by a glacier in the last ice age. Therefore, the prairie potholes must have been created by a continental glacier.*) **learning modality: logical/mathematical**

Ongoing Assessment

Writing Have students write an explanation of what a glacier is, how it forms, and how it moves.

Glacial Deposition, continued

EXPLORING
Glacial Landforms

Invite volunteers to read the annotations for each of the glacial landforms included in the feature. Then ask: **How is the mountain valley shown in this feature different from the valley shown in Exploring the Course of a River in Section 2?** *(A river makes a V-shaped valley; a glacier makes a U-shaped valley.)* Explain that through erosion, a glacier widens, deepens, and straightens a river-cut valley. Where there was once narrow valley, there is now a trough, or U-shaped valley. A fiord is a glacial trough partly filled with water as a result of rising sea level. **learning modality: visual**

Demonstration

Materials *stream table, sand or soil, water, ice cubes*

Time 10 minutes for setup; 10 minutes for observation on 2 days

As students observe, set up a stream table with a steady stream of water. After 10–15 minutes, discontinue the water. Have students examine the resulting valley and sketch what they observe. Then place ice cubes along the length of the stream-formed valley, moving the cubes in succession down the valley. Allow the ice to melt overnight. Again, have students examine the valley and sketch what they see. Finally, invite students to compare the stream-formed valley with the final valley. They should see that the first was V-shaped, while the second had widened to become more U-shaped. **learning modality: visual**

EXPLORING Glacial Landforms

As glaciers advance and retreat, they sculpt the landscape by erosion and deposition.

Horn When glaciers carve away the sides of a mountain, the result is a horn, a sharpened peak.

Cirque A cirque is a bowl-shaped hollow eroded by a glacier.

Arête An arête is a sharp ridge separating two cirques.

Fiord A fiord forms when the level of the sea rises, filling a valley once cut by a glacier in a coastal region.

Retreating glaciers also create features called kettles. A **kettle** is a small depression that forms when a chunk of ice is left in glacial till. When the ice melts, the kettle remains. The continental glacier of the last ice age left behind many kettles. Kettles often fill with water, forming small ponds or lakes called kettle lakes. Such lakes are common in areas that were covered with ice.

The continental glacier of the last ice age also formed the Great Lakes. Before the ice age, there were large river valleys in the area now occupied by the lakes. As the ice advanced over these valleys, it scooped out loose sediment and soft rock, forming broad, deep basins. The Great Lakes formed over thousands of years as the glaciers melted and these basins filled with water.

Background

Integrating Science Earth's biosphere extends even into glaciers. Several species of "ice worms," related to earthworms, live in ice. The worms average about 3 mm long and 1 mm in diameter. They thrive at a temperature of about 0°C, so on sunny days, they burrow deeper into the ice. Biologists believe ice worms feed on red algae, also common in glaciers.

Facts and Figures Perhaps the world's most famous glacial landform is the Matterhorn, a spectacular horn on the border of Italy and Switzerland in the Pennine Alps. This extremely steep peak rises to an elevation of 4,478 m and is a favorite of tourists and mountain climbers. The Matterhorn formed as three glaciers carved cirques on different sides of the original larger mountain.

U-Shaped valley A flowing glacier scoops out a U-shaped valley.

Glacial lake Glaciers may leave behind large lakes in long basins eroded by plucking and abrasion.

Moraine A moraine forms where a glacier deposits mounds or ridges of till. A moraine is made up of a mixture of particles of different sizes—from sand and gravel to boulders.

Drumlin Ice sliding over a moraine may shape it into a drumlin. A drumlin is a long mound of till that is smoothed in the direction of the glacier's flow.

Kettle lake A kettle lake forms when a depression left in till by melting ice fills with water.

 Section 4 Review

1. How are valley glaciers and continental glaciers different?
2. What are two types of glacial erosion?
3. Describe three features formed by glacial deposition.
4. **Thinking Critically** **Relating Cause and Effect** Driving through the countryside in Michigan, you and your family come upon a series of small, round lakes. Explain the process that formed these features.

Check Your Progress · · · **CHAPTER PROJECT 3**

Now you are ready to begin building your second model. Pattern the model after your drawing that predicts the effects of erosion and deposition. The model will show how gravity, water, and glaciers have changed your model landscape. Where on your model would glaciers be likely to form?

Chapter 3 **G ◆ 93**

Section 4 Review Answers

1. Valley glaciers are found in high mountains, and the sides of the mountains keep these glaciers from spreading out. Continental glaciers cover much of a continent or large island.
2. Plucking and abrasion
3. Answers will vary. Students should describe a moraine, prairie pothole, kettle, drumlin, or glacial lake
4. These lakes are kettle lakes, which form when a chunk of glacier is left behind in glacial till. When the ice melts, a depression called a kettle remains in the ice. A kettle filled with water is called a kettle lake.

· **CHAPTER PROJECT 3**

Check Your Progress

Students should make a second drawing that predicts how the second model will look. These drawings should reflect concepts students have learned about mass movement, water erosion and deposition, and glacial erosion and deposition. Advise students to include what they think are the most important changes caused by these processes. For students having trouble, suggest that they use the *Exploring* features in Section 2 and 3 for reference. Students will need more building materials for the second model.

Program Resources

◆ **Teaching Resources** 3-4 Review and Reinforce, p. 79; 3-4 Enrich, p. 80

Media and Technology

Transparencies "Exploring Glacial Landforms," Transparency 12

Performance Assessment

Skills Check Have students make a table that compares and contrasts the features created by glacial erosion and glacial deposition. The table should include a description of each feature, as well as an explanation of how it forms.

portfolio Students can keep their tables in their portfolios.

Objectives

After completing the lesson, students will be able to
◆ identify what gives ocean waves their energy;
◆ describe how ocean waves shape a coast and the landforms waves create.

Key Terms beach, longshore drift, spit

1 Engage/Explore

Activating Prior Knowledge

Encourage students who have been to beaches to share their observations of the sand on the beaches and the waves that flow over the beaches. Elicit descriptions of the color and texture of sand particles, noting any differences among beaches. Then have students describe how they think the waves affect the beaches. Finally, challenge students to develop a hypothesis about how beaches form.

········ **DISCOVER** ·········

Skills Focus posing questions
Materials *sand from 2 beaches, hand lens*
Time 15 minutes
Tips Have student volunteers go as a group to collect sand from a nearby lake or ocean beach. If that is impractical, obtain two different kinds of sand commercially. Suggest that students avoid mixing the two samples by completely removing the first sample before examining the second.
Expected Outcome Students should observe differences in the two samples, such as differences in particle shape, size, color, and texture. Specific differences will depend on the samples used.
Think It Over Questions will vary. *Sample questions:* Is beach sand a result of erosion? How is beach sand deposited? What causes differences in samples of beach sand collected at different places?

DISCOVER ·····················**ACTIVITY**····

What Can Be Learned From Beach Sand?

1. Collect a spoonful of sand from each of two different beaches. The two samples also may come from different parts of the same beach.

2. Examine the first sample of beach sand with a hand lens.

3. Record the properties of the sand grains, for example, color and shape. Are the grains smooth and rounded or angular and rough? Are all the grains in the sample the same shape and color?

4. Examine the second sample and repeat Step 3. How do the two samples compare?

Think It Over
Posing Questions What questions do you need to answer to understand beach sand? Use what you know about erosion and deposition to help you think of questions.

GUIDE FOR READING

◆ What gives waves their energy?
◆ How do waves shape a coast?

Reading Tip As you read, make a concept map showing features formed by wave erosion and deposition.

Ocean waves contain energy—sometimes a great deal of energy. The waves that sweep onto the Pacific coast are especially powerful. Created by ocean winds, they carry energy vast distances across the Pacific Ocean. Acting like drills or buzzsaws, the waves erode the solid rock of the coast into cliffs and caves. Waves also carry sediment that forms features such as beaches. But these features do not last long. More waves follow to change the shoreline yet again.

How Waves Form

The energy in waves comes from wind that blows across the water's surface. As the wind makes contact with the water, some of its energy transfers to the water. Large ocean waves are the result of powerful storms far out at sea. But ordinary breezes can produce waves in lakes or small ponds.

The energy that water picks up from the wind causes water particles to move up and down as the wave goes by. But the water particles themselves don't move forward. Only the form of the wave moves. Have you ever watched a wave in a field of tall grass? Each blade of grass moves back and forth but doesn't move from its place. But the energy of the wave moves across the field.

Waves on the Oregon coast ▼

94 ◆ G

READING STRATEGIES

Reading Tip If necessary, review how to make a concept map. A typical concept map of this section will begin with the general title "Waves." The map can then be divided into "Wave Formation," "Wave Erosion," and "Wave Deposition." Landforms created by wave erosion should fall under "Wave Erosion." Make sure students include linking words between circled words.

Study and Comprehension To help students understand waves, generate a wave in a length of rope. Tie one end of a rope about 2 m long to a pipe, post, or door handle. Then pull the rope straight and, as students observe, flip it with your wrist to make waves that are analogous to ocean waves. Like ocean water, the rope itself does not move forward. Rather, energy moves forward while the rope moves up and down.

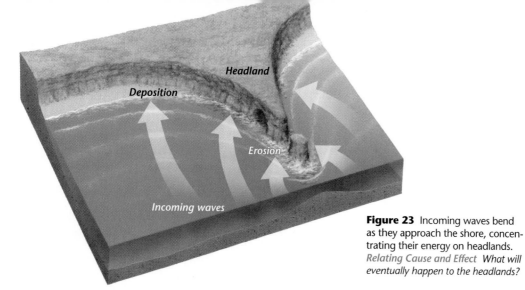

Figure 23 Incoming waves bend as they approach the shore, concentrating their energy on headlands. *Relating Cause and Effect What will eventually happen to the headlands?*

A wave changes as it approaches land. In deep water, a wave only affects the water near the surface. But as the wave approaches shallow water, the wave begins to drag the bottom. The friction between the wave and the bottom causes the wave to slow down. Now the water actually does move forward with the wave. This forward-moving water provides the force that shapes the land along the shoreline.

Erosion by Waves

Waves are the major force of erosion along coasts. One way waves erode the land is by impact. Large waves can hit rocks along the shore with great force. This energy in waves can break apart rocks. Over time, waves can make small cracks larger. Eventually, the waves cause pieces of rock to break off.

Waves also erode land by abrasion. As a wave approaches shallow water, it picks up sediment, including sand and gravel. This sediment is carried forward by the wave. When the wave hits land, the sediment wears away rock like sandpaper wearing away wood.

Waves coming to shore gradually change direction. The change in direction occurs as different parts of a wave begin to drag on the bottom. Notice how the waves in Figure 23 change direction as they approach the shore. The energy of these waves is concentrated on headlands. A headland is a part of the shore that sticks out into the ocean. Headlands stand out from the coast because they are made of harder rock that resists the waves. But, over time, waves erode the headlands and even out the shoreline.

☑ *Checkpoint* *What are two of the processes by which waves can cause erosion?*

Calculating

A sandy coast erodes at a rate of 1.25 meters per year. But a severe storm can erode an additional 3.75 meters from the shore. If 12 severe storms occur during a 50-year period, how much will the coast erode? If you wish, you may use an electronic calculator to find the answer.

Program Resources

◆ **Teaching Resources** 3-5 Lesson Plan, p. 81; 3-5 Section Summary, p. 82
◆ **Guided Study Workbook** Section 3-5

Media and Technology

 Transparencies "Wave Erosion and Wind Erosion," Transparency 13

Answers to Self-Assessment

Caption Question

Figure 23 They will erode back, evening out the shoreline.

☑ *Checkpoint*
Waves cause erosion by impact and abrasion.

2 Facilitate

How Waves Form

Using the Visuals: Figure 23

After students have examined the figure, ask: **Where will an incoming wave first make contact with the bottom as it approaches the shore?** *(Directly in front of the headland)* **What happens when a wave drags the bottom?** *(It slows down.)* Thus, as the wave on either side of the headland continues on, the wave approaching the headland slows down, causing the wave to "wrap" around the headland, as the arrows show. This section of the wave is concentrated in a smaller space, and its energy is concentrated as well. **learning modality: visual**

Erosion by Waves

Sharpen your Skills

Calculating

Time 10 minutes
Tips Some students may need calculators to do the multiplication required to determine how much the coast will erode.
Expected Outcome In 50 years at the normal 1.25 m/yr, the coast will erode 62.5 m. In addition, each of the 12 storms will cause a further 3.75 m of erosion, or 45 m together. Therefore, the total over the period is 62.5 + 45, or 107.5 m of erosion.
Extend After students have read the rest of the section, have them look again at this problem. Ask: **Since waves steadily erode sandy coasts, and storms erode them even more, why are there any sandy coasts left?** *(Although waves do erode coasts, they also deposit sediments on coasts. Thus, waves both wear down and build up coasts.)* **learning modality: logical/mathematical**

Ongoing Assessment

Writing Have students explain in their own words how waves erode the land.

Landforms Created by Wave Erosion

Inquiry Challenge

Materials *aluminum baking pan, sand, water, metric ruler, piece of cardboard*
Time 15 minutes

Ask students: **Do large waves erode more than small waves?** Then challenge students to use the materials to investigate the question and draw a conclusion. A typical experiment will involve building a sand hill on one side of the pan, adding water, and making waves with the piece of cardboard, first small waves and then large waves. Students should observe that the larger the wave, the more the erosion.
learning modality: kinesthetic

Deposits by Waves

Including All Students

Support students who need more help by first sketching a beach on the board. Then, with an arrow, show an ocean wave hitting the shore diagonally, at about a 30° angle. Explain that waves usually hit shores diagonally because a shoreline's shape varies. Then ask: **What happens to the water that travels onto the beach with the wave?** (*Once the wave's energy is spent, the water runs back down the beach to the ocean.*) **What force causes this "backwash"?** (*Gravity causes the water to run back down the beach.*) Explain that waves often push water up onto a beach at an angle, but gravity pulls it back down the beach perpendicular to the shore, just as gravity pulls sediment down a hill in mass movement. Draw an arrow that shows this perpendicular movement of water. Draw several more pairs of arrows, zigzagging up or down the beach. Ask: **How does this affect particles of sediment on the beach?** (*They move up the beach with the combination of incoming waves and backwash.*) The combination of waves and backwash is responsible for longshore drift. Have students draw a copy of the sketch on the board. **limited English proficiency**

Figure 24 Waves cut these cliffs on the coast of Australia. The blocks of rock offshore are sea stacks.
Developing Hypotheses Develop a hypothesis to explain how these sea stacks formed.

Landforms Created by Wave Erosion

When waves hit a steep, rocky coast, they strike the area again and again. Think of an ax striking the trunk of a tree. The cut gets bigger and deeper with each strike of the blade. Finally the tree falls. In a similar way, ocean waves erode the base of the land along a steep coast. Where the rock is softer, the waves erode the land faster. Over time the waves may erode a hollow area in the rock called a sea cave.

Eventually, waves may erode the base of a cliff so much that the rock above collapses. The result is a wave-cut cliff. You can see an example of such a cliff in Figure 24.

Another feature created by wave erosion is a sea arch. A sea arch forms when waves erode a layer of softer rock that underlies a layer of harder rock. If an arch collapses, the result might be a sea stack, a pillar of rock rising above the water.

✓ *Checkpoint* *How can waves produce a cliff on a rocky coast?*

Deposits by Waves

Waves not only erode the land, they also deposit sediment. **Waves shape the coast through both erosion and deposition.** Deposition occurs when waves slow down and the water drops its sediment. This process is similar to the deposition that occurs on a river delta when the river slows down and drops its sediment load.

96 ◆ G

As waves reach the shore, they drop the sediment they carry, forming a beach. A **beach** is an area of wave-washed sediment along a coast. The sediment deposited on beaches is usually sand. Most sand comes from rivers that carry eroded particles of rock into the ocean. But not all beaches are made of sand carried by rivers. Some beaches are made of small fragments of coral or sea shells piled up by wave action. Florida has many such beaches.

The sediment on a beach usually moves down the beach after it has been deposited. Waves usually hit the beach at an angle instead of straight on. These angled waves create a current that runs parallel to the coastline. As repeated waves hit the beach, some of the beach sediment moves down the beach with the current, in a process called **longshore drift.**

One result of longshore drift is the formation of a spit. A **spit** is a beach that projects like a finger out into the water. Spits form as a result of deposition by longshore drift. Spits occur where a headland or other obstacle interrupts longshore drift, or where the coast turns abruptly. Incoming waves carrying sand may build up sandbars, long ridges of sand parallel to the shore.

 INTEGRATING ENVIRONMENTAL SCIENCE A barrier beach is similar to a sandbar, but a barrier beach forms when storm waves pile up sand above sea level. Barrier beaches are found in many places along the Atlantic coast of the United States, such as the Outer Banks of North Carolina. People have built homes on many of these barrier beaches. But the storm waves that build up the beaches can also wash them away. Barrier beach communities must be prepared for the damage that hurricanes and other storms can bring.

Figure 25 This satellite image of Cape Cod in Massachusetts shows how longshore drift can carry sand and deposit it to form a spit. *Observing How many spits can you find in this image?*

Section 5 Review

1. How do ocean waves form?
2. Describe two landforms created by wave erosion and two landforms created by wave deposition.
3. Why are headlands eroded faster than the land at the ends of inlets and bays?
4. **Thinking Critically** **Predicting** You visit a rocky headland by the ocean that has a sea arch and several sea stacks. How might this area change in the next 500 years?

Check Your Progress
CHAPTER PROJECT 3
Now you are ready to add the effects of wave erosion to your model. What landforms will wave erosion produce along the coastline on your model? What materials will you use to model these landforms? When you have finished your second model, make labels for the landforms on your models.

Chapter 3 **G ◆ 97**

Answers to Self-Assessment

Caption Questions

Figure 24 *Sample hypothesis:* Sea stacks can form when waves erode a layer of soft rock faster than hard rock.

Figure 25 At least five spits can be seen.

☑ *Checkpoint*
When they erode the base of the land so much that the rock above collapses.

 Integrating Environmental Science

Display a large map of the United States. Direct students' attention to the barrier islands along the Atlantic and Gulf coasts, especially off the North Carolina coast. Ask: **How permanent do you think these barrier beaches are?** (*Ocean waves are constantly eroding and depositing sediment, thus making changes in these beaches every day.*) **learning modality: visual**

3 Assess

Section 5 Review Answers

1. Ocean waves form when wind makes contact with ocean water and transfers some of its energy to the water.

2. Answers will vary. Students should describe any two landforms created by wave erosion: sea cave, wave-cut cliff, sea arch, and sea stack. They should also describe any two landforms created by wave deposition: beach, spit, and barrier beach.

3. Headlands are eroded faster because waves change direction as they approach the shore, thereby concentrating their energy on headlands.

4. In 500 years, the headland may have eroded back, evening out the shore. Erosion by waves may also have caused the sea arch to collapse, creating more sea stacks.

Check Your Progress
CHAPTER PROJECT 3
At this point, students should be putting the finishing touches on their second models. To add features related to wave erosion, students will need more of the sand-glue mixture, as well as some additional sand or gravel. Help students think ahead to their presentations by questioning them about why they included various features.

Performance Assessment

Drawing Have students make a labeled drawing of the landforms created by wave erosion and deposition.

G ◆ 97

Objectives

After completing the lesson, students will be able to
◆ describe the process by which wind causes erosion;
◆ identify the features resulting from deposition by wind.

Key Terms sand dune, deflation, loess

1 Engage/Explore

Activating Prior Knowledge

Encourage students who have lived near or visited a desert or have seen deserts in films or books to describe what they've seen. Ask: **Are there any natural landforms that are most common in a sandy desert?** (*Most students will know about sand dunes.*) Have students speculate on how sand dunes form. Then ask: **Are there any other places where you might expect to see sand dunes?** (*beaches*) **What characteristics are common to deserts and sandy areas?** (*Both contain little vegetation, and both are often windy.*)

········ DISCOVER ········

Skills Focus observing
Materials *shallow pan, cornmeal, plastic straw*

Time 10 minutes
Tips Caution students to avoid blowing the cornmeal in the direction of another student. Have each student immediately clean up any cornmeal he or she blows out of the pan. Emphasize that students should blow through the straw *gently*.
Think It Over Students should observe that blowing gently through the straw created ripples in the cornmeal or piles that are similar to sand dunes.

DISCOVER •••••••••••••••••••••••••••• ACTIVITY

How Does Moving Air Affect Sediment?

1. Cover the bottom of a pan with a flat layer of cornmeal 1–2 centimeters deep.

2. Gently blow over the layer of cornmeal using a straw to direct your breath. Observe what happens.

CAUTION: *Do not blow the cornmeal in the direction of another student.*

Think It Over

Observing What changes did the wind you created make in the flat layer of cornmeal?

GUIDE FOR READING

◆ How does wind cause erosion?

◆ What features result from deposition by wind?

Reading Tip Before you read, preview Figure 27. In your notebook, write some predictions about the characteristics of wind erosion.

Figure 26 Wind erosion continues to shape the giant sand dunes in the Namib Desert along Africa's southwestern coast.

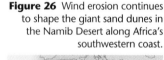

AFRICA

ATLANTIC
OCEAN

NAMIB
DESERT

I magine a landscape made almost entirely of sand. One such place is the Namib Desert. The desert stretches for about 1,900 kilometers along the coast of Namibia in Africa. In the southern half of the Namib are long rows of giant sand dunes. A **sand dune** is a deposit of wind-blown sand. Some sand dunes in the Namib are more than 200 meters high and 15 kilometers long. Much of the sand in the dunes originally came from the nearby Orange River. Over thousands of years, wind has swept the sand across the desert, piling up huge, ever-changing dunes.

How Wind Causes Erosion

Wind by itself is the weakest agent of erosion. Water, waves, moving ice, and even mass movement have more effect on the land. Yet wind can be a powerful force in shaping the land in areas where there are few plants to hold the soil in place. As you might guess, wind is very effective in causing erosion in deserts. There few plants can grow, and wind can easily move the grains of dry, light sand.

READING STRATEGIES

Reading Tip After students have previewed the figure, have them explain in writing how they think different sizes of sediment are affected by wind. Once they have read the section, suggest that they rewrite their explanation to conform to their better understanding of the process of wind erosion.

Vocabulary Call students' attention the key term *deflation*. Explain that it derives from a Latin word meaning "to blow away." Use a balloon to drive home this meaning. When you blow the balloon up, the balloon "inflates"—air "blows in" the balloon. When you allow the air to escape, the balloon "deflates"—air "blows away" from the balloon. In wind deflation, the wind blows sediment away. Also point out the key term *loess*. Explain that it derives from a German word for "loose."

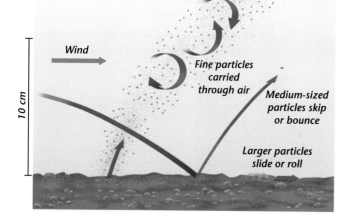

Wind

Fine particles
carried
through air

Medium-sized
particles skip
or bounce

Larger particles
slide or roll

10 cm

Figure 27 Wind erosion moves sediment particles of different sizes in the three ways shown above. *Comparing and Contrasting Compare the movement of sediment by wind with the movement of sediment by water in Figure 16 on page 86. How are the processes similar? How are they different?*

The main way that wind causes erosion is by deflation. Geologists define **deflation** as the process by which wind removes surface materials. When wind blows over the land, it picks up the smallest particles of sediment. This sediment is made of bits of clay and silt. The stronger the wind, the larger the particles that it can pick up and move through the air. Slightly heavier particles, such as sand, might skip or bounce for a short distance. But sand soon falls back to the ground. Strong winds can even roll heavier sediment particles over the ground. Figure 27 shows how wind erodes by deflation.

Deflation does not usually have a great effect on the land. However, in parts of the Great Plains in the 1930s, deflation caused the loss of about 1 meter of topsoil in just a few years. In deserts, deflation can sometimes create an area of rock fragments called desert pavement. You can see an area of desert pavement in Figure 28. There, wind has blown away the smaller sediment. All that remains are rocky materials that are too large and heavy to be moved. Where there is already a slight depression in the ground, deflation can produce a bowl-shaped hollow called a blowout.

Abrasion by wind-carried sand can polish rock, but it causes little erosion. At one time, geologists thought that the sediment carried by wind cut the stone shapes seen in deserts. But now evidence shows that most desert landforms are the result of weathering and water erosion.

Figure 28 Wind erosion formed this desert pavement in the Arizona desert. Wind-driven sand may polish and shape individual stones.

☑ *Checkpoint Where would you be most likely to see evidence of wind erosion?*

Program Resources

◆ **Teaching Resources** 3-6 Lesson Plan, p. 85; 3-6 Section Summary, p. 86
◆ **Guided Study Workbook** Section 3-6

Media and Technology

Transparencies "Wave Erosion and Wind Erosion," Transparency 13

Answers to Self-Assessment

Caption Question

Figure 27 In both, larger particles slide or roll and smaller particles are carried along suspended. One major difference is that, in water, some sediment is transported dissolved in solution.

☑ *Checkpoint*

Wind erosion is powerful in areas where there are few plants to hold soil in place.

2 Facilitate

How Wind Causes Erosion

Inquiry Challenge

Materials *coarse and fine sand, hair dryer, block of wood, ice-cube tray*
Time 15 minutes

Ask students: **Does wind move different sizes of sediment different distances?** Then have small groups investigate the question by mixing coarse and fine sand together, making a pile of sand on a block of wood, placing an ice-cube tray next to the block, and using a hair dryer on a low setting to blow the sand in the direction of the ice-cube tray. Students should observe that the coarse sand will blow into the near sections of the ice-cube tray, while the fine sand will blow into the far sections. Have students draw a conclusion in writing. (Make sure students wear goggles for this activity. You may want students to put down a plastic dropcloth before beginning the activity.) **learning modality: kinesthetic**

Demonstration

Materials *sand, large funnel, sheet of plastic, books, hair dryer, extension cord*
Time 10 minutes

To demonstrate abrasion by wind-carried sediment, set up a table outside and prop a sheet of plastic against a stack of books. Have a student volunteer—wearing goggles—use a hand to cover the bottom of a funnel and fill it with sand. Then, as the class observes, invite the student to release the sand from the funnel 3–4 cm in front of the piece of plastic as you aim a hair dryer on high speed at the plastic. Repeat the process several times. Then have students examine the plastic to observe pits and other signs of abrasion. **learning modality: visual**

Ongoing Assessment

Oral Presentation Call on students at random to explain how wind transports different-sized sediment particles.

Deposits Resulting From Wind Erosion

Using the Visuals: Figure 29

After students have examined the photo, ask: **Which of the three ways shown in Figure 27 would likely have carried the sediment to this loess deposit?** *(By fine particles carried through the air)* Explain that winds can carry fine particles great distances. **learning modality: verbal**

3 Assess

Section 6 Review Answers

1. Wind erodes by deflation. When wind blows over the land, it picks up smaller sediment and bounces or rolls larger sediment over the ground.
2. Sand dunes form when wind carrying sediment strikes an obstacle, such as a boulder or clump of grass, which traps the windblown sediment. Loess deposits form when wind lays down fine sediments in layers.
3. A blowout is a bowl-shaped hollow produced when deflation removes sediment from a slight depression in the ground.
4. The sediment that makes up the sand dune may eventually blow away, since wind is a powerful force where plants don't hold soil in place.

Science at Home

Materials *coins, shallow pan, plastic straw, flour*

ACTIVITY

Tips Encourage students to carry out this demonstration at home. Caution them to make sure family members are far enough away to avoid getting flour in their eyes. Students should be prepared to explain what deflation is and what the coins and flour represent.

Performance Assessment

Writing Have students write a story in which they imagine being a sand particle blown from desert pavement to a sand dune.

Figure 29 Wind carrying fine particles of silt built up this loess deposit near Natchez, Mississippi.

Deposits Resulting From Wind Erosion

All the sediment picked up by wind eventually falls to the ground. This happens when the wind slows down or some obstacle, such as a boulder or a clump of grass, traps the windblown sand and other sediment. **Wind erosion and deposition may form sand dunes and loess deposits.** When the wind strikes an obstacle, the result is usually a sand dune. Sand dunes can be seen on beaches and in deserts where wind-blown sediment has built up.

Sand dunes come in many shapes and sizes. Some are long, with parallel ridges, while others are U-shaped. They can also be very small or very large—some sand dunes in China have grown to heights of 500 meters. Sand dunes move over time. Little by little, the sand shifts with the wind from one side of the dune to the other. Sometimes plants begin growing on a dune. Plant roots can help to anchor the dune in one place.

Sand dunes are most often made of the coarser sediments carried by wind. The finer sediments, including particles of clay and silt, are sometimes deposited in layers far from their source. This fine, wind-deposited sediment is **loess** (LES). Large loess deposits are found in central China and in such states as Nebraska, South Dakota, Iowa, Missouri, and Illinois. Loess helps to form fertile soil. Many areas with thick loess deposits are valuable farmlands.

Section 6 Review

1. Describe how wind erodes the land.
2. How do sand dunes and loess deposits form?
3. What is a blowout and what is the process that produces one?
4. **Thinking Critically Predicting** You visit a beach that has sand dunes covered with dune grass. But where people take a shortcut over one dune, the grass has been worn away. What may eventually happen to the dune if people keep taking this path?

Science at Home

Here's how to make a model of desert pavement. Put a few coins in a shallow pan about 1 centimeter deep. Sprinkle enough flour over the coins to bury them beneath a thin layer of flour. Then blow air gently through a straw across the surface of the flour. Be careful not to draw in any flour through the straw. Be certain the blown flour will not get in your or anyone else's eyes. Ask your family to predict what the surface of the pan would look like if the "wind" continued to blow for a long time.

Background

Facts and Figures There are two main sources of the wind-deposited clay and silt that form loess deposits: deserts and glacial meltwater flood plains. The loess deposits of China derived mainly from great desert regions of Asia. The loess deposits of the U.S. Midwest originated in the deflation of the dry flood plains of meltwater rivers as continental glaciers melted back at the end of the Pleistocene Ice Age.

Program Resources

◆ **Teaching Resources** 3-6 Review and Reinforce, p. 87; 3-6 Enrich, p. 88

SECTION 1

Changing Earth's Surface

Key Ideas
◆ Weathering, erosion, and deposition act to wear down and build up Earth's surface.
◆ Gravity pulls sediment downhill in the process of mass movement. There are four main types of mass movement: landslides, mudslides, slump, and creep.

Key Terms
erosion   deposition
sediment   mass movement

 SECTION 2

Water Erosion

Key Ideas
◆ Moving water is the major force of erosion that has shaped Earth's land surface.
◆ A river may form V-shaped valleys, waterfalls, meanders, oxbow lakes, and flood plains.
◆ When a river slows down, it deposits some of the sediment load it carries, forming features such as alluvial fans and deltas.

Key Terms
runoff   drainage basin   delta
rill   divide   groundwater
gully   flood plain   stalactite
stream   meander   stalagmite
river   oxbow lake   karst topography
tributary   alluvial fan

 SECTION 3

The Force of Moving Water
INTEGRATING PHYSICS

Key Ideas
◆ When gravity pulls water down a slope, water's potential energy changes to kinetic energy, and it does work.
◆ Most sediment washes or falls into streams, or is eroded from the streambed by abrasion.
◆ The greater a river's slope or volume of flow, the more sediment it can erode.

Key Terms
energy   abrasion   friction
potential energy   load   turbulence
kinetic energy

 SECTION 4

Glaciers

Key Ideas
◆ The two kinds of glaciers are valley glaciers and continental glaciers.
◆ Glaciers erode the land through plucking and abrasion. Melting glaciers deposit sediment.

Key Terms
glacier   ice age   moraine
valley glacier   plucking   kettle
continental glacier   till

 SECTION 5

Waves

Key Ideas
◆ The energy of ocean waves comes from wind blowing across the water's surface and transferring energy to the water.
◆ Ocean waves hitting land cause erosion through impact and abrasion. Waves also move and deposit sediment along the shore.

Key Terms
beach   longshore drift   spit

 SECTION 6

Wind Erosion

Key Ideas
◆ Wind causes erosion mainly through deflation, the blowing of surface materials.
◆ Landforms created by wind deposition include sand dunes and loess deposits.

Key Terms
sand dune   deflation   loess

Organizing Information

Flowchart Make a flowchart showing how a stream forms. Your flowchart should include the following terms in the correct order: rills, runoff, gullies, stream, raindrops. Give your flowchart a title. (For tips on making a flowchart, see the Skills Handbook.)

Chapter 3 **G ◆ 101**

Organizing Information

Flow Chart Sample flowchart:

How a Stream Forms

Raindrops
↓
Runoff
↓
Rills
↓
Gullies
↓
Stream

Program Resources

◆ **Teaching Resources** Chapter 3 Project Scoring Rubric, p. 64; Chapter 3 Performance Assessment, pp. 152–154; Chapter 3 Test, pp. 155–158

Media and Technology

 Computer Test Bank *Earth's Changing Surface,* Chapter 3

Reviewing Content
Multiple Choice
1. c 2. a 3. b 4. d 5. b

True or False
6. deposition 7. karst topography 8. true
9. true 10. moraine

Checking Concepts

11. The agents of erosion that are in part caused by the force of gravity are moving water and glaciers. Gravity itself causes mass movement and is therefore also an agent of erosion.

12. If a river's slope increases, its speed also increases. And the greater the volume of flow, the greater the speed. A fast-flowing river carries more and larger particles of sediment.

13. Where a river bends, the water moves faster along the outside of the curve. There, the river tends to cut into its bank. Sediment is deposited on the inside curve, where the water speed is slowest.

14. Any time moving water slows down, it deposits some of its sediment. When a river flows into a still body of water, such as an ocean or a lake, the sediment in the water drops to the bottom. This deposited sediment builds up a landform called a delta.

15. Erosion occurs when groundwater containing carbonic acid flows into cracks in limestone. The rock changes chemically and some of it gets carried away in solution by water, creating holes and caves. Deposition results when water dripping from a cave's roof evaporates, depositing calcite.

16. Ice ages are times when continental glaciers cover large parts of Earth's surface.

17. Students' letters will vary. An adequate response should describe the features described in *Exploring the Course of a River* on pages 78–79. For each feature, there should be some explanation about how it formed. An excellent response should weave the information together in a creative and interesting way.

Thinking Critically

18. Abrasion occurs when particles of sediment in flowing water bump into the

---

Reviewing Content

 For more review of key concepts, see the Interactive Student Tutorial CD-ROM.

Multiple Choice
Choose the answer that best completes the sentence.

1. The eroded materials carried by water or wind are called
   a. stalactites.
   b. desert pavement.
   c. sediment.
   d. moraines.
2. The downhill movement of eroded materials is known as
   a. mass movement.
   b. abrasion.
   c. deposition.
   d. deflation.
3. A mass of rock and soil deposited directly by a glacier is called
   a. load.   b. till.
   c. loess.   d. erosion.
4. When waves strike a shoreline, they concentrate their energy on
   a. beaches.
   b. cirques.
   c. sand dunes.
   d. headlands.
5. The erosion of sediment by wind is
   a. deposition.   b. deflation.
   c. plucking.   d. glaciation.

True or False
If the statement is true, write true. If it is false, change the underlined word or words to make the statement true.

6. The process by which sediment in water settles in new locations is <u>mass movement</u>.
7. An area of <u>alluvial fans</u> may be found where groundwater erodes limestone to form valleys, sinkholes, and caverns.
8. Because it is moving, flowing water has a type of energy called <u>kinetic energy</u>.
9. A looplike bend in the course of a river is a <u>meander</u>.
10. The sediment deposited at the edge of a glacier forms a ridge called a <u>kettle</u>.

Checking Concepts

11. What agents of erosion are in part caused by the force of gravity?
12. How do a river's slope and volume of flow affect the river's sediment load?
13. Describe how the speed of flowing water changes where a river bends. How does this affect a river's deposition of sediment?
14. Why does a delta develop when a river flows into a larger body of water?
15. Describe the process by which groundwater can cause erosion and deposition in limestone beneath Earth's surface.
16. What are ice ages?
17. Writing to Learn You go on a rafting journey that takes you down a river from the mountains to the sea. Write a letter to a friend describing the features created by erosion and deposition that you see as you travel down the river. Include features near the river's source, along the middle of its course, and where it reaches the ocean.

Thinking Critically

18. Applying Concepts Under what conditions would you expect abrasion to cause the most erosion of a riverbed?
19. Relating Cause and Effect In a desert, you see an area that looks as if it were paved with rock fragments. Explain how this situation occurred naturally.
20. Problem Solving Suppose you are a geologist studying a valley glacier. What method could you use to tell if it is advancing or retreating?
21. Making Judgments A salesperson offers to sell your family a new house right on a riverbank for very little money. Why might your family hesitate to buy this house?
22. Inferring You see a sandy beach along a coastline. What can you infer about where the sand came from?
23. Comparing and Contrasting How are landslides similar to mudflows? How are they different?

---

streambed again and again. A very turbulent stream or the fast-flowing water of a flooding river would cause the most erosion of a streambed.

19. Deflation removed all the sand and smaller sediment, leaving behind the rocky materials that were too large and heavy to be moved by wind.

20. Answers may vary. *Sample answer:* You could observe the landforms in front of the

---

glacier. If it is retreating, then the landforms would be those recently sculpted by glacial erosion and deposition.

21. If the house was right on a riverbank, then it would be within the river's flood plain. A family should hesitate because the house might be damaged or destroyed by a flood in the future.

22. The sand came from rivers that carried the particles to the ocean, where waves dropped them to form the beach.

Applying Skills

The table below shows how a river's volume of flow and sediment load change over six months. Use the table to answer Questions 24–26.

Month	Volume of Flow (cubic meters/second)	Sediment Load (metric tons/day)
January	1.5	200
February	1.7	320
March	2.6	725
April	4.0	1600
May	3.2	1100
June	2.8	900

24. Graphing Make one graph with the month on the x-axis and the volume of flow on the y-axis. Make a second graph with the sediment load on the y-axis. Compare your two graphs. When were the river's volume of flow and load the greatest? The lowest?

25. Developing Hypotheses Use your graphs to develop a hypothesis about the relationship between volume of flow and sediment load.

26. Relating Cause and Effect What may have occurred in the river's drainage basin in April to cause the changes in volume of flow and sediment load? Explain.

Performance CHAPTER PROJECT 3 Assessment

Project Wrap Up Now you are ready to explain your models of erosion to your class. Label your models to indicate the features that changed during erosion.

Reflect and Record In your journal, write about the easiest and hardest parts of this project. How would you do each model differently if you did the project again?

Test Preparation
Use these questions to prepare for standardized tests.

Read the passage. Then answer Questions 27–30.

This is the story of a great river. The Missouri River is America's second longest river after the Mississippi River. Its vast drainage basin covers parts of 10 states and 2 Canadian provinces. Early settlers called the Missouri the "Big Muddy" because its waters carry a heavy sediment load.

The Missouri River begins in the Rocky Mountains near Three Forks, Montana, where three small streams join. The upper Missouri flows through a deep valley called the Gates of the Mountains. Then at Great Falls, Montana, it plunges down a series of waterfalls and rapids.

Leaving the mountains, the middle Missouri flows across the Great Plains. Major tributaries, such as the Yellowstone and Platte rivers, flow into it. The Missouri has eroded a wide valley as it winds through the plains. Steep ridges called bluffs sometimes form the edges of the valley.

The Missouri ends just north of St. Louis, Missouri, where it flows into the Mississippi.

27. A good title for this passage is
   a. The Rivers of America.
   b. Following the Missouri River.
   c. Tributaries of the Missouri River.
   d. Sedimental Journey.

28. A deep valley, waterfalls, and rapids can be found
   a. where the Missouri crosses the Plains.
   b. nowhere along the Missouri.
   c. on the upper Missouri.
   d. on the lower Missouri.

29. Along the middle Missouri's valley are features called
   a. gullies.   **b.** drainage basins.
   c. gates.   **d.** bluffs.

30. The nickname "Big Muddy" refers to the Missouri's
   a. sediment load.
   b. source.
   c. meanders.
   d. tributaries.

Chapter 3   **G ◆ 103**

Program Resources

♦ **Inquiry Skills Activity Book** Provides teaching and review of all inquiry skills
♦ **Standardized Test Preparation Book** Provides standardized test practice
♦ **Reading in the Content Area** Provides strategies to improve science reading skills
♦ **Teacher's ELL Handbook** Provides multiple strategies for English language learners

---

23. Both are types of mass movement that result from the rapid downhill movement of earth materials and both can be triggered by an earthquake. Unlike landslides, which are mostly rock and soil, mudslides are up to 60 percent water and can occur on very gentle slopes.

Applying Skills

24. The flow and load were greatest in April. They were lowest in January.
25. A river's load varies directly with its volume of flow.
26. Rainfall or melting snow probably increased throughout the drainage basin in April, creating more runoff and eroding more sediment.

Performance CHAPTER PROJECT 3 Assessment

Project Wrap Up As each student presents his or her models to the class, assess whether the student effectively and comprehensively showed changes from the first to the second model, how well-made the model is, and how well-done the presentation is. Students should explain the natural processes that result in the changes shown in their models.

Reflect and Record In judging how they would make the models differently if they could redo the project, students should compare their own models with those of other students. As they assess the results of their presentations, students should mention the benefits of preparing for their talk, since they knew they had to understand erosion in order to explain their models.

Test Preparation
27. b 28. c 29. d 30. a

Sections	Time	Student Edition Activities	Other Activities	
CHAPTER PROJECT 4 **A Journey Back in Time** p. G105	Ongoing (3 weeks)	Check Your Progress, p. G117 Check Your Progress, p. G125 Check Your Progress, p. G140 Project Wrap Up, p. G143		
1 Fossils pp. G106–112 ◆ 4.1.1 Explain what fossils are and how most fossils form. ◆ 4.1.2 Describe what fossils tell about how organisms have changed over time. ◆ 4.1.3 Identify and describe different types of fossils.	2–3 periods/ 1–1½ blocks	**Discover** What's in a Rock?, p. G106 **Try This** Sweet Fossils, p. G108 **Science at Home,** p. G112	TE TE TE	Demonstration, p. G107 Building Inquiry Skills: Making Models, p. G108; Inferring, p. G109; Comparing and Contrasting, p. G110 Inquiry Challenge, p. G110
2 Finding the Relative Age of Rocks pp. G113–118 ◆ 4.2.1 Describe several ways that scientists determine the relative age of rocks. ◆ 4.2.2 Describe how geologists use index fossils to date rocks.	2–3 periods/ 1–1½ blocks	**Discover** In What Order Are Sediments Deposited?, p. G113 **Try This** Sampling a Sandwich, p. G114 **Real-World Lab: You Be the Detective** Finding Clues to Rock Layers, p. G118	TE TE ISLM	Music Connection, p. G115 Building Inquiry Skills: Comparing and Contrasting, p. G116; Observing, p. G116 G-4, "Exploring Geologic Time Through Core Samples"
3 _INTEGRATING CHEMISTRY_ **Radioactive Dating** pp. G119–122 ◆ 4.3.1 Describe the process of radioactive decay. ◆ 4.3.2 Explain how the absolute age of a rock can be determined using radioactive dating.	1–2 periods/ ½–1 block	**Discover** How Long 'Til It's Gone?, p. G119 **Sharpen Your Skills** Calculating, p. G121 **Science at Home,** p. G122	TE	Addressing Naive Conceptions, p. G120
4 The Geologic Time Scale pp. G123–127 ◆ 4.4.1 Describe the geologic time scale and explain why it is used. ◆ 4.4.2 Identify the different units of the geologic time scale.	2–3 periods/ 1–1½ blocks	**Discover** This Is Your Life!, p. G123 **Skills Lab: Making Models** As Time Goes By, pp. G126–127	TE	Building Inquiry Skills: Making Models, p. G124
5 Earth's History pp. G128–140 ◆ 4.5.1 Identify and describe the major events in Earth's geologic history. ◆ 4.5.2 Identify and describe the major developments of life on Earth.	3–4 periods/ 1½–2 blocks	**Discover** What Do Fossils Reveal About Earth's History?, p. G128 **Try This** Life and Times, p. G136	TE TE TE	Building Inquiry Skills: Comparing and Contrasting, pp. G130, G138; Communicating, p. G132; Graphing, p. G133 Using the Visuals: Figure 24, p. G131, Figure 26, p. G136 Inquiry Challenge, p. G139
Study Guide/Assessment pp. G141–143	1 period/ ½ block		ISAB	Provides teaching and review of all inquiry skills

For Standard or Block Schedule The Resource Pro® CD-ROM gives you maximum flexibility for planning your instruction for any type of schedule. Resource Pro® contains Planning Express®, an advanced scheduling program, as well as the entire contents of the Teaching Resources and the Computer Test Bank.

Key: **SE** Student Edition
PLM Probeware Lab Manual
ISAB Inquiry Skills Activity Book

104a

CHAPTER PLANNING GUIDE

Program Resources	Assessment Strategies	Media and Technology
TR Chapter 4 Project Teacher Notes, pp. G94–95 **TR** Chapter 4 Project Student Overview and Worksheets, pp. G96–99	**TE** Performance Assessment: Chapter 4 Project Wrap Up, p. G143 **TE** Check Your Progress, pp. G117, G125, G140 **TR** Chapter 4 Project Scoring Rubric, p. G100	Science Explorer Internet Site Audio CDs and Audiotapes, English-Spanish Section Summaries
TR 4-1 Lesson Plan, Summary, pp. G101-102 **TR** 4-1 Review and Reinforce, p. G103 **TR** 4-1 Enrich, p. G104 **SES** Book F, *Inside Earth,* Chapter 5 **SES** Book K, *Chemical Building Blocks,* Chapter 4 **SES** Book C, *Cells and Heredity,* Chapter 5	**SE** Section 1 Review, p. G112 **TE** Ongoing Assessment, pp. G107, G109, G111 **TE** Performance Assessment, p. G112	Exploring Earth Science Videodisc, Unit 5 Side 1, "Fossils" Transparencies 14, "Formation of a Rock Fossil"; 15, "The Evolution of Elephants"
TR 4-2 Lesson Plan, p. G105 **TR** 4-2 Section Summary, p. G106 **TR** 4-2 Review and Reinforce, p. G107 **TR** 4-2 Enrich, p. G108 **TR** Real-World Lab blackline masters, pp. G121–122 **SES** Book F, *Inside Earth,* Chapter 2	**SE** Section 2 Review, p. G117 **SE** Analyze and Conclude, p. G118 **TE** Ongoing Assessment, p. G115 **TE** Performance Assessment, p. G117	Exploring Earth Science Videodisc, Unit 5 Side 1, "The Earth Library" Lab Activity Videotape, *Earth's Changing Surface,* 7 Transparencies 16, "The Law of Superposition"; 17, "Formation of an Unconformity"
TR 4-3 Lesson Plan, p. G109 **TR** 4-3 Section Summary, p. G110 **TR** 4-3 Review and Reinforce, p. G111 **TR** 4-3 Enrich, p. G112 **SES** Book L, *Chemical Interactions,* Chapter 4	**SE** Section 3 Review, p. G122 **TE** Ongoing Assessment, p. G121 **TE** Performance Assessment, p. G122	Exploring Earth Science Videodisc, Unit 5 Side 1, "Geologic Time" Transparencies 18, "Dating Sedimentary Rock with Intrusions and Extrusions"; 19, "Radioactive Decay"
TR 4-4 Lesson Plan, Summary, pp. G113–114 **TR** 4-4 Review and Reinforce, p. G115 **TR** 4-4 Enrich, p. G116 **TR** Skills Lab blackline masters, pp. G123–125 **SES** Book B, *Animals,* Chapter 1	**SE** Section 4 Review, p. G125 **SE** Analyze and Conclude, p. G127 **TE** Performance Assessment, p. G125	Transparency 20, "The Geologic Time Scale" Lab Activity Videotape, *Earth's Changing Surface,* 8
TR 4-5 Lesson Plan, Section Summary, Review and Reinforce, Enrich, pp. G117–120 **SES** Book A, *From Bacteria to Plants,* Chapters 2, 3, 5 **SES** Book C, *Cells and Heredity,* Chapter 2 **SES** Book B, *Animals,* Chapters 3 and 4 **SES** Book F, *Inside Earth,* Chapters 1 and 2 **SES** Book J, *Astronomy,* Chapter 2	**SE** Section 5 Review, p. G140 **TE** Ongoing Assessment, pp. G129, G131, G133, G135, G137, G139 **TE** Performance Assessment, p. G141	Exploring Life Science Videodisc, Unit 1 Side 2, "Where Did It Come From?"
GSW Provides worksheets to promote student comprehension of content **RCA** Provides strategies to improve science reading skills **ELL** Provides multiple strategies for English language learners	**SE** Study Guide/Assessment, pp. G141–143 **TR** Performance Assessment, pp. G159–161 **TR** Chapter 4 Test, pp. G162–165 **TR** Book Test, pp. G166–169 **CTB** *Earth's Changing Surface,* Chapter 4 **STP** Provides standardized test practice	Interactive Student Tutorial CD-ROM, G-4 Computer Test Bank, *Earth's Changing Surface,* Chapter 4

TE Teacher's Edition **TR** Teaching Resources **CTB** Computerized Test Bank
RCA Reading in the Content Area **ISLM** Integrated Science Laboratory Manual **STP** Standardized Test Preparation Book
GSW Guided Study Workbook **ELL** Teacher's ELL Handbook **SES** Science Explorer Series Text

Meeting the National Science Education Standards and AAAS Benchmarks

National Science Education Standards	Benchmarks for Science Literacy	Unifying Themes
Science As Inquiry (Content Standard A) ◆ **Develop descriptions, explanations, predictions, and models using evidence** Students interpret relative ages of rock layers and make a model of geologic time. (*Real-World Lab; Skills Lab*) ◆ **Communicate scientific procedures and explanations** Students make travel brochures and a time line and use them to present a geologic time period. (*Chapter Project*) **Physical Science** (Content Standard B) ◆ **Properties and changes of properties in matter** During radioactive decay, the atoms of one element break down to form atoms of another element. (*Section 3*) **Life Science** (Content Standard C) ◆ **Diversity and adaptations of organisms** The fossil record provides evidence that many different organisms have existed at different times and that organisms have changed over time. (*Sections 1, 5; Skills Lab*) **Earth and Space Science** (Content Standard D) ◆ **Earth's history** Fossils help scientists infer how Earth's surface has changed. Rock layers provide a record of Earth's geologic history. (*Chapter Project; Real-World Lab; Skills Lab*)	**1B Scientific Inquiry** Students interpret relative ages of rock layers and make a model of geologic time. (*Real-World Lab; Skills Lab*) **3A Technology and Science** Geologists use radioactive dating to determine the absolute ages of rocks. (*Section 3*) **4C Processes That Shape the Earth** Most fossils form when living things die and are buried by sediments that slowly harden into rock. Rock layers provide a record of Earth's geologic history. Scientists first developed the geologic time scale by studying rock layers and index fossils worldwide. (*Sections 1, 2, 4, 5; Chapter Project; Real-World Lab; Skills Lab*) **4D Structure of Matter** During radioactive decay, the atoms of one element break down to form atoms of another element. (*Section 3*) **5F Evolution of Life** The fossil record provides evidence that many different organisms have existed at different times and that groups of organisms have changed over time. Forms of life have evolved continuously throughout Earth's history. (*Sections 1, 5; Skills Lab*) **12D Communication Skills** Students make travel brochures and a time line and use them to present a geologic time period. (*Chapter Project*)	◆ **Energy** Unstable elements break down by releasing particles and energy in a process called radioactive decay. About 2.5 billion years ago, organisms first began using energy from the sun to make food. (*Sections 3, 5*) ◆ **Evolution** Evolution is the process by which all living things have changed over long periods of time. Rock layers provide a record of Earth's geologic history. (*Sections 1, 2, 4, 5; Chapter Project; Real-World Lab; Skills Lab*) ◆ **Modeling** Students interpret relative ages of rock layers and make a model of geologic time. (*Real-World Lab; Skills Lab*) ◆ **Patterns of Change** Most fossils form when living things die and are buried by sediments that slowly harden into rock. Earth's geologic history shows a series of changes in living things, climate, and landmasses. (*Sections 1, 3, 4, 5; Chapter Project; Real-World Lab; Skills Lab*) ◆ **Scale and Structure** Scientists use sedimentary rock layers to determine the relative ages of rocks and radioactive dating to determine the absolute ages of rocks. (*Sections 2, 3; Real-World Lab*) ◆ **Stability** Geologists use the law of superposition to determine the relative ages of rock layers. Half-life is the time it takes for half of the atoms of a radioactive element to decay. (*Sections 2, 3; Real-World Lab*) ◆ **Unity and Diversity** The fossil record provides evidence that many different organisms have existed at different times. (*Sections 1, 4, 5*)

Take It to the Net

 Interactive text at www.phschool.com

Science Explorer comes alive with iText.

- **Complete student text** is accessible from any computer with a browser.

- **Animations, simulations, and videos** enhance student understanding and retention of concepts.

- **Self-tests and online study tools** assess student understanding.

- **Teacher management tools** help you make the most of this valuable resource.

STAY CURRENT with **SCIENCE NEWS**®

Find out the latest research and information about Earth's history at:
www.phschool.com

Go to **www.phschool.com** and click on the Science icon. Then click on Science Explorer under PH@school.

ACTIVITY	Time (minutes)	Materials Quantities for one work group	Skills
Section 1			
Discover, p. 106	10	**Nonconsumable** hand lens, rock sample containing fossils	Inferring
Try This, p. 108	10	**Consumable** 3 sugar cubes, water **Nonconsumable** modeling compound, bowl, plastic spoon	Observing
Science at Home, p. 112	Home	No special materials are required.	Communicating
Section 2			
Discover, p. 113	10	**Nonconsumable** 4-5 different colors of modeling compound, small bowl, cheese slicer or plastic knife	Inferring
Try This, p. 114	15	**Consumable** cylindrical pasta noodle about 1.5 cm in diameter, sandwich made of different kinds of cheese and meats	Observing
Real-World Lab, p. 118	30	No special materials are required.	Interpreting Data, Drawing Conclusions
Section 3			
Discover, p. 119	10	**Nonconsumable** modeling clay, metric ruler, plastic knife	Predicting
Sharpen Your Skills, p. 121	10	No special materials are required.	Calculating
Science at Home, p. 122	Home	No special materials are required.	Inferring
Section 4			
Discover, p. 123	15	**Nonconsumable** metric ruler **Consumable** adding-machine paper	Making Models
Skills Lab, pp. 126–127	30	**Consumable** worksheet with 2,000 asterisks **Nonconsumable** 1 ream of paper, metric ruler, meter stick, calculator	Measuring, Calculating, Drawing Conclusions
Section 5			
Discover, p. 128	15	**Consumable** sheet of unlined paper	Posing Questions
Try This, p. 136	15	**Consumable** adding-machine paper **Nonconsumable** metric ruler	Interpreting Data

A list of all materials required for the Student Edition activities can be found beginning on page T15. You can obtain information about ordering materials by calling 1-800-848-9500 or by accessing the Science Explorer Internet site at: **www.phschool.com**

A Journey Back in Time

Before beginning Chapter 4, most students may have little idea about the extent of Earth's history other than dinosaurs once roamed the land. Few students will have any concept of the richness and complexity of the history of life on Earth.

Purpose In the Chapter 4 Project, students will research a geologic time period, create a travel brochure that shows what life was like in that period, and illustrate a portion of a class time line of Earth's history.

Skills Focus Students will be able to:
◆ interpret data about a selected period of geologic time in reference materials;
◆ apply concepts learned through research in making a travel brochure for a geologic time period;
◆ communicate what they learned about the period of geologic time in a presentation to the class.

Project Time Line The Chapter 4 Project will take about three weeks. The progress of students will depend on how much time they spend working on the project. The Chapter 4 Project can be divided into the following phases.
◆ Make a list of the types of reference materials that could be useful in researching the geologic time period.
◆ Research the geologic time period, using reference books, specialized books on Earth's history or groups of organisms, magazine articles, and Internet sites.
◆ Plan and write the travel brochure.
◆ Create illustrations for the travel brochure and for the time line.
◆ Make a presentation of the geologic time period to the class.

For more detailed information on planning and supervising this chapter project, see Chapter 4 Project Teacher Notes, pages 94–95 in Teaching Resources.

Suggested Shortcuts
◆ You may wish to divide the class into small groups to carry out this project.
◆ You can make this project shorter and less involved by foregoing the travel brochure and simply having students

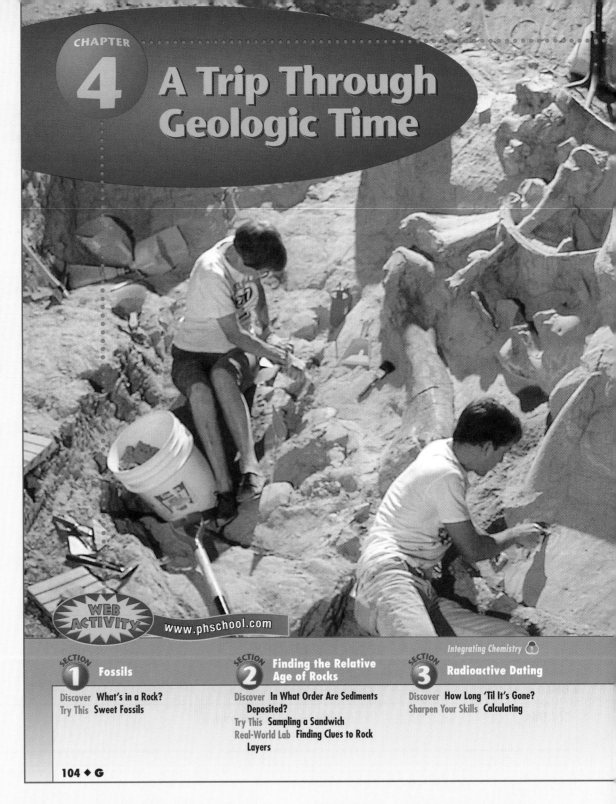

CHAPTER

4 A Trip Through Geologic Time

WEB ACTIVITY www.phschool.com

SECTION 1 Fossils	**SECTION 2** Finding the Relative Age of Rocks	*Integrating Chemistry* **SECTION 3** Radioactive Dating
Discover What's in a Rock? **Try This** Sweet Fossils	**Discover** In What Order Are Sediments Deposited? **Try This** Sampling a Sandwich **Real-World Lab** Finding Clues to Rock Layers	**Discover** How Long 'Til It's Gone? **Sharpen Your Skills** Calculating

work on a large, illustrated geologic time scale. Small groups can be responsible for one or more geologic time periods. Each group can divide up tasks among its members. At the end of the project, the group can present its portion of the geologic time scale.

Possible Materials For research, students will need a wide array of reference materials. Collect books and magazine articles on Earth's history from friends and local libraries. In addition, do an Internet search and make a list

of helpful sites students could visit. Many natural history museums, for example, have Internet sites that provide information about relevant topics. To create their illustrations, students will need colored pencils, markers, or water colors. They will also need tape or glue. For the class time line, you will need butcher or table-covering paper and art materials.

Launching the Project Gather travel brochures that focus on states, foreign countries, and national parks. Travel agents or state tourist bureaus can probably provide

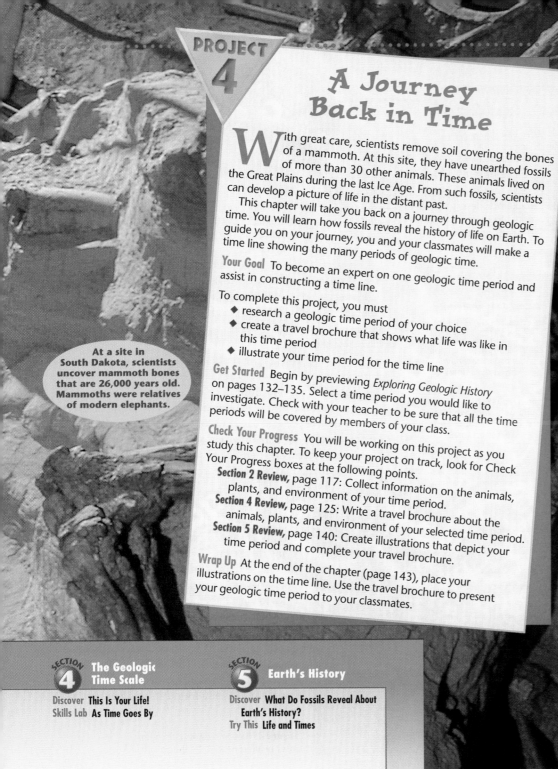

A Journey Back in Time

With great care, scientists remove soil covering the bones of a mammoth. At this site, they have unearthed fossils of more than 30 other animals. These animals lived on the Great Plains during the last Ice Age. From such fossils, scientists can develop a picture of life in the distant past.

This chapter will take you back on a journey through geologic time. You will learn how fossils reveal the history of life on Earth. To guide you on your journey, you and your classmates will make a time line showing the many periods of geologic time.

Your Goal To become an expert on one geologic time period and assist in constructing a time line.

To complete this project, you must
- research a geologic time period of your choice
- create a travel brochure that shows what life was like in this time period
- illustrate your time period for the time line

Get Started Begin by previewing *Exploring Geologic History* on pages 132–135. Select a time period you would like to investigate. Check with your teacher to be sure that all the time periods will be covered by members of your class.

Check Your Progress You will be working on this project as you study this chapter. To keep your project on track, look for Check Your Progress boxes at the following points.

Section 2 Review, page 117: Collect information on the animals, plants, and environment of your time period.

Section 4 Review, page 125: Write a travel brochure about the animals, plants, and environment of your selected time period.

Section 5 Review, page 140: Create illustrations that depict your time period and complete your travel brochure.

Wrap Up At the end of the chapter (page 143), place your illustrations on the time line. Use the travel brochure to present your geologic time period to your classmates.

At a site in South Dakota, scientists uncover mammoth bones that are 26,000 years old. Mammoths were relatives of modern elephants.

SECTION **4** The Geologic Time Scale

Discover **This Is Your Life!**
Skills Lab **As Time Goes By**

SECTION **5** Earth's History

Discover **What Do Fossils Reveal About Earth's History?**
Try This **Life and Times**

G ◆ 105

Program Resources

◆ **Teaching Resources** Chapter 4 Project Teacher Notes, pp. 94–95; Project Overview and Worksheets, pp. 96–99; Project Scoring Rubric, p. 100

WEB ACTIVITY **www.phschool.com**

You will find an Internet activity, chapter self-tests for students, and links to other chapter topics at this site.

Media and Technology

 Audio CDs and **Audiotapes**
English-Spanish Section Summaries

---

these materials. Show them to students, and give students time to examine their features. Then discuss features of the brochures that are most informative and attractive. Explain to students that they will create such a brochure to show what life was like in a specific period of Earth's history. To help students get started, pass out Chapter 4 Project Overview and Worksheets, pages 96–99 in Teaching Resources. You may also wish to pass out the Chapter 4 Project Scoring Rubric, page 100, at this time.

Performance Assessment

Use the Chapter 4 Project Scoring Rubric to assess students' work. Students will be assessed on
- ◆ how accurately and comprehensively the information in the brochure describes the geologic time period;
- ◆ how appropriately and artistically they create the illustrations for the brochure;
- ◆ how well their illustrations enhance the time line;
- ◆ how effectively they present their brochure to the class.

Objectives

After completing the lesson, students will be able to

- explain what fossils are and how most fossils form;
- describe what fossils tell about how organisms have changed over time;
- identify and describe different types of fossils.

Key Terms fossil, paleontologist, sedimentary rock, petrified fossil, mold, cast, carbon film, trace fossil, scientific theory, evolution, extinct

1 Engage/Explore

Activating Prior Knowledge

Ask students: **How do scientists know that different kinds of plants and animals lived in Earth's past?** *(Many students will mention evidence from fossils.)* **What is a fossil?** *(A typical answer might suggest that a fossil is an organism that has turned to rock.)* Explain that in this section they will find out about different types of fossils and the processes that cause each type to form.

···· **DISCOVER** ····

Skills Focus inferring
Materials *hand lens, rock sample containing fossils*
Time 10 minutes
Tips Divide students into small groups and give each group a fossil-bearing rock. Then explain that each student should examine the rock, make a sketch, and write answers before discussing the rock with other group members.
Think It Over Most students should recognize that the rock contains one or more fossils. A typical explanation of how the fossils formed might suggest that an organism fell into sediments that later solidified.

DISCOVER ·············

What's in a Rock?

1. Use a hand lens to carefully observe the rock sample provided by your teacher.

2. Make a drawing of any shapes you see in the rock. Include as many details as you can. Beneath your drawing, write a short description of what you see.

Think It Over
Inferring What do you think the rock contains? How do you think the shapes you observed in the rock got there?

GUIDE FOR READING

- How do fossils form?
- What are the different kinds of fossils?
- What do fossils tell about how organisms have changed over time?

Reading Tip As you read, use the headings to make an outline showing what fossils are, how they form, and why they are important.

Y ou are a geologist at work in the high mountains of western Canada. You carefully split apart a piece of soft rock. Pressed into the rock is the shape of a tiny animal about the size of your thumb. The animal looks like no creature you have ever seen.

The rock is from a layer of rocks called the Burgess shale. The Burgess shale is famous because it contains evidence of life on Earth more than 500 million years ago. The creatures in the Burgess shale are tiny, soft-bodied animals without backbones. Some look like present-day crabs or worms. These animals lived on the bottom of a shallow sea. Scientists hypothesize that a mudslide suddenly buried the animals. Over millions of years, the mud turned to shale. The remains of the animals also became solid rock.

Evidence of Ancient Life

Fossils are the preserved remains or traces of living things. Fossils provide evidence of how life has changed over time. Fossils also help scientists infer how Earth's surface has changed. Fossils are clues to what past environments were like.

Most fossils form when living things die and are buried by sediments. The sediments slowly harden into rock and preserve the shapes of the organisms. Scientists who study fossils are called **paleontologists** (pay lee un TAHL uh jists). Fossils are usually found in sedimentary rock.

Figure 1 Paleontologists chip out the fossil-bearing rock of the Burgess shale.

READING STRATEGIES

Reading Tip If necessary, review with students how to make an outline. Then suggest that the major headings can be used as the first level of the outline's heads, with side headings used for the next level. When there are no side headings in a subsection, students should make their own from information in the subsection. Where there are side headings, students should use details to support those headings.

Vocabulary Help students pronounce *paleontologist*. Point out that *pale-* is derived from a Greek word meaning "ancient," while *-onto* is derived from a Greek word meaning "organism." Therefore, a paleontologist is someone who studies ancient organisms.

Figure 2 A fossil may form when sediment quickly covers an animal's body. *Predicting* What would happen to the fossil if erosion continued after Step D?

A. An animal dies and sinks into shallow water.

B. Sediment covers the animal.

C. The sediment becomes rock, preserving parts of the animal.

D. Mountain building, weathering, and erosion eventually expose the fossil at the surface.

Sedimentary rock is the type of rock that is made of hardened sediment. Most fossils form from animals or plants that once lived in or near quiet water such as swamps, lakes, or shallow seas where sediments build up. In Figure 2, you can see how a fossil might form.

When an organism dies, its soft parts often decay quickly or are eaten by animals. Thus, generally only hard parts leave fossils. These hard parts include bones, shells, teeth, seeds, and woody stems. It is rare for the soft parts of an organism to become a fossil.

Kinds of Fossils

For a fossil to form, the remains or traces of an organism must be protected from decay. Then one of several processes may cause a fossil to form. **Fossils found in rock include petrified fossils, molds and casts, carbon films, and trace fossils. Other fossils form when the remains of organisms are preserved in substances such as tar, amber, or ice.**

Petrified Fossils A fossil may form when the remains of an organism become petrified. The term *petrified* means "turning into stone." **Petrified fossils** are fossils in which minerals replace all or part of an organism. The fossil tree trunks shown in Figure 3 are examples of petrified wood. These fossils formed after sediment covered the wood. Then water rich in dissolved minerals seeped into spaces in the plant's cells. Over time, the water evaporated, leaving the hardened minerals behind. Some of the original wood remains, but the minerals have hardened and preserved it.

Figure 3 Although they look as if they were just cut down, these petrified tree trunks were formed 200 million years ago. These fossils can be seen in the Petrified Forest National Park in Arizona.

G ◆ 107

2 Facilitate

Evidence of Ancient Life

Using the Visuals: Figure 2

Have students brainstorm a list of living things from the area, such as trees, small plants, soil organisms, and larger animals. Then have students identify which organisms and parts could become fossils and which probably would not. Guide students to the understanding that a fossil is the exception, not the rule, when an organism dies. **learning modality: verbal**

Kinds of Fossils

Demonstration

Materials *pan, paper towel, white glue, paper plate, water*

Time 5 minutes twice a day for 2 days

Make a model petrified fossil by mixing two parts water to one part white glue in a pan. Roll a paper towel in the mixture, making sure the whole towel is moistened. Then stand the towel on end on a paper plate and allow it to dry. The result will be a rock-hard "petrified fossil" that retains the original towel's shape. Ask students: **How did this model the formation of a petrified fossil?** (*The glue dissolved in water seeped into spaces in the paper towel and hardened when the water evaporated, just as minerals dissolved in water seep into the cells of an organism and harden.*) **learning modality: visual**

Answers to Self-Assessment

Caption Question

Figure 2 The fossil would erode away with the rest of the rock.

Media and Technology

Transparencies "Formation of a Rock Fossil," Transparency 14

Ongoing Assessment

Skills Check Have students make a flow-chart that represents how an organism becomes a fossil. Their charts should match the steps in Figure 2, but students will have to use words instead of pictures.

 Students can save their flowcharts in their portfolios.

Kinds of Fossils, continued

Skills Focus observing
Materials *modeling compound, 3 sugar cubes, bowl, water, plastic spoon*
Time 10 minutes
Tips Using warm water will cause the sugar to dissolve faster.
Expected Outcome Students should observe that the sugar cube entirely wrapped by clay is preserved, while the other sugar cube has dissolved into the water. The activity models how mud or other sediment can prevent the decay of an organism by protecting it from exposure to water.
Extend Have students explain how an organism could become as completely covered as the second sugar cube.
learning modality: kinesthetic

Building Inquiry Skills: Making Models

Materials *shell, petroleum jelly, modeling compound, plaster of Paris, water, paper cup, plastic spoon*
Time 20 minutes

Have pairs of students make models of a mold and a cast fossil. To make a mold, students should coat a shell with petroleum jelly and then press the shell into modeling compound. From that mold, students can make a cast by pouring plaster of Paris into the mold. (Mix 2 parts plaster of Paris with 1 part water.) Allow the plaster of Paris to harden overnight. Then students can separate the plaster from the modeling compound. Have students write a description of the mold and cast they made. **learning modality: kinesthetic**

Sweet Fossils

1. Wrap a piece of clay around one sugar cube so that half of it is covered with clay.
2. Wrap clay entirely around a second sugar cube and seal it tightly.
3. Drop both cubes into a bowl of water, along with an uncovered sugar cube.
4. Stir until the uncovered sugar cube dissolves completely.
5. Remove the other cubes from the water and examine the remains.

Observing Describe the appearance of the two sugar cubes. Did the clay preserve the sugar cubes? How does this activity model the way fossils form?

Petrified fossils may also form by replacement. In replacement, the minerals in water make a copy of the organism. For example, water containing dissolved minerals may slowly dissolve a clamshell buried in sediment. At the same time, the minerals in the water harden to form rock. The result is a copy of the clamshell made of rock.

Molds and Casts The most common fossils are molds and casts. Both copy the shape of ancient organisms. A **mold** is a hollow area in sediment in the shape of an organism or part of an organism. A mold forms when the hard part of the organism, such as a shell, is buried in sediment.

Later, water carrying dissolved minerals and sediment may seep into the empty space of a mold. If the water deposits the minerals and sediment there, the result is a cast. A **cast** is a copy of the shape of an organism. Figure 4 shows a mold (top) that became filled with minerals to form a cast (bottom). As you can see, a cast is the opposite of its mold. Also notice how the mold and cast have preserved details of the animal's structure.

Figure 4 The fossil mold (top) clearly shows the shape of the animal called *Cryptolithus.* So does the fossil cast (bottom). *Cryptolithus* lived in the oceans about 450 million years ago.

Background

History of Science The Burgess shale is an outcropping of rock in the Canadian Rockies of British Columbia. It contains fossils of some 120 different types of marine invertebrates, and it remains the most important window on the explosion of life that marks the Cambrian Period. The fossils were discovered in 1909 by Charles Walcott, a well-respected paleontologist who at that time headed the Smithsonian Institution in Washington, D.C.

Since its discovery, over 70,000 fossils have been collected from the site.

Facts and Figures Paleontologists estimate that for any given environment, more than 50 percent of the organisms would not usually become fossils, mostly because they lack hard parts. Even for those organisms with hard parts, the conditions must be just right for fossilization. Thus, the fossil record is very incomplete.

Carbon Films Another type of fossil is a **carbon film,** an extremely thin coating of carbon on rock. How does a carbon film form? Remember that all living things contain carbon. When sediment buries an organism, some of the materials that make up the organism evaporate or become gases. These gases escape from the sediment, leaving carbon behind. Eventually, only a thin film of carbon remains. This process can preserve the delicate parts of plant leaves and insects.

INTEGRATING CHEMISTRY

Figure 5 This carbon film fossil of insects is between 5 million and 23 million years old.

Trace Fossils Most types of fossils preserve the shapes of ancient animals and plants. In contrast, **trace fossils** provide evidence of the activities of ancient organisms. A fossilized footprint is one example of a trace fossil. A dinosaur made the fossil footprint shown in Figure 6. The mud or sand that the animal stepped into eventually was buried by layers of sediment. Slowly the sediment became solid rock, preserving the footprints for millions of years.

Fossil footprints provide clues about an animal's size and behavior. How fast could the animal move? Did it walk on two or four legs? Did it live alone or with others of its kind? A scientist can infer the answers to such questions by looking at fossil footprints.

Other examples of trace fossils include the trails that animals followed or the burrows that they lived in. A trail or burrow can give clues about the size and shape of the organism, where it lived, and how it obtained food.

☑ *Checkpoint* *What can a trace fossil reveal about an early animal?*

Preserved Remains Some processes preserve the remains of organisms with little or no change. For example, some remains are preserved when organisms become trapped in tar. Tar is sticky oil that seeps from Earth's surface. Many fossils preserved in tar have been found at the Rancho La Brea tar pits in Los Angeles, California. Thousands of years ago, animals came to drink the water that covered these pits. Somehow, they became stuck in the tar

Figure 6 These dinosaur footprints are in the Painted Desert in Arizona. *Inferring What can you infer about this dinosaur from its footprints?*

Chapter 4 **G ◆ 109**

Answers to Self-Assessment

☑ *Checkpoint*
A trace fossil can reveal evidence of the activities of an early animal as well as its size.

Caption Question
Figure 6 Answers may vary. A typical answer might suggest that there were perhaps two dinosaurs, a large one and a small one.

Kinds of Fossils, continued

Building Inquiry Skills: Comparing and Contrasting

Materials *samples of each of the different kinds of fossils, hand lens*
Time 15 minutes

Provide examples of the different kinds of fossils, including petrified fossils, molds, casts, and amber. Have each student make a sketch and write a description of each fossil. Then in class discussion, invite students to compare and contrast the different kinds of fossils.
learning modality: visual

Change Over Time

Addressing Naive Conceptions

Many students understand the word *theory* to mean an opinion put forward that is less than sure or proven, as in the phrase "that's just your theory about what happened." Explain that this common use of the word is not the scientific use. Ask: **In science, what term is used for a suggested solution to a problem?** *(A hypothesis)* Hypothesis is similar to the common use of the word *theory.* For a scientist, a theory is a broad explanation based on a wealth of observations, as in the "theory of gravity." Scientists know that gravity exists, just as they know that evolution takes place.
learning modality: verbal

Inquiry Challenge

Materials *models or photos of an early automobile and a modern automobile*
Time 15 minutes

Provide small groups with models or photos of early and recent automobiles. (As alternatives, you could use early and recent airplanes or old and recent athletic shoes.) Then have each group make a list of automobile features that have changed over time. Finally, challenge each group to make drawings of two or three intermediate steps in the evolution of the automobile, showing how they think cars probably looked, for example, in the 1940s and the 1960s.
cooperative learning

and then died. The tar soaked into their bones, preserving the bones from decay.

Ancient organisms also have been preserved in amber. Amber is the hardened resin, or sap, of evergreen trees. First, an insect is trapped on sticky resin. After the insect dies, more resin covers it, sealing it from air and protecting its body from decay.

Freezing is another way in which remains can be preserved. The frozen remains of relatives of elephants called woolly mammoths have been found in very cold regions of Siberia and Alaska. Freezing has preserved even the mammoths' hair and skin.

☑ *Checkpoint* **What are three ways in which the remains of an organism can be preserved?**

Figure 7 A fossil preserved in amber provides a window into the history of past life on Earth. Body parts, including the hairlike bristles on an insect's legs, its antennae, and its delicate wings, are often perfectly preserved.

Change Over Time

Paleontologists collect fossils from sedimentary rocks all over the world. They use this information to determine what past life forms were like. They want to learn what these organisms ate, what ate them, and in what environment they lived.

Paleontologists also classify organisms. They group similar organisms together. They arrange organisms in the order in which they lived, from earliest to latest. Together, all the information that paleontologists have gathered about past life is called the fossil record. **The fossil record provides evidence about the history of life on Earth. The fossil record also shows that different groups of organisms have changed over time.**

The fossil record reveals a surprising fact: Fossils occur in a particular order. Older rocks contain fossils of simpler organisms. Younger rocks contain fossils of more complex organisms. In other words, the fossil record shows that life on Earth has evolved, or changed. Simple, one-celled organisms have given rise to complex plants and animals.

The fossil record provides evidence to support the theory of evolution. A **scientific theory** is a well-tested concept that explains a wide range of observations. **Evolution** is the gradual change in living things over long periods of time. You can trace the evolution of one group of animals in *Exploring the Evolution of Elephants.*

The fossil record shows that millions of types of organisms have evolved. But many others have become extinct. A type of organism is **extinct** if it no longer exists and will never again live on Earth.

Background

History of Science The English scientist Charles Darwin (1809–1882) explained his theory of evolution in his book *On the Origin of Species*, published in 1859. The theory has been revised since then, but it remains much as Darwin explained it. The variety and regular sequence of life forms found in the fossil record has made the theory of evolution central to an understanding of life on Earth, how life has changed over time, and how living things are related today.

Integrating Science The two types of modern elephants are actually the last of a once abundant and diverse group. At various times during the Cenozoic Era, ancestors of elephants lived on all the continents except Australia and Antarctica. The early evolution of elephants, including *Moeritherium*, occurred in Africa.

EXPLORING the Evolution of Elephants

Here are some members of the elephant family. Modern elephants, mammoths, and mastodons all evolved from a common ancestor that lived about 34 million years ago.

Asian Elephant present day
Asian elephants live in India and Southeast Asia. They can be trained to move objects with their trunks and to carry heavy loads on their backs.

African Elephant present day
About 4 meters high at the shoulder, the African elephant is larger than the Asian elephant. African elephants are fierce and difficult to tame.

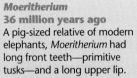

Woolly Mammoth 2 million years ago
The woolly mammoth lived during the last Ice Age. Hunting by humans may have led to their extinction about 10,000 years ago.

Mastodon 25–30 million years ago
Mastodons developed long, flexible trunks and long tusks. Later mastodons looked similar to mammoths, but were smaller and stockier. Mastodons became extinct about 10,000 years ago.

Gomphotherium 23 million years ago
Gomphotherium stood over 2 meters at the shoulder. It had a small trunk, two tusks on the upper jaw, and two tusks on the lower jaw.

Moeritherium 36 million years ago
A pig-sized relative of modern elephants, *Moeritherium* had long front teeth—primitive tusks—and a long upper lip.

Paleomastodon 34 million years ago
Paleomastodons had a short trunk and short tusks on both upper and lower jaws. The paleomastodon was an ancestor of later elephantlike animals.

EXPLORING the Evolution of Elephants

Invite volunteers to read aloud the annotations for each example in the feature. Then ask: **Did modern elephants evolve from the Woolly Mammoth?** (*Students should recognize that the pathway to modern elephants does not include the Woolly Mammoth. Rather, modern elephants and the Woolly Mammoth had common ancestors.*) Emphasize that the evolution of a group is often very complicated, and the fossil record is not complete enough to show every step in the process. **learning modality: verbal**

Fossils and Past Environments

Building Inquiry Skills: Inferring

Have students turn back to Figure 6, and ask: **In what kind of material are these dinosaur footprints?** (*rock*) **Could dinosaurs have left footprints in rock?** (*no*) **What can you infer about the environment in which these fossils were made?** (*At the time the footprints were made, the environment probably was much wetter; the dinosaur likely stepped in mud or wet sand.*) Therefore, a scientist can infer that the environment of the area has probably changed since the fossils were made. **learning modality: logical/mathematical**

Program Resources

 Science Explorer Series *Cells and Heredity*, Chapter 5, provides evidence for the theory of evolution.

Media and Technology

Transparencies "The Evolution of Elephants," Transparency 15

Answers to Self-Assessment

☑ *Checkpoint*

Remains of an organism can be preserved in tar and in amber. Freezing is a third way in which remains can be preserved.

Ongoing Assessment

Writing Have students define the term evolution and use the *evolution* of elephants as an example.

3 Assess

Section 1 Review Answers

1. Most fossils form when living things die and are buried by sediments. The sediments slowly harden into rock and preserve the shapes of the organisms.

2. Petrified fossils, molds, casts, carbon films, and trace fossils

3. The fossil record provides evidence that many different organisms have existed at different times. The fossil record also shows that groups of organisms have changed over time.

4. Students should describe preservation in tar or amber or preservation by freezing.

5. The area was once under water.

Science at Home

Tips Encourage students to ask the older members of their families to find something that has been passed down from generation to generation. Suggest that they write down why the object was preserved to help them remember in telling the story to the class. Caution students not to bring these objects to school; rather, they should make a drawing of the object.

Figure 8 These are fossils of brachiopods and crinoids that lived more than 435 million years ago. Similar organisms still live in the oceans today. From these fossils, scientists know that the environment where they were found was once a shallow sea.

Fossils and Past Environments

Paleontologists use fossils to build up a picture of Earth's environments in the past. The fossils found in an area tell whether the area was a shallow bay, an ocean bottom, or a fresh-water swamp.

Fossils also provide evidence of Earth's climate in the past. For example, coal has been found in Antarctica. But coal only forms from the remains of plants that grow in warm, swampy regions. As you probably know, thick layers of ice and snow now cover Antarctica. The presence of coal shows that the climate of Antarctica was once much warmer than it is today.

Scientists can use fossils to learn about changes in Earth's surface. For example, corals are organisms that thrive in warm, shallow seas. Yet fossil corals are often found in many areas of the midwestern United States. From this fact, scientists infer that shallow seas once covered those areas.

Section 1 Review

1. Describe the process by which most fossils are formed in rock.
2. What are the five types of fossils that can be found in rock?
3. How does the fossil record support the theory of evolution?
4. Describe one way in which the remains of an organism can be preserved.
5. **Thinking Critically** **Inferring** Fossil seashells have been found in rock beds on land. What can you infer about how the area has changed?

Science at Home

A fossil is something old that has been preserved. Why is it that some old things are preserved, while others are destroyed? With your parents' permission, look around your house for the oldest object you can find. Interview family members to determine how old the object is, why it has been preserved, and how it may have changed since it was new. Make a drawing of the object and bring it to class. Tell your class the story of this "fossil."

Performance Assessment

Skills Check Have students make a table that compares and contrasts the different kinds of fossils, including preserved fossils, molds, casts, carbon films, trace fossils, and preserved remains.

 Students can save their tables in their portfolios.

Background

Facts and Figures Shallow seas covered much of what is now Texas during the Devonian Period. There, coral animals built extensive reefs, formed from their outer skeletons. The movement of continents raised the reefs above sea level. Today, those Devonian reefs form part of the Guadalupe Mountains east of El Paso.

Program Resources

◆ **Teaching Resources** 4-1 Review and Reinforce, p. 103; 4-1 Enrich, p. 104

SECTION 2 Finding the Relative Age of Rocks

SECTION
2 Finding the Relative Age of Rocks

DISCOVER

In What Order Are Sediments Deposited?

1. Make a stack of different-colored layers of clay. Each layer should be about the size and thickness of a pancake. If these flat layers are sediments, which layer of sediment was deposited first? (*Hint:* This is the oldest layer.)

2. Now form the stack into a dome by pressing it over a small rounded object, such as a small bowl. With a cheese-slicer or plastic knife, carefully cut off the top of the dome. Look at the layers that you have exposed. Which layer is the oldest?

Think It Over

Inferring If you press the stack into a small bowl and trim away the clay that sticks above the edge, where will you find the oldest layer?

Have you ever seen rock layers exposed on a cliff beside a road? Often the rock layers differ in color or texture. What are these layers, and how did they form?

The sediment that forms sedimentary rocks is deposited in flat layers one on top of the other. Over years, the sediment becomes deeply buried. Then it hardens and changes into sedimentary rock. At the same time, remains of organisms in the sediment may become fossils. Over time, many layers of sediment become different layers of rock. These rock layers provide a record of Earth's geologic history.

Relative and Absolute Ages

When you look at a rock containing a fossil, your first question may be, "How old is it?" The **relative age** of a rock is its age compared to the ages of other rocks. You have probably used the idea of relative age when comparing your age with someone else's age. For example, if you say that you are older than your brother but younger than your sister, you are describing your relative age.

The relative age of a rock does not provide its absolute age. The **absolute age** of a rock is the number of years since the rock formed. It may be impossible to know a rock's absolute age exactly. But sometimes geologists can determine a rock's absolute age to within a certain number of years.

GUIDE FOR READING

◆ How do geologists determine the relative age of rocks?

◆ How are index fossils useful to geologists?

Reading Tip Before you read, rewrite the headings in the section as *how, why,* or *what* questions. As you read, look for answers to these questions.

Objectives

After completing the lesson, students will be able to
◆ describe several ways that scientists determine the relative age of rocks;
◆ describe how geologists use index fossils to date rocks.

Key Terms relative age, absolute age, law of superposition, unconformity, fault, intrusion, extrusion, index fossil

1 Engage/Explore

Activating Prior Knowledge

Guide students in recalling the deposition of sediments they learned about in Chapter 3. Ask: **What happens to the sediment load carried to an ocean by a river?** (*Some is deposited on beaches. Students should infer that some is deposited on the ocean floor.*) Explain that this sediment can harden over time into layers of rock.

DISCOVER

Skills Focus inferring
Materials *4–5 different colors of modeling compound, small bowl, cheese slicer or plastic knife*
Time 10 minutes

Tips Have students make a four- or five-layered stack, using a different color for each layer. When they begin cutting off the top of the dome, advise them not to cut all the way to the bowl; rather, they should leave one layer covering the bowl.
Expected Outcome Students should infer that the oldest layer is the bottom layer when the layers are flat. When the layers are pressed over the bowl and the top of the dome cut off, the oldest layer is in the center of the dome, even if it rises above the other layers.
Think It Over The oldest layer is found on the outside ring, touching the bowl.

READING STRATEGIES

Reading Tip Students should look for answers to these questions: "What are relative and absolute ages?" "What does the position of rock layers tell us about their age?" "How are fossils used to date rocks?" Suggest students use their questions and answers as a study guide to the section.

Program Resources

◆ **Teaching Resources** 4-2 Lesson Plan, p. 105; 4-2 Section Summary, p. 106
◆ **Guided Study Workbook** Section 4-2

Media and Technology

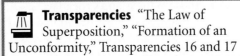
Transparencies "The Law of Superposition," "Formation of an Unconformity," Transparencies 16 and 17

2 Facilitate

Relative and Absolute Ages

Building Inquiry Skills: Classifying

Write the following statements about children in a family on the board: "Anthony is the youngest." (*Relative*) "Melony is 4 years old." (*Absolute*) "Michael is older than Shatiqua." (*Relative*) "Shatiqua is 16 years old." (*Absolute*) "Ashley is older than Melony but younger than Shatiqua." (*Relative*) Then challenge students to classify each statement as either an absolute age or a relative age and place the children in order, from oldest to youngest. (*Michael, Shatiqua, Ashley, Melony, Anthony*) **learning modality: logical/mathematical**

The Position of Rock Layers

Skills Focus observing
Materials *cylindrical pasta noodle about 1.5 cm in diameter, sandwich made of different kinds of cheese and meats*
Time 15 minutes
Tips Using only slices of cheese and meats in a sandwich will make the "coring" easier. One sandwich can be used for several core samples. Explain that geologists use powerful drills to cut through sediment layers and bring core samples to the surface to study the different layers.
Expected Outcome Students should infer that the oldest layer is the bottom-most layer, in this case the bottom slice of bread. The youngest layer is the top-most, the top slice of bread. Scientists study core samples to find out about the layers of rock beneath the surface.
Extend Ask: **If these were layers of sedimentary rock, why couldn't layer 4 be younger than layer 3?** (*The sediment that formed layer 3 could not have been deposited underneath the hardened rock of layer 4.*) **learning modality: kinesthetic**

Kaibab limestone
250 million years old

Toroweap limestone
255 million years old

Coconino sandstone
260 million years old

Hermit shale
265 million years old

Supai sandstone
285 million years old

Younger

Older

Figure 9 More than a dozen rock layers make up the walls of the Grand Canyon. You can see five layers clearly in the photograph. *Applying Concepts In which of the labeled layers in the diagram would you find the oldest fossils? Explain.*

Sampling a Sandwich

Your teacher will give you a sandwich that represents rock layers in Earth's crust.

1. Use a round, hollow, uncooked noodle as a coring tool. Push the noodle through the layers of the sandwich.

2. Pull the noodle out of the sandwich. Break the noodle gently to remove your core sample.

3. Draw a picture coloring and labeling what you see in each layer of the core.

Observing If this were a real sample of rock layers, which layer would be the oldest? The youngest? Why do you think scientists study core samples?

The Position of Rock Layers

It can be difficult to determine the absolute age of a rock. So geologists use a method to find a rock's relative age. Geologists use the **law of superposition** to determine the relative ages of sedimentary rock layers. **According to the law of superposition, in horizontal sedimentary rock layers the oldest layer is at the bottom. Each higher layer is younger than the layers below it.** If you did the Discover activity at the beginning of this section, you have already used the law of superposition.

The walls of the Grand Canyon in Arizona illustrate the law of superposition. The sedimentary rock layers in the canyon walls represent 2 billion years of Earth's history. You can see some of the rock layers found in the Grand Canyon in Figure 9. Scientists have given names to all the layers of rock exposed on the walls of the Grand Canyon. By using the law of superposition, you should be able to determine the relative ages of these layers.

If you were to start at the top of the Grand Canyon, you would see Kaibab limestone. Because it is on top, it is the youngest layer. As you began your descent into the canyon, you would pass by Toroweap limestone. Next, you would see Coconino sandstone. The deeper you traveled into the canyon, the older the rocks would become. Your trip into the canyon is like a trip into Earth's history. The deeper you go, the older the rocks.

✓ Checkpoint How would a geologist find the relative age of a rock?

Background

History of Science Danish geologist Nicolaus Steno (1638–1686) developed the law of superposition in the 1660s. On a visit to the Mediterranean island of Malta, Steno noticed that the "tongue-stones" sold there as good-luck charms were actually fossilized shark teeth from the island's rock layers. Steno hypothesized that the island had once been under water and that the rock layers had been laid down in succession. He concluded that the deepest rocks were the oldest, thus demonstrating "Steno's law," or the law of superposition.

Facts and Figures The Grand Canyon is about 1.6 km deep. The oldest rock, at the bottom of the canyon, is about 2 billion years old. The canyon was cut by the erosive power of the Colorado River, which continues to cut down at a rate of about 16.5 cm per 1,000 years.

Other Clues to Relative Age

There are other clues to the relative ages of rocks. Geologists find some of these clues by studying extrusions and intrusions of igneous rock and faults.

Clues From Igneous Rock Igneous rock forms when magma or lava hardens. Magma is molten material beneath Earth's surface. Magma that flows onto the surface is called lava.

Lava that hardens on the surface is called an **extrusion.** The rock layers below an extrusion are always older than the extrusion.

Beneath the surface, magma may push into bodies of rock. There, the magma cools and hardens into a mass of igneous rock called an **intrusion.** An intrusion is always younger than the rock layers around and beneath it. Figure 10A shows an intrusion. Geologists study where intrusions and extrusions formed in relation to other rock layers. This helps geologists understand the relative ages of the different types of rock.

Clues From Faults More clues come from the study of faults. A **fault** is a break in Earth's crust. Forces inside Earth cause movement of the rock on opposite sides of a fault.

A fault is always younger than the rock it cuts through. To determine the relative age of a fault, geologists find the relative age of the most recent rock layer through which the fault slices.

Movements along faults can make it harder for geologists to determine the relative ages of rock layers. In Figure 10B you can see how the rock layers no longer line up because of movement along the fault.

Music CONNECTION

The Grand Canyon provides one of Earth's best views of the geologic record. The American composer Ferde Grofé composed his *Grand Canyon Suite* for orchestra in 1931. The music paints a picture of desert scenery and a trip on muleback into the Grand Canyon.

In Your Journal

Listen to a recording of the *Grand Canyon Suite.* How does Grofé's music express what it's like to visit the Grand Canyon? What words would you use to describe what you heard?

Figure 10 Intrusions and faults give clues to the relative ages of rocks. In 10A, an intrusion cuts through rock layers. In 10B, rock layers are broken and shifted along a fault. *Inferring Which is older, the intrusion in 10A or the rock layers it crosses?*

Chapter 4 **G ◆ 115**

Program Resources

🔵 **Science Explorer Series** *Inside Earth,* Chapter 2, can provide more information about faults.
◆ **Integrated Science Laboratory Manual** G-4, "Exploring Geologic Time Through Core Samples"

Answers to Self-Assessment

Caption Question

Figure 9 In the Supai sandstone. The law of superposition says that each layer is older than the layer above it.
Figure 10 The rock layers it crosses

☑ Checkpoint

By observing the rock's position in relation to the rock layers above and below it

---

Music CONNECTION

Materials *CD or cassette player, recording of Grofé's Grand Canyon Suite, photos of Grand Canyon*
Time 30 minutes

Ferde Grofé (1892–1972) was born in New York City and grew up mainly in Los Angeles. The *Grand Canyon Suite* is "program music," which is music that attempts to paint a picture or describe an action without using words. The suite has five movements, or related sections. Hear the voices of early morning birds in "Sunrise," and listen to the "he-haw" of a donkey in "On the Trail."

In Your Journal Display a photo of the Grand Canyon while playing one movement of the suite for the class. Have students write down their ideas as the music plays. Then call on volunteers to share the words that came to mind.
learning modality: verbal

Other Clues to Relative Age

Building Inquiry Skills: Comparing and Contrasting

Materials *hand lens, samples of granite, basalt, sandstone, and shale*
Time 15 minutes

Have students compare sedimentary and igneous rock. Label the samples: granite, an igneous rock that forms intrusions; basalt, an igneous rock that forms extrusions; sandstone, a sedimentary rock formed mainly of sandy sediment; and shale, a sedimentary rock formed mainly of muddy sediment. Have students write descriptions of the rocks, including texture and grain size. Then discuss these differences. **learning modality: visual**

Ongoing Assessment

Drawing Have students make a drawing of several sedimentary rock layers; add and label an intrusion, an extrusion, and a fault; then label the layers from oldest to youngest.

G ◆ 115

Gaps in the Geologic Record

1. Sedimentary rocks form in horizontal layers.

2. Folding tilts the rock layers.

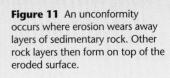

Figure 11 An unconformity occurs where erosion wears away layers of sedimentary rock. Other rock layers then form on top of the eroded surface.

3. The surface is eroded.

Unconformity

4. New sediment is deposited, forming rock layers above the unconformity.

Gaps in the Geologic Record

The geologic record of sedimentary rock layers is not always complete. Deposition slowly builds layer upon layer of sedimentary rock. But some of these layers may erode away, exposing an older rock surface. Then deposition begins again, building new rock layers.

The surface where new rock layers meet a much older rock surface beneath them is called an unconformity. An **unconformity** is a gap in the geologic record. An unconformity shows where some rock layers have been lost because of erosion. Figure 11 shows how an unconformity forms.

Using Fossils to Date Rocks

To date rock layers, geologists first give a relative age to a layer of rock at one location. Then they can give the same age to matching layers of rock at other locations.

Certain fossils, called index fossils, help geologists match rock layers. To be useful as an **index fossil,** a fossil must be widely distributed and represent a type of organism that existed only briefly. A fossil is considered widely distributed if it occurs in many different areas. Geologists look for index fossils in layers of rock. **Index fossils are useful because they tell the relative ages of the rock layers in which they occur.**

Geologists use particular types of organisms as index fossils—for example, certain types of trilobites. Trilobites (TRY luh byts) were a group of hard-shelled animals whose bodies had three

Figure 12 Trilobite fossils are widely distributed. Some types of trilobites serve as index fossils.

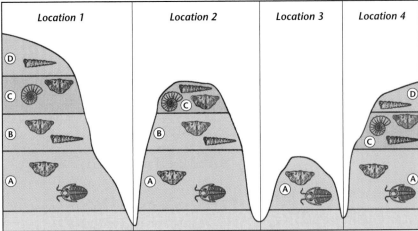

| Location 1 | Location 2 | Location 3 | Location 4 |

distinct parts. Trilobites evolved in shallow seas more than 500 million years ago. Over time, many different types of trilobites appeared. They became extinct about 245 million years ago. Trilobite fossils have been found in many different places.

To serve as an index fossil, a type of trilobite must be different in some way from other trilobites. One example is a type of trilobite with large eyes. These large-eyed trilobites survived for a time after other trilobites became extinct. Suppose a geologist finds large-eyed trilobites in a rock layer. The geologist can infer that those rocks are younger than rocks containing other types of trilobites.

You can use index fossils to match rock layers. Look at Figure 13, which shows rock layers from four different locations. Notice that two of the fossils are found in only one of these rock layers. These are the index fossils.

Figure 13 Scientists use index fossils to match up rock layers at locations that may be far apart. The trilobites in Layer A are index fossils. *Interpreting Diagrams Can you find another index fossil in the diagram?* (*Hint:* Look for a fossil that occurs in only one time period, but in several different locations.)

Section 2 Review

1. What is the law of superposition?
2. What characteristics are necessary for a fossil to be considered an index fossil?
3. What do unconformities show?
4. **Thinking Critically Applying Concepts** Horseshoe crabs are common in the ocean along the east coast of North America. They have existed with very little change for about 200 million years. Would horseshoe crabs be useful as an index fossil? Explain why or why not.

Check Your Progress

CHAPTER PROJECT 4

Locate reference materials you will need to research your chosen geologic time period. Possible sources include library books, magazines, encyclopedias, and Internet articles. Also keep a list of the resources you used. As you do your research, keep in mind the pictures and facts you will need for the class time line and travel brochure. Be sure to include the organisms and environment of the time period.

Program Resources

◆ **Teaching Resources** 4-2 Review and Reinforce, p. 107; 4-2 Enrich, p. 108

Media and Technology

Exploring Earth Science Videodisc Unit 5, Side 1, "The Earth Library"

Chapter 3

Answers to Self-Assessment

Caption Questions

Figure 13 The ammonites in Layer C

✓ *Checkpoint*

Intrusions are always younger than the rock layers through which they pass. Extrusions are always younger than the rock layers below them.

As students examine the figure, suggest that they use the symbol key at the bottom of the Real-World Lab on page 118. Explain that an ammonite was a marine animal in the same group as the modern nautilus; ammonites, important index fossils of the Mesozoic, became extinct at the end of the Cretaceous Period along with dinosaurs. Ask: **Why are there no ammonite fossils at Location 3?** (*Layers B, C, and D either did not form there or were eroded away.*) **learning modality: visual**

3 Assess

Section 2 Review Answers

1. The law of superposition states that in horizontal layers of sedimentary rock, the oldest layer is at the bottom, and each higher layer is younger than the layers below it.
2. Index fossils are fossils of organisms that were widely distributed but only lasted a short time.
3. Unconformities show where an old, eroded surface is in contact with a newer rock layer.
4. They would not be useful because they have existed with little change for too long. A fossil of a horseshoe crab would therefore not tell the relative age of the rock layer in which it was found.

Check Your Progress

CHAPTER PROJECT 4

Point students toward research materials that will provide information about their chosen time periods. Emphasize the need for keeping a list of sources used, since students will need to refer to their sources both in the brochure and in the presentation to the class.

Performance Assessment

Drawing Have students make a drawing that includes sedimentary rock layers, an unconformity, a fault, an intrusion, an extrusion, and several index fossils.

Portfolio Students can save their drawings in their portfolios.

Finding Clues to Rock Layers

Preparing for Inquiry

Key Concept Index fossils as well as intrusions and extrusions can be used to determine the relative ages of rock layers.

Skills Objectives Students will be able to:
- interpret data about the various fossils found in rock layers;
- draw conclusions about the relative ages of rock layers.

Time 30 minutes

Guiding Inquiry

Introducing the Procedure
- Allow students time to read through the entire procedure. Then ask: **Where can you find out what kinds of fossils are in the different rock layers?** *(In the key to symbols)*
- **What kind of fossils do geologists use to match rock layers?** *(index fossils)*

Analyze and Conclude
Site 1

1. Fossils of marine animals in layers A and B indicate a marine environment. Dinosaur tracks and a leaf suggest a land environment created layer D.
2. According to the law of superposition, layer A is the oldest because it is below all other layers.
3. According to the law of superposition, layer G formed most recently because it is above all other layers.
4. Layers C and E are extrusions of igneous rock, in which fossils can't form.
5. Dinosaur, plant, and bird fossils
6. Layer B
7. Rock layers that are missing from the sequence at Site 2 provide clues of an unconformity. Layers E and D are missing between layers X and Y, which suggests that the boundary between Y and X is an unconformity. Layer A is also missing, which suggests that there's an unconformity below W.
8. Layer Y is older because an intrusion is always younger than the layer through which it passes.

9. You would need to know if any layers at Site 1 contained the same fossils.

Extending the Inquiry

More to Explore Since faults can occur only after rock layers have formed, any layers the fault cuts across would be older than the fault. Encourage students to test one another with their sketches.

You Be the Detective

Finding Clues to ROCK LAYERS

Fossil clues give geologists a good idea of what life on Earth was like millions or even billions of years ago.

Problem

How can you use fossils and geologic features to interpret the relative ages of rock layers?

Skills Focus

interpreting data, drawing conclusions

Procedure

1. Study the rock layers at Sites 1 and 2. Write down the similarities and differences between the layers at the two sites.
2. List the kinds of fossils that are found in each rock layer of Sites 1 and 2.

Analyze and Conclude

Site 1

1. What "fossil clues" in layers A and B indicate the kind of environment that existed when these rock layers were formed? How did the environment change in layer D?
2. Which layer is the oldest? How do you know?

3. Which of the layers formed most recently? How do you know?
4. Why are there no fossils in layers C and E?
5. What kind of fossils occurred in layer F?

Site 2

6. Which layer at Site 1 might have formed at the same time as layer W at Site 2?
7. What clues show an unconformity or gap in the horizontal rock layers? Which rock layers are missing? What might have happened to these rock layers?
8. Which is older, intrusion V or layer Y? How do you know?
9. **Think About It** Working as a geologist, you find a rock containing fossils. What information would you need in order to determine this rock's age relative to one of the rock layers at Site 1?

More to Explore

Draw a sketch similar to Site 2 and include a fault that cuts across the intrusion. Have a partner then identify the relative age of the fault, the intrusion, and the layers cut by the fault.

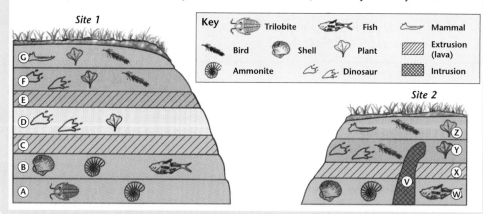

Program Resources

- **Teaching Resources** Real-World Lab blackline masters, pp. 121–122

Media and Technology

 Lab Activity Videotape *Earth's Changing Surface, 7*

SECTION 3 Radioactive Dating

DISCOVER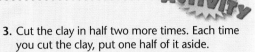

How Long 'Til It's Gone?

1. Make a small cube—about 5 cm × 5 cm × 5 cm—from modeling clay.

2. Carefully use a knife to cut the clay in half. Put one half of the clay aside.

3. Cut the clay in half two more times. Each time you cut the clay, put one half of it aside.

Think It Over
Predicting How big will the remaining piece of clay be if you repeat the process several more times?

In Australia, scientists have found sedimentary rocks that contain some of the world's oldest fossils—stromatolites (stroh MAT uh lyts). Stromatolites are the remains of reefs built by organisms similar to present-day bacteria. The bacteria grew together in dense mats shaped like stacks of pancakes. The mats formed reefs in shallow water near the shores of ancient oceans. Sediment eventually covered these reefs. As the sediments changed to rock, so did the reefs.

Paleontologists have determined that some stromatolites are more than 3 billion years old. But how did scientists determine the age of these fossils? To understand the methods of absolute dating, you need to learn more about the chemistry of rocks.

GUIDE FOR READING

◆ What happens during radioactive decay?

◆ What can be learned from radioactive dating?

◆ How did scientists determine the age of Earth?

Reading Tip As you read, use the headings to make an outline showing what radioactive elements are and how they are used by geologists to find the absolute age of rocks.

Changing From One Element to Another

What do you, the air you breathe, a lemon, and a puddle of water have in common? All are kinds of matter. In fact, everything around you is made of matter. Although different kinds of matter look, feel, or smell different, all the matter you see is made of tiny particles called **atoms.** When all the atoms in a particular type of matter are the same, the matter is an **element.** Carbon, oxygen, iron, lead, and potassium are just some of the more than 110 currently known elements.

Figure 14 Stromatolites were formed by clumps of one-celled organisms that lived in shallow seas more than 3 billion years ago. Similar organisms grow in the ocean near Australia today.

G ◆ 119

INTEGRATING CHEMISTRY

SECTION 3 Radioactive Dating

Objectives

After completing the lesson, students will be able to

◆ describe the process of radioactive decay;

◆ explain how the absolute age of a rock can be determined using radioactive dating.

Key Terms atom, element, radioactive decay, half-life

1 Engage/Explore

Activating Prior Knowledge

Ask students: **What is an atom?** *(Students may know that an atom is the smallest part of an element that has all the properties of that element.)* **What does an atom contain?** *(A typical answer might mention electrons, protons, neutrons, and energy.)* Use these responses to judge how much review individual students need to understand this section.

DISCOVER

Skills Focus predicting
Materials *modeling clay, metric ruler, plastic knife*
Time 10 minutes
Tips Advise students that exact measurements are unnecessary. They should do their best to cut the clay in half each time.
Expected Outcome By cutting the clay in half three times, students will reduce the size of the cube to one-eighth the original size.
Think It Over Students should predict that the remaining piece will be very small, possibly too small to cut in half again with the knife.

---

2 Facilitate

Changing From One Element to Another

Addressing Naive Conceptions

Materials *Geiger counter, digital clock, watch with luminous hands, smoke detector, rock samples including uraninite and carnotite*

Time 10 minutes

Students may think radioactivity is always dangerous. However, some rocks and common items found in the home give off low levels of radiation. Have students use a Geiger counter to measure the radioactivity of common objects and rocks. If a Geiger counter is not available, a cloud chamber is an alternative.

learning modality: kinesthetic

The Rate of Radioactive Decay

Using the Visuals: Figure 16

After students have examined the figure, ask: **In a rock, when does "start" begin?** (*The moment molten material cools to become igneous rock.*) **Where would you find igneous rock among rock layers at a location?** (*In an intrusion or extrusion.*)

learning modality: logical/ mathematical

Absolute Ages From Radioactive Dating

Sharpen your *Skills*

Calculating

Time 10 minutes

Expected Outcome

After 4 half-lives, the mass would be $\frac{1}{2} \times \frac{1}{2} \times \frac{1}{2} \times \frac{1}{2} \times 3$ g = 0.1875 g. The time elapsed would be $4 \times 1.3 = 5.2$ billion years. Each additional half-life would halve the remaining amount of potassium-40.

Extend Ask students: **What happened to the missing mass of potassium-40?** (*It decayed to form argon-40.*) **learning modality: logical/mathematical**

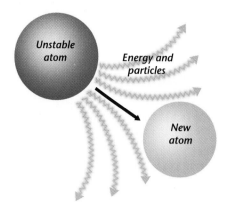

Figure 15 In the process of radioactive decay, an atom releases energy.

Most elements are stable. They do not change under normal conditions. But some elements exist in forms that are unstable. Over time, these elements break down, or decay, by releasing particles and energy in a process called **radioactive decay.** These unstable elements are said to be radioactive. **During radioactive decay, the atoms of one element break down to form atoms of another element.** Radioactive elements occur naturally in igneous rocks. Scientists use the rate at which these elements decay to calculate the rock's age.

The Rate of Radioactive Decay

You have a birthday, a specific day from which you calculate your age. What's the "birthday" of a rock? For an igneous rock, that "birthday" is when it first hardens to become rock. (Recall that igneous rocks form from molten magma and lava.) As a radioactive element within the igneous rock decays, it changes into another element. So the composition of the rock changes slowly over time. The amount of the radioactive element goes down. But the amount of the new element goes up.

The rate of decay of each radioactive element is constant—it never changes. This rate of decay is the element's half-life. The **half-life** of a radioactive element is the time it takes for half of the radioactive atoms to decay. You can see in Figure 16 how a radioactive element decays over time.

Figure 16 The half-life of a radioactive element is the amount of time it takes for half of the radioactive atoms to decay. *Calculating After three half-lives, how much of the radioactive element remains?*

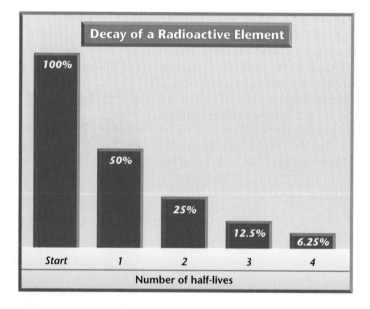

Decay of a Radioactive Element

100%	50%	25%	12.5%	6.25%
Start	1	2	3	4

Number of half-lives

Background

Integrating Science Each element has a specific number of protons in its atoms, and this number never varies. Thus, all carbon atoms have 6 protons. Atoms of the same element, however, can have different numbers of neutrons. Atoms of the same element with different numbers of neutrons are called isotopes. In some isotopes— radioactive isotopes—the forces that bind protons and neutrons together are weak. The result is that these nuclei spontaneously decay.

Unstable radioactive isotopes occur naturally in Earth's crust. For instance, granite forms when molten material hardens underground (an intrusion). Within that granite may be some potassium-40. The moment the rock hardens, the "clock" starts running, as the potassium-40 in the granite begins to decay into argon-40.

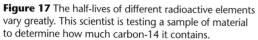

Elements Used in Radioactive Dating		
Radioactive Element	Half-life (years)	Dating Range (years)
Carbon-14	5,730	500–50,000
Potassium-40	1.3 billion	50,000–4.6 billion
Rubidium-87	47 billion	10 million–4.6 billion
Thorium-232	14.1 billion	10 million–4.6 billion
Uranium-235	713 million	10 million–4.6 billion
Uranium-238	4.5 billion	10 million–4.6 billion

Figure 17 The half-lives of different radioactive elements vary greatly. This scientist is testing a sample of material to determine how much carbon-14 it contains.

Absolute Ages From Radioactive Dating

Geologists use radioactive dating to determine the absolute ages of rocks. In radioactive dating, scientists first determine the amount of a radioactive element in a rock. Then they compare that amount with the amount of the stable element into which the radioactive element decays. Figure 17 lists several common radioactive elements and their half-lives.

Potassium–Argon Dating Scientists often date rocks using potassium-40. This form of potassium decays to stable argon-40 and has a half-life of 1.3 billion years. Potassium-40 is useful in dating the most ancient rocks because of its long half-life.

Carbon-14 Dating A radioactive form of carbon is carbon-14. All plants and animals contain carbon, including some carbon-14. As plants and animals grow, carbon atoms are added to their tissues. After an organism dies, no more carbon is added. But the carbon-14 in the organism's body decays. It changes to stable nitrogen-14. To determine the age of a sample, scientists measure the amount of carbon-14 that is left in the organism's remains. From this amount, they can determine its absolute age. Carbon-14 has been used to date fossils such as frozen mammoths, as well as pieces of wood and bone. Carbon-14 even has been used to date the skeletons of prehistoric humans.

Carbon-14 is very useful in dating materials from plants and animals that lived up to about 50,000 years ago. Carbon-14 has a half-life of only 5,730 years. For this reason, it can't be used to date really ancient fossils or rocks. The amount of carbon-14 left would be too small to measure accurately.

☑ *Checkpoint* *What are two types of radioactive dating?*

Sharpen your **Skills**

Calculating ACTIVITY

You have 3 grams of the radioactive element potassium-40. Calculate the mass of the remaining potassium-40 after 4 half-lives. Now calculate how much time has gone by. (*Hint:* One half-life of potassium-40 takes 1.3 billion years.) What would happen to the amount of potassium-40 if you continued through several more half-lives?

Radioactive Dating of Rock Layers

Using the Visuals: Figure 18

Ask students: **Is an extrusion younger or older than a layer above it?** (*Older, because it already had to have been in place for the layer above it to form on top.*) **What is the oldest that the shale layer could possibly be?** (*150 million years old*) **Is an intrusion younger or older than a layer through which it passes?** (*It is always younger, because the layer had to be there for the intrusion to pass through.*) **What is the youngest that the shale layer could be?** (*120 million years*) **learning modality: logical/mathematical**

The Age of Earth

Building Inquiry Skills: Relating Cause and Effect

Help students recall conditions on the moon by asking: **Does the moon have an atmosphere or running water?** (*The moon has neither.*) **How much weathering and erosion would you expect to take place on the moon?** (*Without water and an atmosphere, there would be no weathering and erosion.*) Guide students to an understanding that there could be no sedimentary moon rocks. Unlike Earth, there is no rock cycle on the moon. Therefore, any moon rock dated with radioactive dating would indicate steady decay since the moon's formation. **learning modality: logical/mathematical**

Program Resources

◆ **Guided Study Workbook** Section 4-3
 Science Explorer Series *Chemical Interactions,* Chapter 4, provides more information on radioactive elements.

Media and Technology

🖿 **Transparencies** "Radioactive Decay," Transparency 19

Answers to Self-Assessment

Caption Question
Figure 16 12.5%

☑ *Checkpoint*
Potassium-argon dating and carbon-14 dating.

Ongoing Assessment

Oral Presentation Call on students at random to use these terms in sentences: *radioactive decay, half-life, radioactive dating, potassium-argon dating,* and *carbon-14 dating.*

3 Assess

Section 3 Review Answers

1. During radioactive decay, the atoms of one element break down to form atoms of another element. In the process of radioactive decay, the atoms of the element release particles and energy.
2. The half-life of a radioactive element is the time it takes for half of the radioactive atoms to decay. To determine the absolute age of a rock, scientists determine the amount of a radioactive element in a rock and compare it with the amount of the stable element into which the radioactive element decays.
3. Scientists use both when dating a sedimentary layer by finding the absolute age of the intrusions and extrusions near the layer.
4. Scientists used radioactive dating to determine the absolute age of moon rocks. Since the moon and Earth were formed at about the same time, the age of Earth is the same as the age of the moon rocks.
5. Frozen remains and remains preserved in tar can be dated using carbon-14 because they contain plant or animal material. Molds, casts, and trace fossils do not.

Science at Home

Tips Encourage students to carry out the activity **ACTIVITY** at home and then bring a list of the 10 items to class. Clues used to determine relative ages might include the memories of family members and the condition of an item. Some items, such as coins, may contain dates that indicate an absolute age.

Performance Assessment

Writing Have students explain the method a geologist would use to date a sedimentary rock layer through radioactive dating of an extrusion and an intrusion.

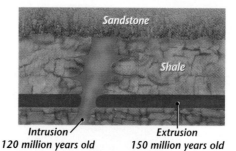

Sandstone

Shale

Intrusion
120 million years old

Extrusion
150 million years old

Figure 18 Radioactive dating has been used to determine the absolute ages of the intrusion and extrusion in the diagram. The shale lies above the extrusion and is crossed by the intrusion. Therefore the shale is younger than the extrusion, but older than the intrusion—between 150 million years old and 120 million years old. *Inferring What can you infer about the age of the sandstone?*

Radioactive Dating of Rock Layers

Radioactive dating cannot usually be used for dating rocks other than igneous rocks. As you recall, sedimentary rocks form as sediments are deposited by water or wind. The rock particles in sedimentary rocks are from other rocks, all of different ages. Radioactive dating would provide the age of the particles. It would not provide the age of the sedimentary rock.

How, then, do scientists date sedimentary rock layers? They date the igneous intrusions and extrusions near the sedimentary rock layers. Look at Figure 18. As you can see, sedimentary rock above an igneous intrusion must be younger than that intrusion.

How Old is Earth?

Radioactive dating has been used to calculate the age of Earth. The oldest rocks ever found on Earth have been dated at about 4.0 billion years old. But scientists think Earth formed even earlier than that. According to one theory, Earth and the moon are about the same age. When Earth was very young, a large object from space collided with Earth. This collision threw a large amount of material from both bodies into orbit around Earth. This material combined to form the moon. Scientists have dated moon rocks brought to Earth by astronauts during the 1970s. **Radioactive dating shows that the oldest moon rocks are about 4.6 billion years old. Scientists infer that Earth is only a little older than those moon rocks—roughly 4.6 billion years old.**

Section 3 Review

1. Describe the process of radioactive decay.
2. What is a half-life? How is it used to determine the absolute age of a rock?
3. When do scientists use both radioactive dating and relative dating to find the age of a rock?
4. How were moon rocks used to determine the age of Earth?
5. Thinking Critically **Applying Concepts** Which of the following types of fossils can be dated using carbon-14: molds and casts, trace fossils, frozen remains, remains preserved in tar? Explain your answer.

Science at Home

Collect 10 items out of a drawer that is full of odds and ends such as keys, coins, receipts, photographs, and souvenirs. Have your family members put them in order from oldest to newest. What clues will you use to determine their relative ages? Do you remember when certain items were bought or a photograph was taken? How can you determine the oldest object of all? Make a list of the ten items in order by relative age. Are there any items for which you know the absolute age?

Answers to Self-Assessment

Caption Question

Figure 18 The sandstone is younger than the intrusion below it, which is 120 million years old.

Program Resources

◆ **Teaching Resources** 4-3 Review and Reinforce, p. 111; 4-3 Enrich, p. 112

Media and Technology

Transparencies "Dating Sedimentary Rock with Intrusions and Extrusions," Transparency 18

SECTION 4 The Geologic Time Scale

DISCOVER ·· ACTIVITY ····

This Is Your Life!

1. Make a list of about 10 to 15 important events that you remember in your life.

2. On a sheet of paper, draw a time line to represent your life. Use a scale of 3.0 cm to 1 year.

3. Write each event in the correct year along the time line.

4. Now divide the time line into parts that describe major periods in your life, for example: preschool years, elementary school years, and middle school years.

Think It Over

Making Models Along which part of your time line are most of the events located? Which period of your life does this part of the time line represent? Why do you think this is so?

Imagine squeezing Earth's 4.6-billion-year history into a 24-hour day. Earth forms at midnight. About seven hours later, the earliest one-celled organisms appear. Over the next 14 hours, simple, soft-bodied organisms such as jellyfish and worms develop. A little after 9:00 P.M.—21 hours later—larger, more complex organisms evolve in the oceans. Reptiles and insects first appear about an hour after that. Dinosaurs arrive just before 11:00 P.M., but are extinct by 11:30 P.M. Modern humans don't appear until less than a second before midnight!

The Geologic Time Scale

Months, years, or even centuries aren't very helpful for thinking about Earth's long history. **Because the time span of Earth's past is so great, geologists use the geologic time scale to show Earth's history.** The **geologic time scale** is a record of the life forms and geologic events in Earth's history. You can see this time scale in Figure 19.

Scientists first developed the geologic time scale by studying rock layers and index fossils worldwide. With this information, scientists placed Earth's rocks in order by relative age. Later, radioactive dating helped determine the absolute age of the divisions in the geologic time scale. As geologists studied the fossil record, they found major changes in life forms at different times. They used these changes to mark where one unit of geologic time ends and the next begins. Therefore the divisions of the geologic time scale depend on events in the history of life on Earth.

GUIDE FOR READING

◆ Why is the geologic time scale used to show Earth's history?

◆ What are the different units of the geologic time scale?

Reading Tip As you read, make a list of the units of geologic time scale. Write a sentence about each.

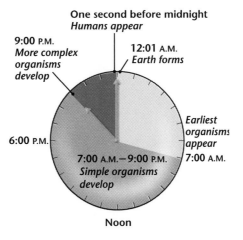

One second before midnight
Humans appear

9:00 P.M.
More complex organisms develop

12:01 A.M.
Earth forms

6:00 P.M.

Earliest organisms appear

7:00 A.M.

7:00 A.M.—9:00 P.M.
Simple organisms develop

Noon

Figure 19 If geologic time went by in a single day, all of human history would take place in less than the last second!

Chapter 4 **G ◆ 123**

READING STRATEGIES

Reading Tip Students should write a sentence for *era, period,* and *epoch,* using the definitions of each term in the text. Point out that these three terms have a specific meaning in the context of Earth history, but all three are also used in common speech. Encourage students to look up the words in a dictionary. Help them determine that the amount of time indicated by each word in normal use is much less.

Program Resources

◆ **Teaching Resources** 4-4 Lesson Plan, p. 113; 4-4 Section Summary, p. 114; 4-4 Review and Reinforce, p.115; 4-4 Enrich, p. 116
◆ **Guided Study Workbook** Section 4-4

SECTION 4 The Geologic Time Scale

Objectives

After completing the lesson, students will be able to

◆ describe the geologic time scale and explain why it is used;

◆ identify the different units of the geologic time scale.

Key Terms geologic time scale, era, invertebrate, period, epoch

1 Engage/Explore

Activating Prior Knowledge

Ask students: **How long ago did dinosaurs live?** *(A typical answer may mention millions of years.)* **How long before that did Earth form?** *(Again students will likely mention millions of years.)* Explain that the dinosaurs lived much longer ago than most people think and Earth formed so long ago that it is almost unimaginable. In this section, students will learn how scientists organize the long history of Earth.

········· DISCOVER ·········

Skills Focus making models

Materials *metric ruler, adding-machine paper*

Time 15 minutes

Tips Emphasize that students don't have to list very personal events. Suggest they list birth date, graduations, important birthdays, and so on. Precut paper strips to a little more than the needed length for each student; a 13-year-old will make a time line of 39 cm.

Expected Outcome Each student should be able to place 10 or more events along the time line.

Think It Over If students follow the suggested divisions, most important events of their lives will probably fall within the middle school years, because students can more easily remember recent events than events earlier in life.

2 Facilitate

The Geologic Time Scale

Building Inquiry Skills: Calculating

Explain that the "simple organisms" mentioned on Figure 19 are mostly single-celled organisms, including bacteria and algae, whereas "complex organisms" include organisms with even the simplest organs and organ systems. Ask: **On this model of geologic time, how many hours pass before complex organisms appear?** *(21 hours, from 12:00 A.M. to 9:00 P.M.)* **What percentage of Earth's history is that?** *(21 ÷ 24, or about 88%)* **learning modality: logical/mathematical**

Divisions of Geologic Time

Using the Visuals: Figure 20

After students have examined the figure, ask: **Which is the largest division of geologic time?** *(era)* **How long is a geologic period?** *(A period doesn't have exact length; they vary from 30 million years of the Silurian to 78 million years of the Cretaceous.)* **Which era are we in now?** *(Cenozoic)* **learning modality: verbal**

Building Inquiry Skills: Making Models

Materials *calculator, large spool of string, ruler*
Time 15 minutes

After students have examined Figure 20, guide them in developing an analogy that will help them understand the relative proportions of eras and periods. Challenge small groups to place the 4.6 billion years of Earth history on a football field. Precambrian Time should encompass about 88 yards; the Paleozoic should be from about the 12-yard line to the 5-yard line. **learning modality: logical/mathematical**

124 ♦ G

Geologic Time Scale

Era	Period	Millions of Years Ago	Duration (millions of years)
Cenozoic	Quaternary	– – 1.6 – –	1.6 to present
	Tertiary		65
		– 66.4 –	
Mesozoic	Cretaceous		78
		– – 144 – –	
	Jurassic		64
		– – 208 – –	
	Triassic		37
		– – 245 – –	
Paleozoic	Permian		41
		– – 286 – –	
	Carboniferous		74
		– – 360 – –	
	Devonian		48
		– – 408 – –	
	Silurian		30
		– 438 –	
	Ordovician		67
		– – 505 – –	
	Cambrian		39
		– – 544 – –	
Precambrian			544 million years ago– 4.6 billion years ago

Figure 20 The eras and periods of the geologic time scale are used to date the events in Earth's long history. *Interpreting Diagrams* How long ago did the Paleozoic Era end?

124 ♦ G

Divisions of Geologic Time

When speaking of the past, what names do you use for different spans of time? You probably use such names as *century, decade, year, month, week,* and *day.* You know that a month is longer than a week but shorter than a year. Scientists use similar divisions for the geologic time scale.

Geologic time begins with a long span of time called Precambrian Time (pree KAM bree un). Precambrian Time, which covers about 88 percent of Earth's history, ended 544 million years ago. **After Precambrian Time, the basic units of the geologic time scale are eras, periods, and epochs.**

☑ *Checkpoint* *How much of Earth's history is included in Precambrian Time?*

Eras, Periods, and Epochs

Geologists divide the time between Precambrian Time and the present into three long units of time called **eras.** They are the Paleozoic Era, the Mesozoic Era, and the Cenozoic Era.

Eras The Paleozoic (pay lee uh ZOH ik) began about 544 million years ago and lasted for 300 million years. The word part *paleo-* means "ancient or early," and *-zoic* means "life." Many animals that lived during the Paleozoic were animals without backbones, or **invertebrates.**

The Mesozoic (mez uh ZOH ik) began about 245 million years ago and lasted about 180 million years. The word part *meso-* means "middle." People often call the Mesozoic the Age of Dinosaurs. Yet dinosaurs were only one of the many groups of organisms that lived during this era. For example, mammals began to evolve during the Mesozoic Era.

Background

History of Science The concept of geologic time was first developed in the late 1700s and early 1800s. Geologists in England and other parts of Europe devised the geologic time scale during the 1800s. They established these eras, periods, and epochs through relative dating methods, carefully correlating rock layers throughout the world using index fossils—a monumental achievement.

Facts and Figures The Tertiary Period includes these five epochs (with starting date in millions of years ago): Paleocene (66.4), Eocene (57.8), Oligocene (36.6), Miocene (23.7), and Pliocene (5.3). The Quaternary Period includes these two epochs: Pleistocene (1.6) and Holocene (0.01). Geologic time has not ended. Today, we are in the Holocene Epoch of the Quaternary Period of the Cenozoic Era.

Earth's most recent era is the Cenozoic (sen uh ZOH ik). It began about 65 million years ago and continues to the present day. The word part *ceno-* means "recent." The Cenozoic is sometimes called the Age of Mammals, because mammals became common during this time.

Periods Eras are subdivided into units of geologic time called **periods.** Geologic periods range in length from tens of millions of years to less than two million years. You can see in Figure 20 that the Mesozoic Era includes three periods: the Triassic Period, the Jurassic Period, and the Cretaceous Period.

You may wonder where the names of the geologic periods come from. Many come from places around the world where geologists first described the rocks and fossils of that period. The name Cambrian, for example, refers to Cambria, the old Roman name for Wales. Jurassic refers to the Jura Mountains in France.

The Carboniferous Period is named for the large coal deposits that formed during that period. *Carboniferous* means "carbon bearing." Geologists in the United States often divide the Carboniferous Period into the Mississippian Period (320–360 million years ago) and the Pennsylvanian Period (286–320 million years ago.)

Epochs Geologists further subdivide the periods of the Cenozoic Era into **epochs.** Why are epochs used in the time scale? The fossil record in the Cenozoic is much more complete than the fossil record of earlier eras. There are a lot more events to place in sequence, and using epochs makes this task easier.

Figure 21 The sedimentary rock layers (top) were laid down during the Ordovician period. The fossil of the plant (bottom) formed during the Carboniferous period.

Section 4 Review

1. What is the geologic time scale?
2. What are geologic periods?
3. What method of dating did geologists first use when they developed the geologic time scale? How is the scale different today?
4. **Thinking Critically Interpreting Diagrams** Which period in the Paleozoic was the longest? If you could travel back in time 100 million years, what period would you be in? What era would you be in?

Check Your Progress

CHAPTER PROJECT 4

Make a list of illustrations for the time line and travel brochure. Before creating the illustrations, think about what they will look like and the materials you will need to complete them. Will they be three dimensional? Will they be drawn using a computer? Begin to plan how you will use illustrations in your travel brochure. Space in a brochure is limited, so focus on the highlights of your geologic period.

Answers to Self-Assessment

☑ *Checkpoint*
Precambrian Time includes about 88 percent of Earth's history.

Caption Question
Figure 20 The Paleozoic era ended 245 million years ago.

Eras, Periods, and Epochs

Including All Students

Pair students with different language abilities. Then challenge each pair to create a mnemonic device that uses the first letters of periods to help them remember the correct sequence of the periods of the Paleozoic and/or all three eras. The classic for the Paleozoic (which uses Mississippian and Pennsylvanian in place of Carboniferous) is "Campbell's *Ordinary Soup Does Make Peter Pale.*"
learning modality: verbal

3 Assess

Section 4 Review Answers

1. A record of the life forms and geologic events in Earth's history
2. The subdivisions of geologic eras
3. They studied rock layers and fossils worldwide and placed Earth's rock layers in order by relative age. Later, radioactive dating helped determine the absolute ages of the divisions in the geologic time scale.
4. The Carboniferous Period was the longest in the Paleozoic Era. Traveling back 100 million years would put you in the Cretaceous Period of the Mesozoic Era.

Check Your Progress

CHAPTER PROJECT 4

Discuss with each student plans for illustrating the brochure and the time line. Provide materials whenever possible, or direct students to places where they can acquire art materials. In addition, review each student's basic design for the brochure, making suggestions about content and presentation.

Performance Assessment

Drawing Have students make their own geologic time scale.
Portfolio Students can keep their drawings in their portfolios.

As Time Goes By

Preparing for Inquiry

Key Concept Earth's history is an immense amount of time.

Skills Objectives Students will be able to:
- measure the size of a ream of paper;
- calculate how many reams would be necessary to represent various time spans in a model time line;
- draw conclusions about time spans in Earth's history.

Time 30 minutes

Advance Planning One way to make a page that contains 2,000 asterisks is to have 40 lines of 50 asterisks each. An alternative would be to have 30 lines of 60 asterisks plus an additional 4 lines of 50 asterisks. Then print out one of these pages per student.

A 500-sheet ream, or package, of copy or multi-use paper has a thickness of about 4.5 cm, though this thickness varies. The exact measurement is not significant, though all reams used in the activity should be the same. Several of these reams could be shared by students, each taking a turn at measuring the thickness.

A meter stick will be necessary to measure the height of the classroom's ceiling.

Alternative Materials A textbook about the same size as a ream of paper can be used as an alternative.

Guiding Inquiry

Invitation Help students focus on the key concept by asking: **When you tell a friend that something happened a long time ago, what do you mean by "a long time"?** (*Students might say the phrase means a month, a year, or 10 years.*) Explain that the difficulty with grasping the concept of geologic time is that no time span in a human life prepares a person for understanding geologic time. This activity will help students grasp that concept.

Troubleshooting the Experiment
- Review this metric equivalent: 1 m = 100 cm.

As Time Goes By

Earth's history goes back 4.6 billion years. How can people grasp the vast scale of geologic time? In this lab, you will make a model to represent Earth's history.

Problem

How can you make a model of geologic time?

Materials

worksheet with 2,000 asterisks
one ream of paper

Procedure

Part 1 Table A

1. Copy Table A into your lab notebook. Figure how long ago these historic events happened and write the answers on your chart.

2. Obtain a worksheet with 2,000 asterisks printed on it. Each asterisk represents one year. The first asterisk at the top represents one year ago.

3. Starting from this asterisk, circle the asterisk that represents how many years ago each event in Table A occurred.

4. Label each circled asterisk to indicate the event.

5. Obtain a ream of copy paper. There are 500 sheets in a ream. If each sheet had 2,000 asterisks on it, there would be a total of 1 million asterisks. Therefore, each ream would represent 1 million years.

Part 2 Fill in Chart B

6. Copy Table B into your lab notebook. Determine how much paper in reams or sheets would be needed to represent the events in geologic time found in Table B. (*Hint:* Recall that each ream represents 1 million years.)

Table A Historic Events		
Event	**Date**	**Number of Years Ago**
You are born		
One of your parents is born		
Space shuttle *Challenger* explodes	1986	
Neil Armstrong first walks on the moon	1969	
World War I ends	1918	
Civil War ends	1865	
Declaration of Independence signed	1776	
Columbus crosses Atlantic	1492	
Leif Ericson visits North America	1000	

Sample Table A

Event	Date	Years Ago
You are born	1986	14
Parent born	1960	40
Challenger	1986	14
Neil Armstrong	1969	31
World War I ends	1918	82
Civil War ends	1865	135
Declaration signed	1776	224
Columbus	1492	508
Leif Ericson	1000	1,000

Sample Table B

Event	Reams/Sheets	Thickness
Ice Age	5 sheets	0.01 cm
Whales	50 reams	225 cm
Pangaea	225 reams	10.125 m
Vertebrates	520 reams	23.4 m
Multicellular	1,000 reams	45 m
First life	3,500 reams	157.5 m
Oldest rocks	4,000 reams	180 m
Age of Earth	4,600 reams	207 m

Table B Geologic Events			
Event	Number of Years Ago	Reams or Sheets of Paper	Thickness of Paper
End of the last Ice Age	10,000		
Whales evolve	50 million		
Pangaea begins to break up	225 million		
First vertebrates develop	530 million		
Multicellular organisms develop (algae)	1 billion		
First life (bacteria)	3.5 billion		
Oldest known rocks form	4.0 billion		
Age of Earth	4.6 billion		

7. Measure the thickness of a ream of paper. Use this thickness to calculate how thick a stack of paper would need to be to represent how long ago each geologic event occurred. (*Hint:* Use a calculator to multiply the thickness of the ream of paper by the number of reams.) Enter your results in Table B.

Analyze and Conclude

1. Measure the height of your classroom. How many reams of paper would you need to reach the ceiling? How many years would the height of the ceiling represent? Which geologic events listed in Table B would fall on a ream of paper inside your classroom?
2. At this scale, how many classrooms would have to be stacked on top of each other to represent the age of Earth? The time when vertebrates appeared?
3. How many times higher would the thickness of the stack be for the age of Earth than for the breakup of Pangaea?
4. On your model, how could you distinguish one era or period from another? How could you show when particular organisms evolved and when they became extinct?

5. **Think About It** Is the scale of your model practical? What would be the advantages and disadvantages of a model that fit geologic time on a time line 1 meter long?

More to Explore

This model represents geologic time as a straight line. Can you think of other ways of representing geologic time graphically? Using colored pencils, draw your own version of the geologic time scale so that it fits on a single sheet of typing paper. (*Hint:* You could represent geologic time as a wheel, a ribbon, or a spiral.)

◆ Make sure students have access to a calculator and can use one with some ease. Pair students who have difficulty using a calculator with students who have no trouble.

Program Resources

◆ **Teaching Resources** Skills Lab blackline masters, pp. 123–125

Media and Technology

 Lab Activity Videotape *Earth's Changing Surface, 8*

Expected Outcome

Students will become aware of the immensity of geologic time, especially as compared to the span of their own lives and the length of human history.

Analyze and Conclude

1. Answers will vary depending on the height of the classroom. The height of a classroom is typically about 2.5 m, or 250 cm. About 55 reams of paper, with a width of 4.5 cm each, would be needed to reach the ceiling. That would represent 55 million years. Only two events, the end of the last ice age and the evolution of whales, would fall on a ream inside the classroom.
2. Answers will depend on the figure obtained in Question 1. At 55 reams per classroom, about 84 classrooms (4,600 ÷ 55) would be needed to represent the age of Earth. About 9.5 (520 ÷ 55) would be needed to represent the time when vertebrates appeared.
3. The thickness of the stack would need to be about 20 times higher (4,600 ÷ 225).
4. Answers may vary. A typical answer might suggest using different colors of paper for each of the eras and then marking the divisions between periods with cardboard dividers. Major events can be shown with flags on sticks stuck into the stack.
5. Most students will judge that the scale in not practical. Advantages of a 1-m model include that it could easily fit on a wall and it could be used for quick reference. Disadvantages include that the time from the beginning of the Paleozoic to the present would be such a short length that it would be difficult to include many relatively recent major events.

Extending the Inquiry

More to Explore Students' versions will vary depending on the shape they choose. Have them use the geologic time scale in Section 4 to mark the divisions between eras and each of their periods. Students might draw the outline of a ribbon or spiral with a black pencil and then use the colored pencils to color in the era and period lengths.

Objectives

After completing the lesson, students will be able to
- identify and describe the major events in Earth's geologic history;
- identify and describe the major developments of life on Earth.

Key Terms vertebrate, amphibian, reptile, mass extinction, mammal

1 Engage/Explore

Activating Prior Knowledge

Show students a picture of a wooly mammoth and a familiar dinosaur, both of which students will probably recognize. Then ask: **Did these organisms live at the same time?** *(Many students will say no.)* **Which lived first?** *(Most students will say the dinosaur lived before the mammoth.)* Explain that the students have begun the task of organizing the evolution of life on Earth. This section will focus on the same task.

DISCOVER

Skills Focus posing questions

Materials *sheet of unlined paper*
Time 15 minutes
Tips Divide the class into groups of three. Suggest that each student write a description of how each fossil formed and make a sketch of each organism before talking to other group members. Once students have made their sketches, they should work together to make a list of questions.
Expected Outcome Students should recognize that each fossil is an impression or carbon film. They should recognize that fossil A is a leaf. They will probably not be able to identify fossil B, which is an euripterid.
Think It Over Students' questions will vary. *Typical questions:* When did each of these organisms live? In what type of environment did these organisms live? What organisms ate these organisms?

DISCOVER ·················· ACTIVITY···

What Do Fossils Reveal About Earth's History?

1. Compare the two fossils in photos A and B. How did these organisms become fossils?
2. Work with one or two other students to study the organisms in the two photos. Think about how these organisms may have lived. Then make sketches showing what each of these organisms may have looked like.

Think It Over
Posing Questions If you were a paleontologist, what questions would you want to ask about these organisms?

GUIDE FOR READING

- What were the major events in Earth's geologic history?
- What were the major events in the development of life on Earth?

Reading Tip Preview *Exploring Geologic History* on pages 132–135. Make a list of questions you have about Earth's history. Then look for answers as you read.

Your science class is going on a field trip, but this trip is a little out of the ordinary. You're going to travel back billions of years to the earliest days on Earth. Then you will move forward through time to the present. Enter the time machine and strap yourself in. Take a deep breath—you're off!

A dial on the dashboard shows the number of years before the present. You stare at the dial—it reads 4.6 billion years. You peer out the window as the time machine flies above the planet. Earth looks a little strange. Where are the oceans? Where are the continents? How will Earth change over the next billions of years? You'll answer these and other questions about Earth's history as you take this extraordinary trip.

Precambrian Time

Your journey through the first part of Earth's history will need to be very fast. Remember, Precambrian time includes most of Earth's history!

Precambrian Earth **Earth formed from a mass of dust and gas about 4.6 billion years ago.** Gravity pulled this mass together. Over time, Earth's interior became very hot and molten. Hundreds of millions of years passed. Then lava flowed over the surface, building the first continents. An atmosphere formed, and the world was covered with an ocean.

The Earliest Forms of Life Scientists cannot pinpoint when or where life began on Earth. But scientists have found fossils of single-celled organisms in rocks that formed about 3.5 billion years ago. These earliest life forms were probably similar to

READING STRATEGIES

Reading Tip Give students several minutes to preview *Exploring Geologic History.* Suggest that their list of questions should include questions about terms they don't know as well as about events that surprise or interest them. Use these lists to address gaps in student's knowledge of various kinds of organisms or the terminology used to identify those organisms. For example,

explain that the term *arachnid* includes spiders and ticks. Suggest that students use a dictionary to write a definition of any term on their lists that they don't know. Use questions on their lists that focus on surprises or interests to help you decide on what to emphasize in teaching the section as well as what areas students might choose for independent research.

present-day bacteria. All other forms of life on Earth evolved from these simple organisms.

About 2.5 billion years ago, organisms first began using energy from the sun to make their own food. This process is called photosynthesis. One waste product of photosynthesis is oxygen. As oxygen was released into the air, the amount of oxygen in the atmosphere slowly increased. Over time, organisms evolved that could use oxygen to produce energy from food. These organisms included animals that are like today's sponges and worms. Because they all had soft bodies, these animals left few fossils. However, the evolution of these organisms set the stage for great changes during the Paleozoic Era. You can trace the development of life in *Exploring Geologic History* on pages 132–135.

The Paleozoic Era

Your time machine slows. You watch in fascination as you observe the "explosion" of life that began the Paleozoic Era.

Life Explodes During the Cambrian Period life took a big leap forward. **At the beginning of the Paleozoic Era, a great number of different kinds of organisms evolved.** Paleontologists call this event the Cambrian Explosion because so many new life forms appeared within a relatively short time. For the first time, many organisms had hard parts, including shells and outer skeletons.

At this time, all animals lived in the sea. Invertebrates such as jellyfish, worms, and sponges drifted through the water, crawled along the sandy bottom, or attached themselves to the ocean floors. Recall that invertebrates are animals that lack backbones.

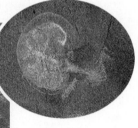

Figure 22 During the early Cambrian period, Earth's oceans were home to many strange organisms unlike any animals that are alive today. The fossil above is an organism of the middle Cambrian called *Burgessia bella* from the Burgess shale.

Chapter 4 **G ◆ 129**

2 Facilitate

Precambrian Time

Cultural Diversity

Explain to students that the origin of Earth and life on Earth is sometimes a controversial issue. Have on hand library books that contain creation stories from a variety of cultures, such as African, Native American, and Asian cultures. Read aloud two or three of these stories, or invite student volunteers to read them aloud to the class. Caution students to respect all such stories, for they are often part of a culture's religion or belief system. Then ask: **How is a scientific explanation of Earth's origin different from a creation story?** (*A scientific explanation must be testable, and thus it can be proved wrong with the collection of new data. A creation story does not depend on such data.*) **learning modality: verbal**

The Paleozoic Era

Using the Visuals: Figure 22

Have students turn back to Figure 1 in Section 1 to examine where the fossil of *Burgessia bella* was found. Explain that this animal was a tiny arthropod, the group that now includes insects and crustaceans, such as lobsters and shrimp. *Burgessia,* only a few cm long, lived on or near the bottom of a shallow sea. Ask: **How was this organism and others of the early Cambrian different from most organisms of Precambrian Time?** (*These organisms were more complex, and many had hard parts such as shells and outer skeletons.*) **learning modality: visual**

Ongoing Assessment

Writing Have students write a brief description of the environment in which *Burgessia bella* lived.

 Students can save their descriptions in their portfolios.

The Paleozoic Era, continued

Using the Visuals: Figure 23

After students have examined the figure, ask: **How do you know just by looking at the picture that this illustration does not depict life in the Cambrian or Ordovician periods?** *(This figure shows plants and vertebrate animals on land, and plants did not reach land until the Silurian and vertebrates did not reach land until the Devonian.)* **Since this is a late-Devonian scene, about how long ago was this?** *(About 360 million years ago)* Point out the two vertebrates on land, and help students with pronunciation of their names. Then ask: **Which of these vertebrates represents an evolutionary advance?** *(The amphibian* Ichthyostega *is more advanced than the fishlike amphibian* Acanthostega.*)* **To represent evolution in sequence, in what order would you place amphibians, fishes, and reptiles?** *(Fishes, amphibians, reptiles)* Emphasize that reptiles evolved from amphibians, which evolved from fishes. **learning modality: visual**

Building Inquiry Skills: Comparing and Contrasting

Materials *frog, lizard*
Time 20 minutes

Bring a frog or other amphibian and a lizard or other reptile to class in separate containers. Have students write a description of each, noting similarities and differences. Ask: **How are these organisms alike and how are they different?** *(A typical answer might suggest that their body shapes are similar. An amphibian has thinner skin and webbed feet, while a reptile has thick skin and clawed feet.)* **Which is more adapted for water, and which is more adapted for land?** *(An amphibian is adapted for water and land, while a reptile is adapted for land.)* Emphasize that reptiles evolved from amphibians and that this evolution was a major event in animals' invasion of land. Also point out that a major difference students cannot observe is the eggs each group lays. Amphibian eggs must be laid in water, while reptile eggs' tough skins allow them to be laid on land. **learning modality: visual**

Brachiopods and trilobites were common in the Cambrian seas. Brachiopods were small ocean animals with two shells. They resembled modern clams. Clams, however, are only distantly related to them.

During the Ordovician (awr duh VISH ee un) and Silurian (sih LOOR ee un) periods, the ancestors of the modern octopus and squid appeared. Some of these organisms, called cephalopods, grew to a length of almost 10 meters. **During this time, jawless fishes evolved. Jawless fishes were the first vertebrates.** A **vertebrate** is an animal with a backbone. These fishes had suckerlike mouths, and they soon became common in the seas.

Life Reaches Land Until the Silurian Period, only one-celled organisms lived on the land. But during the Silurian Period, plants began to grow on land. These first, simple plants grew low to the ground in damp areas. But by the Devonian Period (dih VOH nee un), plants that could grow in drier areas had evolved. Among these plants were the earliest ferns. The first insects also appeared during the Silurian Period.

Figure 23 One of the first amphibians, *Icthyostega* (center), was about 1 meter long. It lived during the late Devonian Period. Another, more fishlike amphibian, *Acanthostega* (bottom), lived at about the same time.

Both invertebrates and vertebrates lived in the Devonian seas. Even though the invertebrates were more numerous, the Devonian Period is often called the Age of Fishes. This is because every main group of fishes was present in the oceans at this time. Most fishes now had jaws, bony skeletons, and scales on their bodies. Sharks appeared in the late Devonian Period.

During the Devonian Period, animals began to invade the land. The first vertebrates to crawl onto land were lungfish with strong, muscular fins. The first amphibians evolved from these fishes. An **amphibian** (am FIB ee un) is an animal that lives part of its life on land and part of its life in water. *Ichthyostega,* shown in Figure 23, was one of the first amphibians.

Throughout the rest of the Paleozoic Era, life expanded over Earth's continents. Other groups of

---

Figure 24 Forests flourished during the Carboniferous Period. Insects such as dragonflies were common. *Predicting What types of fossils would you expect to find from the Carboniferous Period?*

vertebrates evolved from the amphibians. For example, small reptiles developed during the Carboniferous Period. **Reptiles** have scaly skin and lay eggs with tough, leathery shells. Some types of reptiles became very large during the later Paleozoic.

During the Carboniferous Period, winged insects evolved into many forms, including huge dragonflies and cockroaches. Giant ferns and cone-bearing plants and trees formed vast swampy forests called "coal forests." How did the coal forest get its name? The remains of the coal forest plants formed thick deposits of sediment that changed into coal over millions of years.

Mass Extinction Ends the Paleozoic At the end of the Paleozoic Era, many kinds of organisms died out. This was a **mass extinction,** in which many types of living things became extinct at the same time. **The mass extinction at the end of the Paleozoic affected both plants and animals, on land and in the seas. Scientists do not know what caused the mass extinction, but as much as 95 percent of the life in the oceans disappeared.** For example, trilobites, which had existed since early in the Paleozoic, suddenly became extinct. Many amphibians also became extinct. But not all organisms disappeared. The mass extinction did not affect fishes. Many reptiles also survived.

✓ *Checkpoint* *What were three major events in the development of life during the Paleozoic Era?*

Figure 25 *Dimetrodon,* which lived during the Permian Period, was one of the first reptiles. This meat-eater was about 3.5 meters long.

Chapter 4 **G ◆ 131**

Program Resources

🔵 **Science Explorer Series** *Animals,* Chapter 3, can provide information about fishes, amphibians, and reptiles.

Answers to Self-Assessment

Caption Question

Figure 24 Fossils of amphibians, reptiles, insects, ferns, and cone-bearing plants

✓ *Checkpoint*

Answers may vary. A typical answer might mention the explosion of life in the Cambrian, the invasion of land by plants and animals, and the mass extinction at the end of the era.

Materials *colored pencils, examples of ferns, horsetails, and club mosses*

ACTIVITY ◆

Time 15 minutes

Show students examples or photos of modern ferns, horsetails, and club mosses. Point out that flowering plants had not yet evolved by the Carboniferous Period. The vast swamp forests of the time contained giant ancestors of these modern plants, as well as some conifers. Allow students to examine and feel the plants. Then have students make a drawing of what a swamp forest might have been like, using these plants as models. **learning modality: visual**

Portfolio Students can keep their drawings in their portfolios.

Building Inquiry Skills: Relating Cause and Effect

Use a map of the United States to show students the general area of the coal deposits of North America that formed from plants that grew during the Carboniferous. These deposits extend from western Ohio and eastern Pennsylvania in the north, through West Virginia, eastern Kentucky, and Tennessee, and to Alabama in the south. Explain that geologists call coal an organic rock, because it forms from plant material that has been compacted beneath sediment over millions of years. Ask: **How old are these North American coal deposits?** *(As old as the Carboniferous Period, or 360–286 million years old)* **What are these coal deposits used for today?** *(For energy in electric power plants, steel-making plants, and other factories)* Point out that the energy that powers a television or microwave oven in many parts of the nation today is energy that was captured from the sun for photosynthesis by a plant about 300 million years ago. **learning modality: verbal**

Ongoing Assessment

Oral Presentation Call on students at random to explain these events: Cambrian explosion, life reaches land, evolution of vertebrates, and Paleozoic mass extinction.

EXPLORING
Geologic History

Invite a student volunteer to read the items in the column for Precambrian Time. Then answer any questions students have about the landmark events listed. If you or a student cannot readily answer a question, write it on the board. Also help students with the figures that illustrate the Precambrian. For any question that cannot be answered or figure that cannot be explained, assign a student volunteer to find the answer or explanation in reference books. Continue this process through the three eras. **learning modality: verbal**

Building Inquiry Skills: Communicating

Invite students to choose one group of animals or **ACTIVITY** plants, research the evolution of that group, and then prepare a brief presentation to the class. A student's choice might be related to the period that student is focusing on in the Chapter 4 Project, but not necessarily. Guide students in choosing a variety of organisms, so that most students aren't researching dinosaurs. A student might choose to focus on a large group, such as fishes or insects, or the evolution of a specific organism, such as trilobites or horses. Encourage students to make a "tree" that shows evolution through time, such as in *Exploring the Evolution of Elephants* in Section 1. **learning modality: verbal**

EXPLORING Geologic History

Using the fossil record, paleontologists have created a picture of the different types of common organisms in each geologic period.

PRECAMBRIAN TIME
4.6 billion–544 million years ago

PALEOZOIC ERA
544–245 million years ago

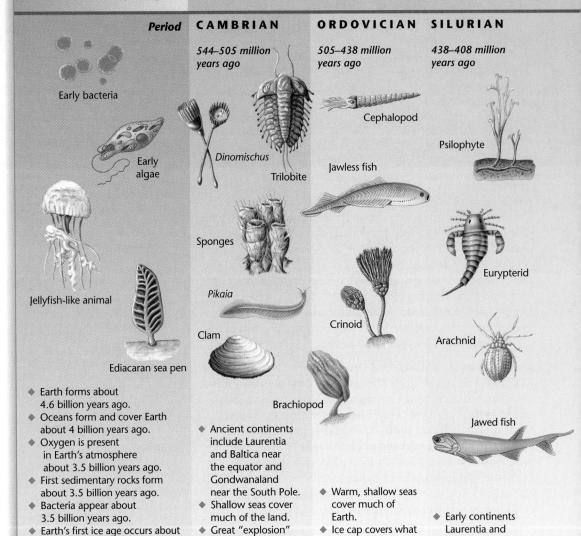

Period

CAMBRIAN
544–505 million years ago

ORDOVICIAN
505–438 million years ago

SILURIAN
438–408 million years ago

Early bacteria

Early algae

Jellyfish-like animal

Ediacaran sea pen

Dinomischus

Trilobite

Sponges

Pikaia

Clam

Cephalopod

Jawless fish

Crinoid

Brachiopod

Psilophyte

Eurypterid

Arachnid

Jawed fish

Precambrian Time
- Earth forms about 4.6 billion years ago.
- Oceans form and cover Earth about 4 billion years ago.
- Oxygen is present in Earth's atmosphere about 3.5 billion years ago.
- First sedimentary rocks form about 3.5 billion years ago.
- Bacteria appear about 3.5 billion years ago.
- Earth's first ice age occurs about 2.3 billion years ago.
- Soft-bodied, multicellular organisms develop late in the Precambrian.
- First mass extinction probably occurs near the end of the Precambrian.

Cambrian
- Ancient continents include Laurentia and Baltica near the equator and Gondwanaland near the South Pole.
- Shallow seas cover much of the land.
- Great "explosion" of invertebrate life occurs in seas.
- Invertebrates with shells appear, including trilobites, mollusks, and brachiopods.

Ordovician
- Warm, shallow seas cover much of Earth.
- Ice cap covers what is now North Africa.
- Invertebrates dominate the oceans.
- Early vertebrates—jawless fish—become common.

Silurian
- Early continents Laurentia and Baltica collide.
- Coral reefs develop.
- Fish with jaws develop.
- Land plants appear.
- Insects and spiders appear.

132 ◆ G

Background

Integrating Science The ancient sea pen, from about 590 million years ago, is an example of an early but complex animal. It was about 50 cm long, and its bulblike holdfast held it to the ocean bottom.

Both *Dinomischus* and *Pikaia* were two of the many Burgess Shale animals. *Dinomischus*, about 2.5 cm long, captured floating particles with its tentacles. *Pikaia* was a wormlike swimmer about 5 cm long.

Pikaia had a chordlike mass running lengthwise through its body, possibly making it one of the earliest examples of the phylum Chordata, which includes the vertebrates.

The psilophyte is an example of a late-Silurian, low-growing land plant. The eurypterids were some of the most aggressive predators of the early seas. One type grew as long as 3 m. Eurypterids used their large claws to catch and dismember prey.

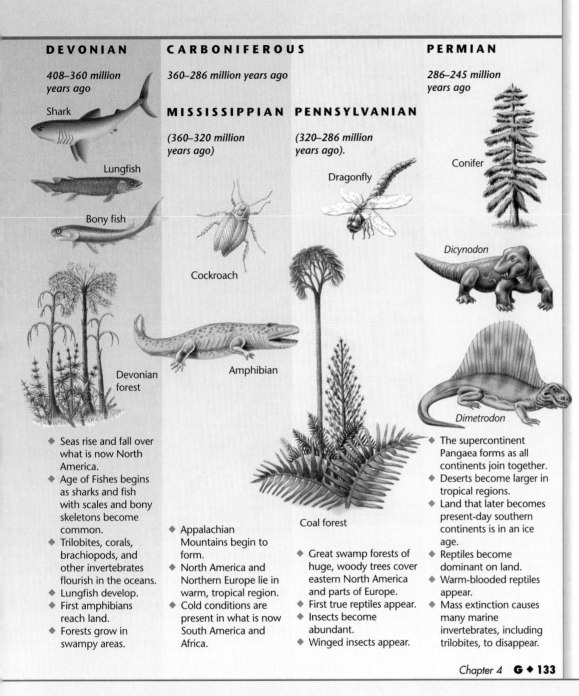

DEVONIAN

408–360 million years ago

Shark

Lungfish

Bony fish

Devonian forest

- ◆ Seas rise and fall over what is now North America.
- ◆ Age of Fishes begins as sharks and fish with scales and bony skeletons become common.
- ◆ Trilobites, corals, brachiopods, and other invertebrates flourish in the oceans.
- ◆ Lungfish develop.
- ◆ First amphibians reach land.
- ◆ Forests grow in swampy areas.

CARBONIFEROUS

360–286 million years ago

MISSISSIPPIAN

(360–320 million years ago)

Cockroach

Amphibian

- ◆ Appalachian Mountains begin to form.
- ◆ North America and Northern Europe lie in warm, tropical region.
- ◆ Cold conditions are present in what is now South America and Africa.

PENNSYLVANIAN

(320–286 million years ago).

Dragonfly

Coal forest

- ◆ Great swamp forests of huge, woody trees cover eastern North America and parts of Europe.
- ◆ First true reptiles appear.
- ◆ Insects become abundant.
- ◆ Winged insects appear.

PERMIAN

286–245 million years ago

Conifer

Dicynodon

Dimetrodon

- ◆ The supercontinent Pangaea forms as all continents join together.
- ◆ Deserts become larger in tropical regions.
- ◆ Land that later becomes present-day southern continents is in an ice age.
- ◆ Reptiles become dominant on land.
- ◆ Warm-blooded reptiles appear.
- ◆ Mass extinction causes many marine invertebrates, including trilobites, to disappear.

Chapter 4 **G ◆ 133**

Building Inquiry Skills: Graphing

Materials *graph paper, metric ruler*
Time 20 minutes

Challenge students to make a bar graph that shows when different groups of organisms first appear in the fossil record and, if appropriate, when they disappear. Students could begin the vertical axis at the start of the Paleozoic and then mark 50-million-year intervals to the present. A bar for each group of organisms would be displayed along the horizontal axis. One difference between this graph and most bar graphs is that many bars will begin above the horizontal axis. For example, the bar for dinosaurs will begin at about 245 million years ago and end at 65 million years ago. **learning modality: logical/mathematical**

Real-Life Learning

Contact a geology department of a local university (or a science/natural history museum) and request that a paleontologist make a visit to your classroom for a brief talk and questions from students. Before the visit, have students brainstorm a list of questions to ask. These questions might focus on specific eras or periods, specific animal or plant groups, or dramatic events in Earth's history. Have students also ask about a career in paleontology, what they would need in terms of preparation and what jobs are available. **learning modality: verbal**

Program Resources

Science Explorer Series *From Bacteria to Plants,* Chapters 2 and 3, can provide more information on bacteria, protists, and fungi.

Ongoing Assessment

Skills Check Have students make a table that includes each instance on pages 132–133 when a new group of organisms appears and match each group with the correct geologic period. **Portfolio** Students can keep their tables in their portfolios.

Exploring Geologic History

Addressing Naive Conceptions

Students may have a difficult time grasping the enormous spans of time represented by each geologic period. As a consequence, they might think that all the organisms listed and shown in each period lived at the same time. Refer students back to *Exploring the Evolution of Elephants* in Section 1. Then ask: **How long did it take for Paleomastodons to evolve into modern elephants?** (*About 34 million years*) **How much of the Cenozoic Era did that evolution take?** (*Less than half of that era*) **learning modality: logical/mathematical**

Real-Life Learning

Many museums of natural history or centers of science and technology have exhibits or activities related to Earth's geologic history and the history of life on Earth. For example, several museums have set up a model paleontological dig in which students can get hands-on experience with how scientists search for fossils. Encourage student volunteers to phone or visit the websites of any such local institutions, find out about relevant exhibits or programs, and report back to the class. Then urge students to take advantage of such resources with members of their families. **learning modality: verbal**

MESOZOIC ERA
245–65 million years ago

Period **TRIASSIC**

245–208 million years ago

Coelophysis

Morganucodon

Cycad

◆ Pangaea holds together for much of the Triassic.
◆ Hot, dry conditions dominate center of Pangaea.
◆ Age of Reptiles begins.
◆ First dinosaurs appear.
◆ First mammals, which evolve from warm-blooded reptiles, appear.
◆ First turtles and crocodiles appear.
◆ Conifers, palmlike trees, and ginkgo trees dominate forests.

JURASSIC

208–144 million years ago

Stegosaurus

Megazostrodon

Archaeopteryx

Diplodocus

◆ Pangaea continues to break apart as North America separates from Africa and South America.
◆ Sea levels rise in many parts of the world.
◆ Largest dinosaurs thrive, including *Stegosaurus, Diplodocus,* and *Apatosaurus.*
◆ First birds appear.
◆ First flying reptiles, pterosaurs, appear.

Background

Integrating Science *Coelophysis* ("hollow face") was an early dinosaur carnivore. Dozens of *Coelophysis* skeletons were discovered in 1947 in a quarry in New Mexico. Possibly, a whole herd was washed away by a river and then deposited together on a sandbar.

Both *Morganucodon* and *Megazostrodon* were examples of the earliest mammals. These tiny animals, about 10 cm long, were

much like modern shrews. Mammals stayed small for the next 160 million years.

The creodonts were early mammal carnivores. Although many of these animals were catlike carnivores, others were related to ungulates.

Hyracotherium, an early ancestor of modern horses, was about the size of a small dog. Instead of a single hoof on each leg, it had several hooved toes.

CENOZOIC ERA
65 million years ago to the present

CRETACEOUS
144–65 million years ago

Magnolia

Tyrannosaurus rex

Creodonts

Triceratops

◆ Continents move toward their present-day positions, as South America splits from Africa.
◆ Widespread volcanic activity occurs.
◆ First flowering plants appear.
◆ Dinosaurs dominate, including *Tyrannosaurus rex*.
◆ First snakes appear.
◆ Mass extinction at end causes disappearance of many land and marine life forms, including dinosaurs.

TERTIARY
65–1.6 million years ago

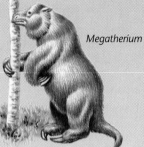
Uintatherium

Hyracotherium

Plesiadapis

◆ The Rocky Mountains, Alps, Andes, and Himalayas form.
◆ Continents move into present-day positions.
◆ Continental glacier covers Antarctica about 25 million years ago.
◆ Flowering plants thrive.
◆ First grasses appear.
◆ Age of Mammals begins.
◆ Modern groups such as horses, elephants, bears, rodents, and primates appear.
◆ Mammals return to the seas in the forms of whales and dolphins.
◆ Ancestors of humans evolve.
◆ Continental glaciers repeatedly cover part of North America beginning about 2.5 million years ago.

QUATERNARY
1.6 million years ago to the present

Saber-toothed cat

Megatherium

Homo sapiens

◆ Thick glaciers advance and retreat over much of North America and Europe, parts of South America and Asia, and all of Antarctica.
◆ The Great Lakes form.
◆ Giant mammals flourish in parts of North America and Eurasia not covered by ice. But they become extinct when the Ice Age ends about 10,000 years ago.
◆ Mammals, flowering plants, and insects dominate land.
◆ Modern humans evolve in Africa about 100,000 years ago.

Chapter 4 **G ◆ 135**

Including All Students

Encourage students who need additional challenges to investigate the giant mammals, or "megafauna," that lived during the Pliocene and Pleistocene epochs of the Quaternary Period. These mammals include wooly mammoths, large rhinoceroses, saber-toothed tigers, giant camels, and moose-sized deer called "Irish elk." Students should especially research the mastodons and other animals found preserved in the ice of northern Siberia. Have students work together to make a poster or bulletin board display with illustrations and captions. Challenge students to write a brief caption that explains the evolution of such animals. Paleontologists believe large mammals had an advantage in adapting to the cold climate of the ice ages. **cooperative learning**

TRY THIS

 **ACTIVITY**

Skills Focus interpreting data

Materials *adding-machine paper, metric ruler*

Time 15 minutes

Tips Suggest that students use a scale of 1 cm = 100 million years. With that scale, the time line will be 35 cm long.

Expected Outcome Students should place the events in this order: oldest fossils form, 3.5 billion years ago; "explosion" of invertebrates occurs, 544 million years ago; first fishes appear, 400 million years ago; Pangaea forms, 260 million years ago; dinosaurs become extinct, 65 million years ago; human ancestors appear, 3.5 million years ago; continental glaciers retreat, 10,000 years ago. Students should observe that the extinction of dinosaurs is a relatively recent event compared with the time since the oldest fossil.

Extend Have students place as many other events on their time lines as they can. **learning modality: logical/mathematical**

Ongoing Assessment

Skills Check Have students make a table that includes each instance on pages 134–135 when a new group of organisms appears and match each group with the correct geologic period.

The Supercontinent Pangaea

Building Inquiry Skills: Relating Cause and Effect

Ask students: **In general, how is the climate of a region near an ocean different from the climate of a region far inland?** *(A typical answer might suggest that temperatures are more extreme inland compared to the climate near an ocean, where ocean winds produce moderate temperatures.)* Explain that when the continents came together to form Pangaea, much coastal area was lost, as smaller landmasses moved into one another. At some point, there were no longer oceans between the continents, and as a consequence the climate changed throughout the world. Ask: **How might a change of climate affect an animal that was well-adapted to the previous climate?** *(The animal might not do as well in the new climate. For example, plants that it depended on for food might not grow in the new climate.)* Although paleontologists are not sure, many hypothesize that such changes in climate caused the mass extinction at the end of the Paleozoic. **learning modality: logical/mathematical**

Using the Visuals: Figure 26

Materials *atlas, scissors*
Time 15 minutes

Explain that Earth's continents don't drift around like boats on water. Rather, they are attached to great sections of Earth's lithosphere called plates. Forces inside Earth cause these plates to move slowly, and those movements were responsible for the formation and breakup of Pangaea. Then have each student use a world map in an atlas to trace the world's continents, including Africa, North America, South America, Australia, Antarctica, and Europe/Asia. Challenge students to cut out these shapes and form them into Pangaea, as shown in the figure. **learning modality: kinesthetic**

260 million years ago

Present

Figure 26 The supercontinent Pangaea began to break apart about 225 million years ago. *Observing How have North America and South America moved in relation to Africa and Europe?*

Life and Times

1. Place these **ACTIVITY** events in their relative order: continental glaciers retreat; first fish appear; oldest fossils form; human ancestors appear; "explosion" of invertebrates occurs; dinosaurs become extinct; Pangaea forms.

2. Draw a time line and graph these dates:
   3.5 billion years ago
   544 million years ago
   400 million years ago
   260 million years ago
   65 million years ago
   3.5 million years ago
   10,000 years ago
   Choose a scale so the oldest date fits on the paper.

Interpreting Data Match each event with the correct date on your time line. How does the time since the dinosaurs became extinct compare with the time since the oldest fossil formed?

The Supercontinent Pangaea

Scientists aren't sure what caused the mass extinction at the end of the Paleozoic. One theory is that Earth's climate changed. But what caused this climate change? Scientists hypothesize that it may have been caused by the slow movement of the continents.

During the Permian period, about 260 million years ago, Earth's continents moved together to form a great landmass, or supercontinent, called Pangaea (pan JEE uh). The formation of Pangaea caused deserts to expand in the tropics. At the same time, sheets of ice covered land closer to the South Pole. Many organisms could not survive the new climate. After Pangaea formed, it broke apart again. Figure 26 shows how the continents moved toward their present-day positions. They moved very slowly—only a few centimeters per year.

The movement of continents is sometimes called continental drift. But the continents don't really "drift." The continents move slowly over Earth's surface because of forces inside Earth.

☑ *Checkpoint* *What was Pangaea?*

The Mesozoic Era

Millions of years flash by. Your time machine cruises above Pangaea and the landmasses that formed when it broke apart. Watch out—there's a dinosaur! You're observing an era that you've read about in books and seen in movies.

The Triassic Period Some living things survived the Permian mass extinction. These organisms became the main forms of life early in the Triassic Period (try AS ik). Plants and animals that survived included fish, insects, reptiles, and cone-bearing plants called conifers. **Reptiles were so successful during the Mesozoic Era that this time is often called the Age of Reptiles.**

Background

Facts and Figures Toward the end of the Paleozoic Era, the continents came together to form Pangaea ("all lands"). One result was the formation of the Appalachian Mountains, which dominate eastern North America. These mountains probably rose as Africa collided with North America. The mountains have since weathered and eroded from a once greater height.

Both the formation and breakup of Pangaea were the result of movements of Earth's lithospheric plates, caused in part by currents in the molten material of Earth's mantle. These plates fit closely together along cracks in the lithosphere. As they move, they collide, pull apart, or slide past one another. Near Hawaii, the Pacific plate is moving at the rate of about 8.3 cm per year.

About 225 million years ago, the first dinosaurs appeared. One of the earliest dinosaurs, *Coelophysis*, was a meat eater that had light, hollow bones and ran swiftly on its hind legs. It was about 2.5 meters long.

Mammals also first appeared during the Triassic Period. A **mammal** is a warm-blooded vertebrate that feeds its young milk. Mammals probably evolved from warm-blooded reptiles. The mammals of the Triassic Period were very small, about the size of a mouse or shrew. From these first small mammals, all mammals that live today evolved.

The Jurassic Period During the Jurassic Period (joo RAS ik), dinosaurs became the dominant animal on land. Scientists have identified several hundred different kinds of dinosaurs. Some were plant eaters, while others were meat eaters. Dinosaurs "ruled" Earth for about 150 million years, but different types lived at different times. At 20 meters long, *Dicraeosaurus* was one of the larger dinosaurs of the Jurassic Period. The smallest known dinosaur, *Compsognathus*, was only about 50 centimeters long when fully grown.

Figure 27 *Dicraeosaurus* was a plant-eating dinosaur that lived during the late Jurassic Period.

Program Resources

Science Explorer Series *Inside Earth*, Chapter 1, provides more information on plate tectonics and the formation and breakup of Pangaea.

Answers to Self-Assessment

Caption Question

Figure 26 North and South America have moved away from Africa and Europe.

✓ Checkpoint

Pangaea was a great landmass that included all Earth's continents, which came together about 260 million years ago.

The Mesozoic Era

Using the Visuals: Figure 27

Ask students: **Why is the Mesozoic Era called the Age of Reptiles?** (*During the Mesozoic, reptiles, including dinosaurs, were very successful.*) **How long did the Mesozoic Era last?** (*From 245 million years ago to 65 million years ago, or 180 million years*) **Is that longer or shorter than the period in which we live?** (*Much longer—the Quaternary is only 1.6 million years old.*) **When did *Dicraeosaurus* live?** (*During the Jurassic Period*) Stress to students that familiar dinosaurs did not necessarily live at the same time. For example, Apatosaurus lived during the Jurassic Period, while Tyrannosaurus lived in the Cretaceous Period. **learning modality: verbal**

Building Inquiry Skills: Posing Questions

Divide students into small groups and have each group brainstorm a list of questions about dinosaurs. Questions might include: How large was the largest dinosaur? Were all dinosaurs giants? Did dinosaurs live in herds or were they solitary? What did dinosaurs eat? When groups have finished, have them read their questions to the class. Write the most interesting questions on the board, and invite volunteers to find the answer to a question and report back to the class. **learning modality: verbal**

Ongoing Assessment

Writing Have students explain how the formation of Pangaea affected the Paleozoic and the Mesozoic.

The Mesozoic Era,
continued

Ask students: **During which period was** *Archaeopteryx* **alive?** *(Jurassic)* **What group of organisms were prominent at that time?** *(Reptiles, including dinosaurs)* Challenge students to find a library book or magazine article that compares a bird skeleton with a dinosaur skeleton. Have volunteers research why many paleontologists think birds evolved from dinosaurs and prepare a presentation to the class. **learning modality: visual**

Building Inquiry Skills: Comparing and Contrasting

Materials *small potted evergreen plant, small flowering plant*
Time 10 minutes

Have small groups compare and contrast characteristics of gymnosperms (seed plants with exposed seed, usually in a cone) and angiosperms (flowering plants with seeds within a fruit). Give students time to observe, make sketches, and write a description of each kind of plant. Explain that flowering plants, which first appeared in the Cretaceous, include all the leafy trees and grasses that dominate Earth today. **learning modality: visual**

Integrating Space Science

Explain that the asteroid scientists think collided with Earth was perhaps about 10 km in diameter. Ask: **Why would the blocking of sunlight by dust and heavy clouds affect plants?** *(Plants need sunlight to carry out photosynthesis, the way they make their food.)* **Why would plants dying affect animals?** *(Animals get their food by eating plants.)* Have students write a description of what might happen to life on Earth if an asteroid of the same size collided with our planet now. **learning modality: verbal**

Figure 28 From a fossil (above right), paleontologists can tell that *Archaeopteryx* was about 30 centimeters long, had feathers and teeth, and also had claws on its wings. The artist of the illustration (above) has given *Archaeopteryx* colorful feathers.

One of the first birds, called *Archaeopteryx*, appeared during the Jurassic Period. The name *Archaeopteryx* means "ancient wing thing." Many paleontologists now think that birds evolved from dinosaurs. During the 1990s, scientists discovered fossils in China with the skulls and teeth of dinosaurs. But these creatures had birdlike bodies and feathers.

The Cretaceous Period Reptiles were still the dominant vertebrates throughout the Cretaceous Period (krih TAY shus). Dinosaurs, such as the meat-eating *Tyrannosaurus rex*, ruled the land. But mammals continued to evolve. Flying reptiles and birds competed for places in the sky. The hollow bones and feathers of birds made them better adapted to their environment than the flying reptiles, which became extinct during the Cretaceous Period. In the seas, reptiles such as turtles and crocodiles swam among fishes and marine invertebrates.

The Cretaceous Period also brought new forms of life. Flowering plants evolved. These included leafy trees, shrubs, and small flowering plants like the ones you see today. Unlike the conifers, flowering plants produce seeds that are inside a fruit. The fruit helps the seeds survive.

Another Mass Extinction At the close of the Cretaceous INTEGRATING SPACE SCIENCE Period, about 65 million years ago, another mass extinction occurred. **Scientists hypothesize that this mass extinction occurred when an object from space struck Earth.** This object was probably an asteroid. Asteroids are rocky masses that orbit the sun between Mars and Jupiter. On rare occasions, the orbits of certain asteroids come dangerously close to Earth. Once in many millions of years, an impact may occur.

Background

Integrating Science Paleontologists infer that *Archaeopteryx* flew because of the shape of its feathers. This early bird was about the size of a modern pigeon. Its skeleton is remarkably like that of some smaller dinosaurs, including *Dromaeosaurus*. Such evidence suggests that birds may have evolved from dinosaurs. By the early Cenozoic Era, some birds had evolved into large meat-eaters. *Diatryma*, for example,

was a 2-m tall predator that could catch ancestral horses in its huge beak.

During the Cretaceous, another important type of organism appeared—the flowering plants, or angiosperms. Because the continents were still fairly close together, angiosperms quickly spread throughout the world. It is no coincidence that mammals spread and diversified along with their main food source, angiosperms.

When the asteroid hit Earth, the impact threw huge amounts of dust and water vapor into the atmosphere. Many organisms on land and in the oceans died immediately. Dust and heavy clouds blocked sunlight around the world for years. Without sunlight, plants died, and plant-eating animals starved. This mass extinction wiped out over half of all plant and animal groups. No dinosaurs survived. Many other kinds of reptiles also became extinct.

Not all scientists agree that an asteroid impact caused the mass extinction. Some scientists think that climate changes caused by increased volcanic activity were responsible.

☑ *Checkpoint* *What major groups of organisms developed during the Mesozoic Era?*

The Cenozoic Era

Your voyage through time continues through the Cenozoic Era toward the present. Paleontologists often call the Cenozoic Era the Age of Mammals. During the Mesozoic Era, mammals had a hard time competing with dinosaurs for food and places to live. **The extinction of dinosaurs created an opportunity for mammals. During the Cenozoic Era, mammals evolved adaptations that allowed them to live in many different environments—on land, in water, and even in the air.**

The Tertiary Period During the Tertiary Period, Earth's climates were generally warm and mild. In the oceans, many types of mollusks appeared. Marine mammals such as whales and dolphins evolved. On land, flowering plants, insects, and mammals flourished. When grasses evolved, they provided a food source for grazing mammals. These were the ancestors of today's cattle, deer, sheep, and other grass-eating mammals. Some mammals became very large, as did some birds.

Figure 29 Scientists hypothesize that during the Cretaceous an asteroid hit Earth near the present-day Yucatán Peninsula, in southeastern Mexico.
Relating Cause and Effect How did the asteroid impact affect life on Earth?

Figure 30 This extinct mammal was related to present-day horses. The fossil formed during the Tertiary Period between 36 and 57 million years ago.

Chapter 4 **G ◆ 139**

Inquiry Challenge

Materials *2 potted plants*
Time observation over a week

Challenge small groups to develop a hypothesis and then design an experiment that would model how the impact of an asteroid at the end of the Mesozoic affected plant life on Earth. A typical hypothesis might suggest that lack of sunlight would kill or harm a plant. A typical experiment might include placing one plant in direct sunlight and an identical plant in darkness. After reviewing designs, have groups carry out their experiments.
cooperative learning

The Cenozoic Era

Using the Visuals: Figure 30

Ask students: **What is a mammal?** (*A mammal is a warm-blooded vertebrate that feeds its young with milk.*) **When do they first appear in the geologic record?** (*During the Triassic Period of the Mesozoic Era*) **From what organisms did mammals evolve?** (*From warm-blooded reptiles*) **How would you describe the first mammals?** (*They were small, about the size of a mouse or shrew.*) Show students a picture of a shrew from a book on animals. Then ask: **What event in Earth's history probably allowed mammals to become larger and more diverse?** (*The mass extinction at the close of the Cretaceous, which killed all dinosaurs as well as many other types of organisms, leaving niches available for mammals to fill.*) **learning modality: verbal**

Ongoing Assessment

Writing Have students write a story in which they take the role of a small mammal at the end of the Cretaceous. In this story students should describe how the impact of the asteroid affected life on Earth and also look ahead as the mammal contemplates the future without dinosaurs dominating Earth. **Portfolio** Students can keep their stories in their portfolios.

G ◆ 139

Program Resources

Science Explorer Series *Astronomy,* Chapter 2, has information about asteroids; *From Bacteria to Plants,* Chapter 5, introduces flowering plants; *Animals,* Chapter 4, can provide more information about birds and mammals.

Answers to Self-Assessment

☑ *Checkpoint*
Dinosaurs, mammals, birds, and flowering plants

Caption Question

Figure 29 The asteroid impact caused a mass extinction that wiped out over half of all plant and animal groups, including all dinosaurs.

The Cenozoic Era, continued

Using the Visuals: Figure 31

Explain that this fossil was discovered in eastern Africa in the 1970s, and it remains one of the most complete specimens of human ancestors. Ask: **In which period did "Lucy" live?** (*The Tertiary Period of the Cenozoic Era*) Scientists estimate that this female hominid was about 1.1 m tall and weighed less than 30 kg. **What can you observe in this fossil hominid that makes it different from an ape?** (*The skeleton shows that "Lucy" walked upright, on two legs.*) **learning modality: visual**

3 Assess

Section 5 Review Answers

1. The Cambrian Explosion is when a great number of different kinds of organisms evolved at the beginning of the Paleozoic Era. It was important because so many new life forms appeared.

2. Pangaea was a supercontinent that formed when Earth's continents moved together during the Permian Period, about 260 million years ago.

3. The extinction of dinosaurs created an opportunity for mammals because they no longer had to compete with dinosaurs for food and places to live.

4. The source of oxygen in Earth's atmosphere was the release of oxygen by organisms that carried out photosynthesis.

5. Answers may vary. A typical answer might suggest that each time a mass extinction occurred, the evolution of life changed greatly as many types of organisms were wiped out.

Check Your Progress CHAPTER PROJECT 4

Review students' rough drafts and make suggestions about what to include and what to delete. At this point, have student volunteers make the basic time line for the geologic time scale. The time scale should cover at least one wall of the classroom.

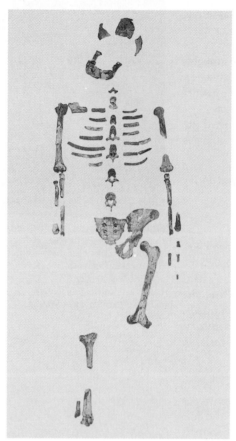

Figure 31 Scientists nicknamed this fossil skeleton Lucy. An early ancestor of modern humans, Lucy lived about 3.3 million years ago.

The Quaternary Period The mammals that had evolved during the Tertiary Period eventually faced a changing environment. **Earth's climate cooled, causing a series of ice ages during the Quaternary Period.** Repeatedly, thick continental glaciers advanced and retreated over parts of Europe and North America.

So much of Earth's water was frozen in continental glaciers that the level of the oceans fell by more than 100 meters. Then, about 20,000 years ago, Earth's climate began to warm. Over thousands of years, the continental glaciers melted. This caused sea level to rise again.

In the oceans, algae, coral, mollusks, fish, and mammals thrived. Insects and birds shared the skies. On land, flowering plants and mammals such as bats, cats, dogs, cattle, and humans—just to name a few—became common.

The fossil record suggests that human ancestors appeared about 3.5 million years ago. Modern humans, or *Homo sapiens,* may have evolved as early as 100,000 years ago. By about 12,000 to 15,000 years ago, humans had migrated around the world to every continent except Antarctica.

Your time machine has now arrived back in the present. You and all organisms on Earth are living in the Quaternary Period of the Cenozoic Era. Is this the end of evolution and the changing of Earth's surface? No, these processes will continue as long as Earth exists. But you'll have to take your time machine into the future to see just what happens!

Section 5 Review

1. What is the "Cambrian explosion"? Why is it important to the history of life on Earth?
2. What was Pangaea? When did it form?
3. How did the extinction of dinosaurs affect the evolution of mammals?
4. What do scientists think was the source of the oxygen in Earth's atmosphere?
5. **Thinking Critically Making Generalizations** How do you think mass extinctions have affected evolution?

Check Your Progress CHAPTER PROJECT 4

Create illustrations of your portion of the time line. How will you show animals, plants, and environments of that time? When you have finished your illustrations, place them on the time line. Then make a rough draft of your travel brochure. Have a classmate or teacher edit your rough draft before you write the final draft. Do you have all the information about your geologic period that will make a person want to travel there?

Background

History of Science The fossil skeleton called Lucy, an example of *Australopithecus afarensis,* was discovered in Ethiopia in the early 1970s. She was named Lucy after the Beatles' song "Lucy in the Sky with Diamonds," popular at the time. She was about 1 m tall and had apelike features such as short legs and curved toe bones. But the leg and pelvis bones show that Lucy walked upright on two legs.

Program Resources

◆ **Teaching Resources** 4-5 Review and Reinforce, p. 119; 4-5 Enrich, p. 120

Fossils

Key Ideas
◆ Most fossils form when living things die and are quickly buried by sediment, which eventually hardens and preserves parts of the organisms.
◆ The major kinds of fossils include petrified remains, molds, casts, carbon films, trace fossils, and preserved remains.
◆ The fossil record shows that many different organisms have lived on Earth at different times and that groups of organisms have changed over time.

Key Terms
fossil	mold	scientific
paleontologist	cast	theory
sedimentary rock	carbon film	evolution
petrified fossil	trace fossil	extinct

Finding the Relative Age of Rocks

Key Ideas
◆ The law of superposition can be used to determine the relative ages of rock layers.
◆ Scientists also study faults, intrusions, and extrusions to find the relative ages of rock layers.
◆ Index fossils are useful in dating rock layers.

Key Terms
relative age	fault
absolute age	intrusion
law of superposition	extrusion
unconformity	index fossil

 Radioactive Dating

INTEGRATING CHEMISTRY

Key Ideas
◆ During radioactive decay, the atoms of one element decay into atoms of another element.
◆ Scientists use radioactive dating to determine the absolute ages of rocks.

Key Terms
atom	radioactive decay
element	half-life

 The Geologic Time Scale

Key Ideas
◆ The basic divisions of the geologic time scale are eras, periods, and epochs.

Key Terms
geologic time scale	invertebrate	epoch
era	period	

Earth's History

Key Ideas
◆ A great number of different kinds of living things evolved during the "Cambrian explosion" at the beginning of the Paleozoic Era.
◆ During the Permian Period, the continents joined to form the supercontinent Pangaea.

Key Terms
vertebrate	reptile	mammal
amphibian	mass extinction	

Organizing Information

Concept Map Copy the concept map about fossils onto a piece of paper. Then complete it and add a title. (For more on concept maps, see the Skills Handbook.)

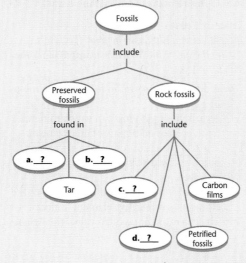

Organizing Information

Concept Map
Sample title: *Kinds of Fossils* **a.** amber
b. ice **c.** trace fossils **d.** casts, molds

Program Resources

◆ **Teaching Resources** Chapter 4 Project Scoring Rubric, p. 100; Chapter 4 Performance Assessment, pp. 159–161; Chapter 4 Test, pp. 162–165; Book Test, pp. 166–169

Media and Technology

 Computer Test Bank *Earth's Changing Surface*, Chapter 4

Performance Assessment

Skills Check Have students make a table that compares the three eras of geologic time. In this table students should include the major geological events as well as the evolution of important groups of organisms.

Reviewing Content
Multiple Choice
1. a **2.** b **3.** c **4.** d **5.** c

True or False
6. true **7.** petrified fossil **8.** absolute age
9. half-life **10.** Mesozoic Era

Checking Concepts

11. Sediment covers the remains of an organism. Then water rich in minerals seeps into the spaces of the organism's cells. Over time, the water evaporates, leaving the hardened minerals behind. Petrified fossils also form by replacement, in which minerals in water make a copy of the organism.

12. A bony fish has a better chance of leaving a fossil because it has hard parts that do not decay quickly, while a jellyfish does not have hard parts.

13. Sometimes, deeply buried layers of rock are lifted up to Earth's surface. At the surface, the exposed rock erodes away. Then sediments are deposited on top of the eroded surface of the older rocks and harden into rock layers. The place where an old eroded surface is in contact with a newer rock layer is called an unconformity.

14. A scientist would use radioactive dating to determine the absolute ages of intrusions and extrusions near the sedimentary rock in which the fossil was found.

15. The Cenozoic Era is called the Age of Mammals because, during the Cenozoic Era, mammals evolved adaptations that allowed them to live in many different environments—on land, in water, and even in the air.

16. Answers will vary. Students should describe an asteroid hitting Earth and the mass extinction of dinosaurs and other organisms that results.

Thinking Critically

17. The paleontologists could conclude that both rock layers formed at about the same time.

18. The movie would not be scientifically accurate because dinosaurs became extinct at the end of the Mesozoic Era, while humans did not evolve until well into the Cenozoic Era, over 60 million years later.

Reviewing Content

 For more review of key concepts, see the Interactive Student Tutorial CD-ROM.

Multiple Choice
Choose the answer that best completes each sentence.

1. A hollow area in sediment in the shape of all or part of an organism is called a
  a. mold.   **b.** cast.
  c. trace fossil.   **d.** carbon film.

2. A gap in the geologic record formed when sedimentary rocks cover an erosion surface is called a(n)
  a. intrusion.
  b. unconformity.
  c. fault.
  d. extrusion.

3. When a radioactive element decays, it releases
  a. atoms.
  b. potassium-40.
  c. particles and energy.
  d. carbon-14.

4. Eras of geologic time are subdivided into
  a. epochs.   **b.** centuries.
  c. decades.   **d.** periods.

5. What is an animal that doesn't have a backbone called?
  a. vertebrate   **b.** mammal
  c. invertebrate   **d.** amphibian

True or False
If the statement is true, write true. If it is false, change the underlined word or words to make the statement true.

6. A dinosaur footprint in rock is an example of a <u>trace fossil</u>.

7. A <u>carbon film</u> is a fossil in which minerals have replaced all or part of an organism.

8. The <u>relative age</u> of something is the exact number of years since an event has occurred.

9. A <u>period</u> is the time required for half of the atoms of a radioactive element to decay.

10. The <u>Paleozoic Era</u> is often called the Age of Reptiles.

Checking Concepts

11. How does a petrified fossil form?

12. Which organism has a better chance of leaving a fossil: a jellyfish or a bony fish? Explain.

13. Describe a process that could cause an unconformity.

14. What evidence would a scientist use to determine the absolute age of a fossil found in a sedimentary rock?

15. What era is often called the Age of Mammals? Why is this appropriate?

16. Writing to Learn Imagine that your time machine comes to a halt just as a big event occurs at the end of the Mesozoic Era. Describe what you see, and then describe how this event affects the life you see on Earth.

Thinking Critically

17. Applying Concepts Suppose that paleontologists found a certain kind of trilobite in a rock layer at the top of a hill in South America. Then they found the same kind of trilobite in a rock layer at the bottom of a cliff in Africa. What could the paleontologists conclude about the two rock layers?

18. Making Judgments If you see a movie in which early humans fight giant dinosaurs, how would you judge the scientific accuracy of that movie? Give reasons for your judgment.

19. Relating Cause and Effect When Pangaea formed, the climate changed and the land on Earth became drier. Why do you think that this climate change favored reptiles over amphibians?

20. Problem Solving Carbon-14 has a half-life of 5,730 years, while uranium-235 has a half-life of 713 million years. Which would be better to use in dating a fossil from Precambrian time? Explain.

---

19. Amphibians live part of their lives in water, while reptiles are land animals. When the climate became drier, the amphibians had less water. A drier climate, then, would favor the reptiles.

20. Precambrian Time begins with the formation of Earth 4.6 billion years ago and ends 544 million years ago. Carbon-14 would be of no use in dating the fossil because its half-life is much too short. Therefore, the uranium-235 would be better to use.

Applying Skills

21. By the law of superposition, layer W is the oldest layer and layer Z is the youngest.

22. A scientist must have used radioactive dating to determine the ages of the intrusion and extrusion.

23. Layer Y is younger than the 60-million-year-old intrusion but older than the 34-million-year-old intrusion.

24. Layer Z is younger than the 34-million-year-old intrusion but older than the 20-million-year-old extrusion.

Applying Skills

Use the diagram of rock layers below to answer Questions 21–24.

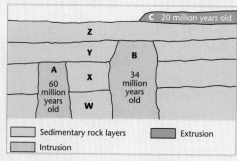

Sedimentary rock layers

Intrusion

Extrusion

21. Inferring Which is the oldest layer of sedimentary rock? Which is the youngest? How do you know?

22. Measuring What method did a scientist use to determine the age of the intrusion and extrusion?

23. Interpreting Data What is the relative age of layer Y (*Hint:* With what absolute ages can you compare it?)

24. Interpreting Data What is the relative age of layer Z?

Performance CHAPTER PROJECT 4 **Assessment**

Project Wrap Up You have completed your illustrations for the time line and travel brochure. Now you are ready to present the story of the geologic time period you researched. Be sure to include the wonderful and awesome things people will see when they travel to this time period. Don't forget to warn them of any dangers that await them.

Reflect and Record In your journal, reflect on what you have learned about Earth's history. What were the most interesting things you found out? If you could travel back in time, how far back would you go?

Test Preparation

Use these questions to prepare for standardized tests.

The diagrams show the index fossils found in rock layers at two different locations. Use the diagrams to answer Questions 25–28.

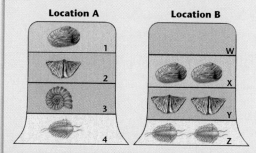

Location A

Location B

Key				
Index fossil	Trilobite	Ammonite	Brachiopod	Clam
Geologic period	Cambrian	Ordovician	Silurian	Devonian

25. According to the law of superposition, the oldest rock layers at Locations A and B are Layers
  a. 2 and Y. **b.** 3 and Y.
  c. 4 and Z **d.** 1 and W.

26. The youngest rock layer at either location is Layer
  a. 1. **b.** X.
  c. 3. **d.** W.

27. The index fossil for the Cambrian period is the
  a. ammonite. **b.** clam.
  c. trilobite. **d.** brachiopod.

28. Layer 1 at Location A and Layer X at Location B both contain fossil clams. These index fossils indicate that both layers formed during the
  a. Devonian Period.
  b. Silurian Period.
  c. Ordovician Period.
  d. Cambrian Period.

Performance CHAPTER PROJECT 4 **Assessment**

Project Wrap Up As each student presents their brochure, assess the amount and quality of the information included, as well as whether the brochure accurately covers the geologic period. Also evaluate the quality and effectiveness of the illustrations the brochure contains. Question students about the sources they used, and make sure they can support any fact or assertion with a good source.

Reflect and Record In their reflections about Earth's history, students should write accurate descriptions of the most interesting things they learned and provide good reasons for the period they would like to travel back to. Also have students reflect on how they could have made their brochures better if they could make them again.

Test Preparation

25. c 26. d 27. c 28. a

Program Resources

◆ **Inquiry Skills Activity Book** Provides teaching and review of all inquiry skills

◆ **Standardized Test Preparation Book** Provides standardized test practice

◆ **Reading in the Content Area** Provides strategies to improve science reading skills

◆ **Teacher's ELL Handbook** Provides multiple strategies for English language learners

The Gift of the Nile

This interdisciplinary feature presents the central theme of the importance of the Nile River to the rise of ancient Egyptian civilization by connecting four different disciplines: language arts, science, social studies, and mathematics. The four explorations are designed to capture student's interest and help them understand how the mechanics and results of Earth's changing surface relate to other school subjects and to real-world events. The unit is particularly suited for team teaching.

1 Engage/Explore

Activating Prior Knowledge

Help students recall what they learned in Chapter 3, Erosion and Deposition, by asking: **How does water change land?** (*Water erodes rock and carries away the sediment, depositing it downstream.*) **How does deposition change Earth's surface?** (*Deposition forms features such as alluvial fans and deltas.*) Then ask: **What do you know about Egypt and the Nile River?** (*Accept all responses without comment.*)

Introducing the Unit

Display a large map of Africa, and invite a volunteer to find the Nile River. Ask: **In which direction does the Nile flow?** (*generally from south to north*) **Through which countries does the Nile flow?** (*Uganda, Sudan, Ethiopia, and Egypt*) Tell students that the Nile River is the longest river in the world and that it travels through a very large, dry desert. Draw students' attention to the photograph at the top of this page. Ask: **How does the Nile River change the land along its banks?** (*It makes the land lush and fertile.*) **How do you think the Nile River affects the lives of the people living near it?** (*Accept all answers without comment at this time.*)

The Gift of the Nile

What water—

Lush, fertile lands along the Nile contrast with the scorching desert beyond.

- *flows from south to north?*
- *travels through a scorching desert for much of its length?*
- *nourished a remarkable ancient culture that lasted for 3,000 years?*
- *is the longest river in the world?*

It's the Nile River, which gives life to the Egyptian desert.

More than 5,000 years ago, people first began planting seeds and harvesting crops in the valley of the Nile. The great civilization of Egypt rose in these fertile lands. The Nile supplied water for drinking, growing crops, raising animals, and fishing. When the river flooded every year, it brought a new layer of rich soil to the flood plain.

This productive strip of land was the envy of many nations. Fortunately, the deserts west and east of the Nile River helped protect ancient Egypt from invaders. The river provided a route for trade from central Africa downstream to the Mediterranean Sea. Around 600 B.C., Egypt expanded its trade by digging a canal to the Red Sea.

During the months when the Nile flooded, peasants worked as builders for the Pharaoh, or king. They constructed magnificent pyramids and temples, some of which still stand in the desert today.

Blue water lilies grow in the Nile.

144 ◆ G

Program Resources

◆ **Teaching Resources** Interdisciplinary Explorations, Language Arts, pp. 126–128; Science, pp. 129–131; Social Studies, pp. 132–134; Mathematics, pp. 135–137

Program Resources

◆ **Teaching Resources** The following worksheets correlate with page 145: Practicing Personification, page 126; Hieroglyphics and the Rosetta Stone, page 127; Nile River Vocabulary, page 128.

Lifeline of Egypt

The wealth of ancient Egypt and the lives of its people depended on the fertile flood plains that bordered the Nile River. Egyptian society was organized in classes to support agriculture. The Pharaoh was the supreme ruler to whom all Egyptians paid taxes. Below the Pharaoh was a small upper class of priests, scribes, and nobles. Traders and skilled workers, who made tools, pottery, and clothing, formed a small middle class. But the largest group in Egyptian society was the peasants. Peasants used the Nile waters to raise crops that fed all of Egypt.

Priests and nobles recorded the history and literature of ancient Egypt on the walls of monuments and temples. They also wrote on papyrus, a paper made from reeds that grew in marshes along the Nile. Many writings were about the Nile.

When scholars finally found the key to hieroglyphics (hy ur oh GLIF iks), Egyptian writing, they discovered hymns, poems, legends, adventure stories, and lessons for young people. The poem at the right is from a hymn to Hapy, the god of the Nile. "Darkness by day" is the Nile filled with silt.

Egyptian writing, called hieroglyphics, decorates the borders of this poem. ▶

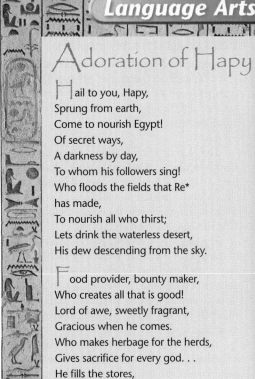

Adoration of Hapy

Hail to you, Hapy,
Sprung from earth,
Come to nourish Egypt!
Of secret ways,
A darkness by day,
To whom his followers sing!
Who floods the fields that Re*
has made,
To nourish all who thirst;
Lets drink the waterless desert,
His dew descending from the sky.

Food provider, bounty maker,
Who creates all that is good!
Lord of awe, sweetly fragrant,
Gracious when he comes.
Who makes herbage for the herds,
Gives sacrifice for every god. . .
He fills the stores,
Makes bulge the barns,
Gives bounty to the poor.

Oh joy when you come!
O joy when you come, O Hapy,
Oh joy when you come!

Amon-Re, god of the sun

Language Arts Activity

In this poem, Hapy is a personification of the Nile River. When writers and poets use personification, they give an object or animal human qualities. Write your own story or poem using personification. Choose a subject found in nature, such as a mountain, stream, river, or glacier. Jot down human behaviors and actions for your subject—"the stream gurgles, murmurs, and sighs." Before writing, think about the time, place, characters, and sequence of events in your story.

G ◆ 145

2 Facilitate

- After students read the poem, encourage them to give their impression of the person who might have written the poem. Ask: **Is it surprising to you that a poem like this was written thousands of years ago?** (*Accept all responses without comment, but encourage students to explain their reactions.*)
- Discuss the power of the written word. Ask: **Why was finding the key to hieroglyphics such an important discovery?** (*It allows us to read and understand the thoughts, feelings, historical events, and daily events that were important in this civilization. This helps us to see the ancient Egyptians as they saw themselves.*)

Language Arts Activity

Before students write their poem or story, have them choose the subject and decide how they will personify it. Then encourage students to think about the time, place, characters, and sequence of events in their poem or story. Suggest that they outline the poem or story first to help them organize their thoughts.

3 Assess

Activity Assessment

Let each student read his or her poem or story aloud to the rest of the class. Encourage other students to identify the personification in the poem or story. Evaluate the student's poem or story based on the presence of personification and its completeness.

Background

History The ancient Egyptian civilization depended on the yearly flood of the Nile River. The Egyptians kept careful written records of the level at which the Nile flooded each year, as well as records of other natural events. Pharaohs, or kings, would often refer to these records to find out if a similar event had occurred before and how the people had reacted to it.

The Nile also provided the inspiration for telling stories. People wrote about the Nile itself and how it affected their lives. The Nile served as a route to distant lands, giving travelers experiences about which they could tell stories.

2 Facilitate

- ◆ Discuss the role of water and silt from the Nile River on the development of the ancient Egyptian civilization. Ask: **How was it possible for the Nile River to support a large and prosperous civilization?** *(The Nile provided water and fertile soil, enabling the Egyptians to grow enough food for them and to trade for things that they couldn't grow or make.)* **Why couldn't a civilization such as this develop in the desert?** *(Without water, people couldn't grow the food they needed to live. They would spend all their time obtaining food and water; there would probably not be time for other kinds of activities such as writing poems.)*

- ◆ Have students trace the course of the Nile River on the map in their books as they read about it. Or, choose student volunteers to read the text aloud as you trace the route of the river on a large map of Africa.

- ◆ Explain that the annual flood was a mysterious event to ancient Egyptians. They believed that gods caused the flood and the severity of the flood depended on the gods' mood. Discuss what really happens when the Nile floods. Ask: **Where do the Nile's floodwaters come from?** *(From heavy rains in the eastern plateau of Ethiopia)*

Fertilizing the Fields

In some parts of Egypt, it hasn't rained in years. Only about 3 percent of Egypt can be farmed. The rest is sun-baked desert. But hot weather and the silt and water brought by the Nile River make the Nile Valley highly productive.

The Nile River is the longest river on Earth, stretching 6,650 kilometers. Its drainage basin is about 3.3 million square kilometers. This is larger than that of the Mississippi River. Three major rivers form the Nile—the White Nile, the Blue Nile, and the Atbara.

The source of the White Nile is just south of the equator near Lake Victoria (about 1,135 meters above sea level). A fairly constant volume of water flows north over rapids and through swamp lands to Khartoum. Here the Blue Nile and the White Nile meet to form the great Nile River.

The Blue Nile starts in the eastern plateau of Ethiopia near Lake Tana (about 1,800 meters above sea level). The Atbara River, the last major tributary of the Nile, also flows in from Ethiopia. Between Khartoum and Aswan, the Nile flows north over six cataracts—huge waterfalls. From Aswan to Cairo, the flood plain stretches out on both sides of the river. It gradually widens to about 19 kilometers. Then in Lower Egypt the river branches out to form the Nile Delta.

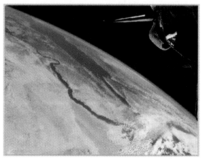

A view from space shows the Nile River winding through the Sahara Desert. A space probe is at the upper right.

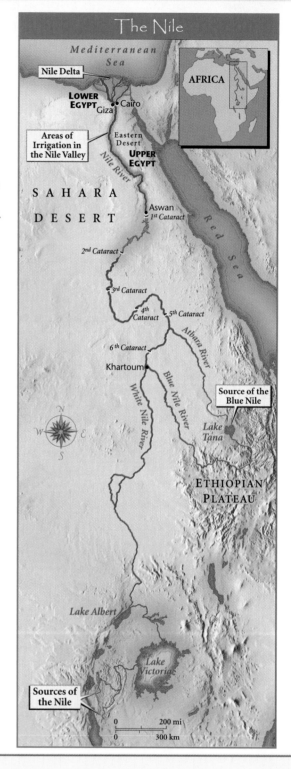

The Nile

- ◆ **Teaching Resources** The following worksheets correlate with pages 146–147: Reading a Map, page 129; Reading a Data Table, page 130; Plotting a River Profile, page 131.

The rushing waters of the Blue Nile carry silt and other sediment from the Ethiopian highlands to the Nile.

Between May and August, heavy rains soak the eastern plateau of Ethiopia and wash rock and silt from the highlands into the Blue Nile. The dark water rushes over rapids and through deep gorges into the Nile River. For thousands of years this rush of water from the Blue Nile and the Atbara caused the seasonal flooding on the Nile. In mid-July, the Nile would begin to rise north of Aswan. When the flood waters went down, the silt remained on the land.

Then in the 1800s and 1900s, Egypt built dams on the Nile to try to control the floodwaters. The Aswan High Dam, the largest of these dams, was completed in 1970. With this dam, the Egyptians finally gained control over annual flooding. The Aswan High Dam holds back water for dry periods and manages surplus water.

In recent years, the population of Egypt and other nations in the Nile basin has grown rapidly. Feeding more people means increasing the area of irrigated cropland. To avoid conflicts, nations must agree to share water. Most of the water in the Blue Nile, for example, comes from Ethiopia.

Yet Egypt and Sudan, the nations farther downstream, use about 90 percent of that water. Today, Ethiopia's growing population needs more Nile water. Using water efficiently and sharing it fairly are essential in the Nile basin.

Science Activities

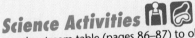

Use the stream table (pages 86–87) to observe how the Nile builds its delta and how the Aswan Dam affects the river. Pour water into the lower end of the stream table to model the sea.

◆ Make a dam. Cut off the top 2 centimeters from a plastic foam cup. Cut a semicircle for your dam. Cut a small notch in the top of the dam for a spillway.

◆ Start the dripper to create the Nile. Allow it to flow for 5 minutes. What do you observe where the river flows into the sea?

◆ Now place the dam halfway down the river. Scoop out a small, shallow reservoir behind the dam. Observe for 5 minutes.

What effect would you say that the Aswan Dam has on the movement of sediment down the Nile?

G ◆ 147

Background

Facts and Figures As the Aswan High Dam was being built in the 1960s, the rising water behind the dam threatened many of the ancient monuments in the Nile Valley. Some of these monuments were moved to safety. The reservoir formed by the Aswan High Dam, Lake Nasser, is about 480 km long and stretches into Sudan. Water is released from Lake Nasser when it is needed for irrigation down river. As the water pours through the dam, it is also used to produce electricity.

The Aswan High Dam has changed life in modern Egypt. With water available year round, Egyptian farmers can grow several crops per year. The water from Lake Nasser, however, does not carry the rich silt that the Nile floods used to deposit on the fields. Now farmers must add fertilizer to the soil.

◆ Discuss the human need for controlling the Nile River by building dams. Point out that people throughout time have tried to manage the Nile River with the technology of the time. Technology always has costs as well as benefits. Ask: **What are some benefits of building dams?** (*Ensure a constant water supply; prevent damage from floods; provide a source of electricity*) **What are some costs of dams?** (*They change the environment and wildlife habitats; cause increased use of fertilizers in floodplains; silt builds up behind the dams and not at the river's mouth.*)

Science Activity

Students can work in the same groups with the same stream tables as they did for the Real-World Lab on pages 86–87. To create the Nile, have students adjust the dripper to 2 drops per second. With the dam in place, the dripper should flow at 3 to 4 drops per second in order to observe the sediment as it reaches the dam. To increase the flow in the dripper, add a drop of soap to the water to cut surface tension, then bend the dripper into more of a U shape. Remind students to keep the diatomaceous earth wet at all times. They can use the spray bottle to wet the surface if it begins to dry out.

3 Assess

Initially, the river will carry sediment to the sea, forming a multi-lobed delta. With the dam in place, water will pool behind the dam, and sediment will build up behind the dam and fill the reservoir. The dam will slow the flow of water and sediment to the sea.

Have students write a short description of their observations and conclusions. They should explain the effect of the Aswan Dam on the movement of sediment down the Nile. (*The Aswan Dam stops the flow of sediment down the Nile.*)

2 Facilitate

◆ Discuss how the ancient Egyptians used technology to control the Nile River. Ask: **How did the shaduf help the Egyptians?** *(It enabled them to take water out of the river and use it to irrigate their fields.)* **What was the advantage of basin irrigation?** *(It forced the river to deposit its sediments into the farm fields.)*

◆ Explain that the wealth of the ancient Egyptians came from their success at farming. Challenge students to identify efficient agricultural practices that led to their farming success. *(Irrigation; inventing tools, such as the shaduf and irrigation ditches; using their land efficiently—allowing animals to graze on the fields after harvest and before the flood; driving sheep over the fields to push the seeds into the ground, using plows pulled by oxen)* Point out that their success at farming gave them surplus food with which they could trade for other goods. Explain that the Nile River helped Egyptians trade with many different people because the river was a very efficient transportation route.

◆ Compare the seasons in your area to the seasons of the ancient Egyptians. Point out how the ancient Egyptian seasons were more dependent on the changes in water level of the Nile than they were on the temperature. Ask: **Why couldn't the ancient Egyptians plant a crop until November?** *(The fields were flooded from July until October.)*

Basin Irrigation

The ancient Egyptians may have been the first to irrigate their lands. The slope of the flood plain in Egypt is good for irrigation. From south to north, the land slopes down slightly. The land also slopes slightly down to the desert from the river banks on either side of the Nile.

Egyptians used basin irrigation. They divided the flood plain into a series of basins by building low banks of dirt. When the Nile flooded from July to October, it filled the basins. Then, the water level in the Nile and in the basins gradually dropped. This left a rich sediment layer ready for planting.

In November, peasants plowed the fields and scattered seeds. To push the seeds into the ground, they drove sheep over the fields. Egyptians grew crops of wheat, barley, lentils, onions, beans, garlic, vegetables, and fruits in the Nile Valley. The crops usually could feed all of Egypt. The Egyptians traded any surplus crops for lumber, copper, and beautiful minerals that they used for decorations.

When the fields became dry, peasants brought water from irrigation channels, or deep ditches. They also used a tool called a shaduf to take water directly from the Nile. After the harvest in April, farm animals grazed on the lands until the Nile rose again in mid-July. Then a new cycle began.

The flooding of the Nile determined the lives of early Egyptians. Their year began on the day the Nile began to rise, about July 19 on our calendar. The Egyptians were the first people to have a calendar of 365 days. Their year was divided into 3 seasons based on the Nile's flood cycle. Each season had 4 months of 30 days. At the end of the twelve months, the Egyptians had 5 festival days to complete the year.

The shaduf, still used today, dates back to about 2200 B.C. A wooden beam balances on a pivot, like a plank on a see-saw. Hanging from one end of the beam is a bucket. Balancing at the other end is a large stone. A farmer rocks the beam to scoop water from the Nile. Then the farmer swivels the bucket and empties it into an irrigation channel.

Program Resources

◆ **Teaching Resources** The following worksheets correlate with pages 148–149: Making a Model Shaduf, pages 132–133; Finding Your Way Around Cairo, page 134.

This painting from around 1200 B.C. was found on the wall of the Tomb of Sennedjem in Thebes. The panels show Sennedjem and his wife farming in the afterworld. Sennedjem's wife plants grain. Sennedjem harvests wheat with a sickle (top panel) and plows (middle panel). Egyptians cultivated fruit-bearing trees, such as the date palm (bottom panel).

Social Studies Activities

Divide into groups of three to make a time line of an Egyptian calendar year. Each member of the group should choose a four-month season—flooding, planting, or harvesting—to label and illustrate.

◆ Draw the time line to begin on July 19 and end on July 18.
◆ Divide the time line into 12 months and 5 days.
◆ Label the months and seasons.
◆ Illustrate the seasonal work of the farmers.

The flooded fields of the Nile Delta are separated into lots by irrigation channels.

◆ Encourage interested students to make their own painting or drawing in which they illustrate an event in the life of an ancient Egyptian.
◆ To extend this exploration, students could learn about the Mayan calendar and compare it to the Egyptian calendar. Students could also compare the way of life in each civilization, as well as the environment and the time period of its greatest strength.

Social Studies Activity

Let students in each group choose which season they will label and illustrate on the time line. You might give students butcher or table-covering paper on which to draw the time lines so that they have enough room for all their drawings and labels. Challenge students to model their illustrations for the time line after the Egyptian painting on this page. Encourage students to use information from the text about Egyptian farming to help them decide what to draw. Remind students to make the divisions on the time line of equal size, especially since each of the 12 months has the same number of days.

3 Assess

Activity Assessment

Display the time lines throughout the classroom and in the hallways. Allow time for students to present their time lines and explain why they chose to illustrate each season as they did. Evaluate the group's construction of the time line, particularly the precision of the time divisions and the accuracy of the labels and illustrations.

Background

Facts and Figures Farming provided the basis for ancient Egyptian civilization. Most Egyptian settlements were villages near the Nile River or in its delta. The farmers contributed some of the wheat and barley they grew to support the elite landowners and the central government. Unlike ancient Mesopotamia, Egypt did not develop large cities until rather late in its history.

Originally, the months of the Egyptian calendar were numbered. Later, the months were named for festivals, and the years were named for major events. These events were recorded, along with the height of the Nile flood, in a register. Later, kings would consult these registers, or annals, to compare the current level of the Nile to the levels in past years. In this way, they could make predictions about the extent of flooding and the success of crops.

2 Facilitate

- Invite students to measure the length of the room using their feet as the unit of measure. Students can step off the length by placing their feet end-to-end across the room. Have students compare their results. Ask: **Why are some measurements different?** *(Everyone's feet are not the same length.)*

- Discuss the importance of measurement to the ancient Egyptians. Ask: **What role did the Nile River play in establishing a standard system of measurement?** *(The yearly floods wiped out field boundaries, requiring farmers to mark off new boundary lines each year. They also measured the depth of floodwaters.)* Explain that ancient Egyptians built many pyramids and monuments of immense size. To do this, they needed an understanding of geometry and a standard system of measurement.

Math Activity

Let students in each group agree on the length of a standard cubit. Students can make a cubit stick from sturdy paper or thin cardboard. Remind students to mark off each cubit on their rope to make it easier to make the triangle. Encourage students to relate the equation for a right triangle to the right triangle they are making. Hint that a triangle has three sides, so they must divide the length of rope into three lengths, but the lengths do not have to be equal.

Measuring the Land

Have you ever measured the length of a room using your feet as the unit of measurement? Around 3000 B.C., ancient Egyptians developed the cubit system of measurement. It was based on the lengths of parts of the arm and hand, rather than the foot. The Egyptian cubit was the length of a forearm from the tip of the elbow to the end of the middle finger. The cubit was subdivided into smaller units of spans, palms, digits, and parts of digits.

Of course, the length of a cubit varied from person to person. So Egypt established a standard cubit, called the Royal Cubit. It was based on the length of the Pharaoh's forearm. The Royal Cubit was a piece of black granite about 52.3 centimeters long. Although the royal architect kept the Royal Cubit, wooden copies were distributed through the land.

Measurement was important to Egyptian life. Every year when the Nile flooded, it wiped out the boundaries for the fields. So after the annual floods, farmers had to measure off new areas. Drawings on the walls of early tombs show that the Egyptians probably had a system for measuring distances and angles on land.

Standard measurement was also necessary for building the massive temples and pyramids that lined the Nile Valley. The cubit stick must have been very accurate, because the lengths of the sides of the Great Pyramid at Giza vary by only a few centimeters.

Egyptians used geometry to measure triangles, squares, and circles to build pyramids. These pyramids at Giza were built around 2500 B.C.

150

Program Resources

- **Teaching Resources** The following worksheets correlate with pages 150–151: Using Different Systems of Measurement, page 135; Building a Pyramid, page 136; Graphing Population Data, page 137.

Mathematics Activities

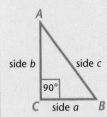

To measure fields and build pyramids, the Egyptians needed to understand geometry. They laid out their fields in squares by first making a right triangle. Look at the diagram. The two shorter sides are the legs. The side opposite the right angle is the hypotenuse. The Egyptians might have known that the sum of the squares of the lengths of the legs is equal to the square of the hypotenuse. The equation is $a^2 + b^2 = c^2$. So if side a is 3, and side b is 4, and side c is 5, then $3^2 + 4^2 = 5^2$, or $9 + 16 = 25$.

Now work in groups of 3 to make your own right triangle.

◆ Measure one student's arm to make a cubit stick.

◆ Use the cubit stick to cut one rope 12 cubits long; mark off each of the 12 cubits.

◆ Have 3 students hold the rope at points A, B, and C so that side a is 3 cubits, side b is 4 cubits, and c is 5 cubits.

Have you made a right triangle? How do you know? How could you make a square?

Tie It Together

Egyptian Exhibition

Plan a brochure to promote a special exhibition on Egypt at a museum. Half the class can focus on ancient Egypt. The other half can find out about the changes that have occurred on the Nile in the last 100 years. Work in small groups to research and assemble the information and illustrations. You might want to include the following:

◆ the Rosetta Stone and hieroglyphics

◆ directions for making a mummy

◆ the Great Pyramid at Giza

◆ history and treasures of King Tutankhamen

◆ religion in ancient Egypt

◆ model of an irrigation system for fields on the Nile

◆ maps of ancient and modern Egypt

◆ construction of the Aswan Dam, 1959–1970

◆ water control on the Nile in Egypt today

◆ Nile Delta today

G ◆ 151

3 Assess

Activity Assessment

Students will have made a right triangle as long as the sides of their triangles are exactly 3 cubits and 4 cubits, with a hypotenuse of 5 cubits (3 + 4 + 5 = 12). They know this because of the equation $a^2 + b^2 = c^2$, where $3^2 + 4^2 = 5^2$, or $9 + 16 = 25$. Students can make a square using the equation for a right triangle by making a and b equal to the same number. Two of these triangles joined together at the hypotenuse will form a square with four equal sides.

Tie It Together

Time 1 week (2 days for research, 2 days for assembling the information and illustrations, 1 day for assembling the brochure as a class)

Tips Have students work in groups of two or three. Encourage groups to choose one of the subjects listed in the text or one of their own based on their interests and knowledge of Egypt. If necessary, help each group divide up the tasks and work out a plan for researching and gathering information. If possible, have students use desktop publishing software to assemble their information into a class brochure.

◆ After the brochure is complete, invite students to reflect on their process. Ask: **What would you do differently to make the task of publishing the brochure more efficient?** (*Accept student answers without comment.*) Discuss the process of desktop publishing and what students have learned to make the next brochure easier to produce.

Extend If your local museum has an exhibit on ancient Egyptian culture, plan to take students there on a field trip. Encourage students to look especially for the subject that they researched for the brochure.

Background

Facts and Figures The Egyptians developed a branch of mathematics, which is now known by its Greek name, *geometry,* meaning "Earth measuring." Egyptians used geometry to survey their land and record boundaries. They also used geometry to measure the squares, triangles, circles, and cubes used for building pyramids and other monuments. About 2000 B.C., they learned how to make a square or rectangle by using a 90° angle.

The ancient Greeks adopted the Egyptian method of making rectangles with a 90° angle. During the sixth century B.C., a Greek philosopher and mathematician, Pythagoras, expanded on the Egyptian method by developing the Pythagorean Theorem, which says that the square of the hypotenuse of a right triangle is equal to the sum of the square of its sides ($a^2 + b^2 = c^2$).

G ◆ 151

Developing scientific thinking in students is important for a solid science education. To learn how to think scientifically, students need frequent opportunities to practice science process skills, critical thinking skills, as well as other skills that support scientific inquiry. The *Science Explorer* Skills Handbook introduces the following key science skills:

◆ Science Process Skills
◆ SI Measuring Skills
◆ Skills for Conducting a Scientific Investigation
◆ Critical Thinking Skills
◆ Information Organizing Skills
◆ Data Table and Graphing Skills

The Skills Handbook is designed as a reference for students to use whenever they need to review a science skill. You can use the activities provided in the Skills Handbook to teach or reinforce the skills.

Think Like a Scientist

Observing

ACTIVITY

Before students look at the photograph, remind them that an observation is what they can see, hear, smell, taste, or feel. Ask: **Which senses will you use to make observations from this photograph?** (*Sight is the only sense that can be used to make observations from the photograph.*) **What are some observations you can make from the photograph?** (*Answers may vary. Sample answers: The boy is wearing sneakers, sports socks, shorts, and a T-shirt; the boy is sitting in the grass holding something blue against his knee; the boy is looking at his knee; there is a soccer ball lying beside the boy.*) List the observations on the board. If students make any inferences or predictions about the boy at this point, ask: **Can you be sure your statement is accurate from just observing the photograph?** Help students understand how observations differ from inferences and predictions.

Inferring

ACTIVITY

Review students' observations from the photograph. Then ask: **What inferences can you make from your observations?** (*Students may*

Think Like a Scientist

Although you may not know it, you think like a scientist every day. Whenever you ask a question and explore possible answers, you use many of the same skills that scientists do. Some of these skills are described on this page.

Observing

When you use one or more of your five senses to gather information about the world, you are **observing.** Hearing a dog bark, counting twelve green seeds, and smelling smoke are all observations. To increase the power of their senses, scientists sometimes use microscopes, telescopes, or other instruments that help them make more detailed observations.

An observation must be an accurate report of what your senses detect. It is important to keep careful records of your observations in science class by writing or drawing in a notebook. The information collected through observations is called evidence, or data.

Inferring

When you interpret an observation, you are **inferring,** or making an inference. For example, if you hear your dog barking, you may infer that someone is at your front door. To make this inference, you combine the evidence—the barking dog—and your experience or knowledge—you know that your dog barks when strangers approach—to reach a logical conclusion.

Notice that an inference is not a fact; it is only one of many possible interpretations for an observation. For example, your dog may be barking because it wants to go for a walk. An inference may turn out to be incorrect even if it is based on accurate observations and logical reasoning. The only way to find out if an inference is correct is to investigate further.

Predicting

When you listen to the weather forecast, you hear many predictions about the next day's weather—what the temperature will be, whether it will rain, and how windy it will be. Weather forecasters use observations and knowledge of weather patterns to predict the weather. The skill of **predicting** involves making an inference about a future event based on current evidence or past experience.

Because a prediction is an inference, it may prove to be false. In science class, you can test some of your predictions by doing experiments. For example, suppose you predict that larger paper airplanes can fly farther than smaller airplanes. How could you test your prediction?

 Use the photograph to answer the questions below.

Observing Look closely at the photograph. List at least three observations.

Inferring Use your observations to make an inference about what has happened. What experience or knowledge did you use to make the inference?

Predicting Predict what will happen next. On what evidence or experience do you base your prediction?

say that the boy hurt his knee playing soccer and is holding a coldpack against his injured knee.) **What experience or knowledge helped you make this inference?** (*Students may have experienced knee injuries from playing soccer, and they may be familiar with coldpacks like the one the boy is using.*) **Can anyone suggest another possible interpretation for these observations?** (*Answers may vary. Sample answer: The boy hurt his knee jogging, and he just happened to sit beside a soccer ball his sister left in the yard.*) **How can you find out whether an inference is correct?** (*by further investigation*)

Predicting

ACTIVITY

After students come to some consensus about the inference that the boy hurt his knee, encourage them to make predictions about what will happen next. (*Students' predictions may vary. Sample answers: The boy will go to the doctor. A friend will help the boy home. The boy will get up and continue playing soccer.*)

Classifying

Could you imagine searching for a book in the library if the books were shelved in no particular order? Your trip to the library would be an all-day event! Luckily, librarians group together books on similar topics or by the same author. Grouping together items that are alike in some way is called **classifying.** You can classify items in many ways: by size, by shape, by use, and by other important characteristics.

Like librarians, scientists use the skill of classifying to organize information and objects. When things are sorted into groups, the relationships among them become easier to understand.

ACTIVITY Classify the objects in the photograph into two groups based on any characteristic you choose. Then use another characteristic to classify the objects into three groups.

Making Models

ACTIVITY This student is using a model to demonstrate what causes day and night on Earth. What do the flashlight and the tennis ball in the model represent?

Have you ever drawn a picture to help someone understand what you were saying? Such a drawing is one type of model. A model is a picture, diagram, computer image, or other representation of a complex object or process. **Making models** helps people understand things that they cannot observe directly.

Scientists often use models to represent things that are either very large or very small, such as the planets in the solar system, or the parts of a cell. Such models are physical models—drawings or three-dimensional structures that look like the real thing. Other models are mental models—mathematical equations or words that describe how something works.

Communicating

Whenever you talk on the phone, write a letter, or listen to your teacher at school, you are communicating. **Communicating** is the process of sharing ideas and information with other people. Communicating effectively requires many skills, including writing, reading, speaking, listening, and making models.

Scientists communicate to share results, information, and opinions. Scientists often communicate about their work in journals, over the telephone, in letters, and on the Internet. They also attend scientific meetings where they share their ideas with one another in person.

ACTIVITY On a sheet of paper, write out clear, detailed directions for tying your shoe. Then exchange directions with a partner. Follow your partner's directions exactly. How successful were you at tying your shoe? How could your partner have communicated more clearly?

Classifying **ACTIVITY**

Encourage students to think of other common things that are classified. Then ask: **What things at home are classified?** *(Clothing might be classified in order to place it in the appropriate dresser drawer; glasses, plates, and silverware are grouped in different parts of the kitchen; screws, nuts, bolts, washers, and nails might be separated into small containers.)* **What are some things that scientists classify?** *(Scientists classify many things they study, including organisms, geological features and processes, and kinds of machines.)* After students have classified the different fruits in the photograph, have them share their criteria for classifying them. *(Some characteristics students might use include shape, color, size, and where they are grown.)*

Making Models **ACTIVITY**

Ask students: **What are some models you have used to study science?** *(Students may have used human anatomical models, solar system models, maps, stream tables.)* **How did these models help you?** *(Models can help you learn about things that are difficult to study, because they are either too big, too small, or complex.)* Be sure students understand that a model does not have to be three-dimensional. For example, a map in a textbook is a model. Ask: **What do the flashlight and tennis ball represent?** *(The flashlight represents the sun, and the ball represents Earth.)* **What quality of each item makes this a good model?** *(The flashlight gives off light, and the ball is round and can be rotated by the student.)*

Communicating **ACTIVITY**

Challenge students to identify the methods of communication they've used today. Then ask: **How is the way you communicate with a friend similar to and different from the way scientists communicate about their work to other scientists?** *(Both may communicate using various methods, but scientists must be very detailed and precise, whereas communication between friends may be less detailed and precise.)* Encourage students to communicate like a scientist as they carry out the activity. *(Students' directions should be detailed and precise enough for another person to successfully follow.)*

On what did you base your prediction? *(Scientific predictions are based on knowledge and experience.)* Point out that in science, predictions can often be tested with experiments.

Making Measurements

Measuring in SI

Review SI units in class with students. Begin by providing metric rulers, graduated cylinders, balances, and Celsius thermometers. Use these tools to reinforce that the meter is the unit of length, the liter is the unit of volume, the gram is the unit of mass, and the degree Celsius is the unit for temperature. Ask: **If you want to measure the length and width of your classroom, which SI unit would you use?** (meter) **Which unit would you use to measure the amount of matter in your textbook?** (gram) **Which would you use to measure how much water a drinking glass holds?** (liter) **When would you use the Celsius scale?** (To measure the temperature of something) Then use the measuring equipment to review SI prefixes. For example, ask: **What are the smallest units on the metric ruler?** (millimeters) **How many millimeters are there in 1 cm?** (10 mm) **How many in 10 cm?** (100 mm) **How many centimeters are there in 1 m?** (100 cm) **What does 1,000 m equal?** (1 km)

Length (Students should state that the shell is 4.6 centimeters, or 46 millimeters, long.)
If students need more practice measuring length, have them use meter sticks and metric rulers to measure various objects in the classroom.

Liquid Volume
(Students should state that the volume of water in the graduated cylinder is 62 milliliters.) If students need more practice measuring liquid volume, have them use a graduated cylinder to measure different volumes of water.

Making Measurements

When scientists make observations, it is not sufficient to say that something is "big" or "heavy." Instead, scientists use instruments to measure just how big or heavy an object is. By measuring, scientists can express their observations more precisely and communicate more information about what they observe.

Measuring in SI

The standard system of measurement used by scientists around the world is known as the International System of Units, which is abbreviated as SI (in French, *Système International d'Unités*). SI units are easy to use because they are based on multiples of 10. Each unit is ten times larger than the next smallest unit and one tenth the size of the next largest unit. The table lists the prefixes used to name the most common SI units.

Common SI Prefixes		
Prefix	**Symbol**	**Meaning**
kilo-	k	1,000
hecto-	h	100
deka-	da	10
deci-	d	0.1 (one tenth)
centi-	c	0.01 (one hundredth)
milli-	m	0.001 (one thousandth)

Length To measure length, or the distance between two points, the unit of measure is the **meter (m)**. The distance from the floor to a doorknob is approximately one meter. Long distances, such as the distance between two cities, are measured in kilometers (km). Small lengths are measured in centimeters (cm) or millimeters (mm). Scientists use metric rulers and meter sticks to measure length.

Common Conversions
1 km = 1,000 m
1 m = 100 cm
1 m = 1,000 mm
1 cm = 10 mm

The larger lines on the metric ruler in the picture show centimeter divisions, while the smaller, unnumbered lines show millimeter divisions. How many centimeters long is the shell? How many millimeters long is it?

Liquid Volume To measure the volume of a liquid, or the amount of space it takes up, you will use a unit of measure known as the **liter (L)**. One liter is the approximate volume of a medium-size carton of milk. Smaller volumes are measured in milliliters (mL). Scientists use graduated cylinders to measure liquid volume.

Common Conversion
1 L = 1,000 mL

The graduated cylinder in the picture is marked in milliliter divisions. Notice that the water in the cylinder has a curved surface. This curved surface is called the *meniscus*. To measure the volume, you must read the level at the lowest point of the meniscus. What is the volume of water in this graduated cylinder?

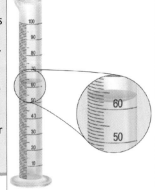

Mass To measure mass, or the amount of matter in an object, you will use a unit of measure known as the **gram (g)**. One gram is approximately the mass of a paper clip. Larger masses are measured in kilograms (kg). Scientists use a balance to find the mass of an object.

Common Conversion

1 kg = 1,000 g

The mass of the apple in the picture is measured in kilograms. What is the mass of the apple? Suppose a recipe for applesauce called for one kilogram of apples. About how many apples would you need?

Temperature
To measure the temperature of a substance, you will use the **Celsius scale**. Temperature is measured in degrees Celsius (°C) using a Celsius thermometer. Water freezes at 0°C and boils at 100°C.

What is the temperature of the liquid in degrees Celsius?

Converting SI Units

To use the SI system, you must know how to convert between units. Converting from one unit to another involves the skill of **calculating**, or using mathematical operations. Converting between SI units is similar to converting between dollars and dimes because both systems are based on multiples of ten.

Suppose you want to convert a length of 80 centimeters to meters. Follow these steps to convert between units.

1. Begin by writing down the measurement you want to convert—in this example, 80 centimeters.
2. Write a conversion factor that represents the relationship between the two units you are converting. In this example, the relationship is *1 meter = 100 centimeters*. Write this conversion factor as a fraction, making sure to place the units you are converting from (centimeters, in this example) in the denominator.

3. Multiply the measurement you want to convert by the fraction. When you do this, the units in the first measurement will cancel out with the units in the denominator. Your answer will be in the units you are converting to (meters, in this example).

Example

80 centimeters = ___?___ meters

$$80 \text{ centimeters} \times \frac{1 \text{ meter}}{100 \text{ centimeters}} = \frac{80 \text{ meters}}{100}$$

$$= 0.8 \text{ meters}$$

Convert between the following units.
1. 600 millimeters = _?_ meters
2. 0.35 liters = _?_ milliliters
3. 1,050 grams = _?_ kilograms

Conducting a Scientific Investigation

Posing Questions

Before students do the activity on the next page, walk them through the steps of a typical scientific investigation. Begin by asking: **Why is a scientific question important to a scientific investigation?** *(It is the reason for conducting a scientific investigation.)* **What is the scientific question in the activity at the bottom of the next page?** *(Is a ball's bounce affected by the height from which it is dropped?)*

Developing a Hypothesis

Emphasize that a hypothesis is a possible explanation for a set of observations or answer to a scientific question, but it is *not* a guess. Ask: **On what information do scientists base their hypotheses?** *(Their observations and previous knowledge or experience)* Point out that a hypothesis does not always turn out to be correct. Ask: **In that case, do you think the scientist wasted his or her time? Explain your answer.** *(No, because the scientist probably learned from the investigation and may be able to develop another hypothesis that could be supported.)*

Designing an Experiment

Have a volunteer read the Experimental Procedure in the box. Then call on students to identify the manipulated variable *(amount of salt added to water)*, the variables that are kept constant *(amount and starting temperature of water, placing containers in freezer)*, the responding variable *(time it takes water to freeze)*, and the control *(Container 3)*.

Ask: **How might the experiment be affected if Container 1 had only 100 mL of water?** *(It wouldn't be a fair comparison with the containers that have more water.)* **What if Container 3 was not included in the experiment?** *(You wouldn't have anything to compare the other two containers with to know if their freezing times were faster or slower than normal.)* Help students understand the importance of keeping all variables constant except the manipulated variable. Also, be sure

Conducting a Scientific Investigation

In some ways, scientists are like detectives, piecing together clues to learn about a process or event. One way that scientists gather clues is by carrying out experiments. An experiment tests an idea in a careful, orderly manner. Although experiments do not all follow the same steps in the same order, many follow a pattern similar to the one described here.

Posing Questions

Experiments begin by asking a scientific question. A scientific question is one that can be answered by gathering evidence. For example, the question "Which freezes faster— fresh water or salt water?" is a scientific question because you can carry out an investigation and gather information to answer the question.

Developing a Hypothesis

The next step is to form a hypothesis. A **hypothesis** is a possible explanation for a set of observations or answer to a scientific question. In science, a hypothesis must be something that can be tested. A hypothesis can be worded as an *If…then…* statement. For example, a hypothesis might be *"If I add salt to fresh water, then the water will take longer to freeze."* A hypothesis worded this way serves as a rough outline of the experiment you should perform.

156 ◆ G

they understand the role of the control. Then ask: **What operational definition is used in this experiment?** *("Frozen" means the time at which a wooden stick can no longer move in a container.)*

Designing an Experiment

Next you need to plan a way to test your hypothesis. Your plan should be written out as a step-by-step procedure and should describe the observations or measurements you will make.

Two important steps involved in designing an experiment are controlling variables and forming operational definitions.

Controlling Variables In a well-designed experiment, you need to keep all variables the same except for one. A **variable** is any factor that can change in an experiment. The factor that you change is called the **manipulated variable.** In this experiment, the manipulated variable is the amount of salt added to the water. Other factors, such as the amount of water or the starting temperature, are kept constant.

The factor that changes as a result of the manipulated variable is called the **responding variable.** The **responding variable** is what you measure or observe to obtain your results. In this experiment, the responding variable is how long the water takes to freeze.

An experiment in which all factors except one are kept constant is a **controlled experiment.** Most controlled experiments include a test called the control. In this experiment, Container 3 is the control. Because no salt is added to Container 3, you can compare the results from the other containers to it. Any difference in results must be due to the addition of salt alone.

Forming Operational Definitions
Another important aspect of a well-designed experiment is having clear operational definitions. An **operational definition** is a statement that describes how a particular variable is to be measured or how a term is to be defined. For example, in this experiment, how will you determine if the water has frozen? You might decide to insert a stick in each container at the start of the experiment. Your operational definition of "frozen" would be the time at which the stick can no longer move.

EXPERIMENTAL PROCEDURE

1. Fill 3 containers with 300 milliliters of cold tap water.

2. Add 10 grams of salt to Container 1; stir. Add 20 grams of salt to Container 2; stir. Add no salt to Container 3.

3. Place the 3 containers in a freezer.

4. Check the containers every 15 minutes. Record your observations.

Interpreting Data

The observations and measurements you make in an experiment are called data. At the end of an experiment, you need to analyze the data to look for any patterns or trends. Patterns often become clear if you organize your data in a data table or graph. Then think through what the data reveal. Do they support your hypothesis? Do they point out a flaw in your experiment? Do you need to collect more data?

Drawing Conclusions

A conclusion is a statement that sums up what you have learned from an experiment. When you draw a conclusion, you need to decide whether the data you collected support your hypothesis or not. You may need to repeat an experiment several times before you can draw any conclusions from it. Conclusions often lead you to pose new questions and plan new experiments to answer them.

ACTIVITY
Is a ball's bounce affected by the height from which it is dropped? Using the steps just described, plan a controlled experiment to investigate this problem.

G ◆ 157

Interpreting Data

Emphasize the importance of collecting accurate and detailed data in a scientific investigation. Ask: **What if you forgot to record some data during your investigation?** *(They wouldn't be able to completely analyze their data to draw valid conclusions.)* Then ask: **Why are data tables and graphs a good way to organize data?** *(They often make it easier to compare and analyze data.)* You may wish to have students review the Skills Handbook pages on Creating Data Tables and Graphs at this point.

Drawing Conclusions

Help students understand that a conclusion is not necessarily the end of a scientific investigation. A conclusion about one experiment may lead right into another experiment. Point out that in scientific investigations, a conclusion is a summary and explanation of the results of an experiment.

Tell students to suppose that for the Experimental Procedure described on this page, they obtained the following results: Container 1 froze in 45 minutes, Container 2 in 80 minutes, and Container 3 in 25 minutes. Ask: **What conclusions can you draw about this experiment?** *(Students might conclude that the more salt that is added to fresh water, the longer it takes the water to freeze. The hypothesis is supported, and the question of which freezes faster is answered—fresh water.)*

You might wish to have students work in pairs to plan the controlled experiment. *(Students should develop a hypothesis, such as "If I increase the height from which a ball is dropped, then the height of its bounce will increase." They can test the hypothesis by dropping balls from varying heights (the manipulated variable). All trials should be done with the same kind of ball and on the same surface (constant variables). For each trial, they should measure the height of the bounce (responding variable).)* After students have designed the experiment, provide rubber balls and invite them to carry out the experiment so they can collect and interpret data and draw conclusions.

ACTIVITY

Thinking Critically

Comparing and Contrasting

Emphasize that the skill of comparing and contrasting often relies on good observation skills, as in this activity. *(Students' answers may vary. Sample answer: Similarities—both are dogs and have four legs, two eyes, two ears, brown and white fur, black noses, pink tongues; Differences—smooth coat vs. rough coat, more white fur vs. more brown fur, shorter vs. taller, long ears vs. short ears.)*

Applying Concepts

Point out to students that they apply concepts that they learn in school in their daily lives. For example, they learn to add, subtract, multiply, and divide in school. If they get a paper route or some other part-time job, they can apply those concepts. Challenge students to practice applying concepts by doing the activity. *(Antifreeze lowers the temperature at which the solution will freeze, and thus keeps the water in the radiator from freezing.)*

Interpreting Illustrations

Again, point out the need for good observation skills. Ask: **What is the difference between "interpreting illustrations" and "looking at the pictures"?** *("Interpreting illustrations" requires thorough examination of the illustrations, captions, and labels, while "looking at the pictures" implies less thorough examination.)* Encourage students to thoroughly examine the diagram as they do the activity. *(Students' paragraphs will vary, but should describe the internal anatomy of an earthworm, including some of the organs in the earthworm.)*

Thinking Critically

Has a friend ever asked for your advice about a problem? If so, you may have helped your friend think through the problem in a logical way. Without knowing it, you used critical-thinking skills to help your friend. Critical thinking involves the use of reasoning and logic to solve problems or make decisions. Some critical-thinking skills are described below.

Comparing and Contrasting

When you examine two objects for similarities and differences, you are using the skill of **comparing and contrasting.** Comparing involves identifying similarities, or common characteristics. Contrasting involves identifying differences. Analyzing objects in this way can help you discover details that you might otherwise overlook.

Compare and contrast the two animals in the photo. First list all the similarities that you see. Then list all the differences.

Applying Concepts

When you use your knowledge about one situation to make sense of a similar situation, you are using the skill of **applying concepts.** Being able to transfer your knowledge from one situation to another shows that you truly understand a concept. You may use this skill in answering test questions that present different problems from the ones you've reviewed in class.

You have just learned that water takes longer to freeze when other substances are mixed into it. Use this knowledge to explain why people need a substance called antifreeze in their car's radiator in the winter.

Interpreting Illustrations

Diagrams, photographs, and maps are included in textbooks to help clarify what you read. These illustrations show processes, places, and ideas in a visual manner. The skill called **interpreting illustrations** can help you learn from these visual elements. To understand an illustration, take the time to study the illustration along with all the written information that accompanies it. Captions identify the key concepts shown in the illustration. Labels point out the important parts of a diagram or map, while keys identify the symbols used in a map.

Bristles · Upper blood vessel · Reproductive organs · Arches · Brain · Mouth · Digestive tract · Lower blood vessel · Waste-removal organs · Intestine · Nerve cord

▲ Internal anatomy of an earthworm

Study the diagram above. Then write a short paragraph explaining what you have learned.

Relating Cause and Effect

If one event causes another event to occur, the two events are said to have a cause-and-effect relationship. When you determine that such a relationship exists between two events, you use a skill called **relating cause and effect.** For example, if you notice an itchy, red bump on your skin, you might infer that a mosquito bit you. The mosquito bite is the cause, and the bump is the effect.

It is important to note that two events do not necessarily have a cause-and-effect relationship just because they occur together. Scientists carry out experiments or use past experience to determine whether a cause-and-effect relationship exists.

You are on a camping trip and your flashlight has stopped working. List some possible causes for the flashlight malfunction. How could you determine which cause-and-effect relationship has left you in the dark?

Making Generalizations

When you draw a conclusion about an entire group based on information about only some of the group's members, you are using a skill called **making generalizations.** For a generalization to be valid, the sample you choose must be large enough and representative of the entire group. You might, for example, put this skill to work at a farm stand if you see a sign that says, "Sample some grapes before you buy." If you sample a few sweet grapes, you may conclude that all the grapes are sweet—and purchase a large bunch.

A team of scientists needs to determine whether the water in a large reservoir is safe to drink. How could they use the skill of making generalizations to help them? What should they do?

Making Judgments

When you evaluate something to decide whether it is good or bad, or right or wrong, you are using a skill called **making judgments.** For example, you make judgments when you decide to eat healthful foods or to pick up litter in a park. Before you make a judgment, you need to think through the pros and cons of a situation, and identify the values or standards that you hold.

Should children and teens be required to wear helmets when bicycling? Explain why you feel the way you do.

Problem Solving

When you use critical-thinking skills to resolve an issue or decide on a course of action, you are using a skill called **problem solving.** Some problems, such as how to convert a fraction into a decimal, are straightforward. Other problems, such as figuring out why your computer has stopped

working, are complex. Some complex problems can be solved using the trial and error method—try out one solution first, and if that doesn't work, try another. Other useful problem-solving strategies include making models and brainstorming possible solutions with a partner.

Relating Cause and Effect

Emphasize that not all events that occur together have a cause-and-effect relationship. For example, tell students that you went to the grocery and your car stalled. Ask: **Is there a cause-and-effect relationship in this situation? Explain your answer.** *(No, because going to the grocery could not cause a car to stall. There must be another cause to make the car stall.)* Have students do the activity to practice relating cause and effect. *(Students should identify that the flashlight not working is the effect. Some possible causes include dead batteries, a burned-out light bulb, or a loose part.)*

Making Generalizations

Point out the importance of having a large, representative sample before making a generalization. Ask: **If you went fishing at a lake and caught three catfish, could you make the generalization that all fish in the lake are catfish? Why or why not?** *(No, because there might be other kinds of fish you didn't catch because they didn't like the bait or they may be in other parts of the lake.)* **How could you make a generalization about the kinds of fish in the lake?** *(By having a larger sample)* Have students do the activity in the Student Edition to practice making generalizations. *(The scientists should collect and test water samples from a number of different parts of the reservoir.)*

Making Judgments

Remind students that they make a judgment almost every time they make a decision. Ask: **What steps should you follow to make a judgment?** *(Gather information, list pros and cons, analyze values, make judgment)* Invite students to do the activity, and then to share and discuss the judgments they made. *(Students' judgments will vary, but should be supported by valid reasoning. Sample answer: Children and teens should be required to wear helmets when bicycling because helmets have been proven to save lives and reduce head injuries.)*

Problem Solving

Challenge student pairs to solve a problem about a soapbox derby. Explain that their younger brother is building a car to enter in the race. The brother wants to know how to make his soapbox car go faster. After student pairs have considered the problem, have them share their ideas about solutions with the class. *(Most will probably suggest using trial and error by making small changes to the car and testing the car after each change. Some students may suggest making and manipulating a model.)*

Organizing Information

Concept Maps

Challenge students to make a concept map with at least three levels of concepts to organize information about types of transportation. All students should start with the phrase *types of transportation* at the top of the concept map. After that point, their concept maps may vary. *(For example, some students might place* private transportation *and* public transportation *at the next level, while other students might have* human-powered *and* gas-powered. *Make sure students connect the concepts with linking words. Challenge students to include cross-linkages as well.)*

Compare/ Contrast Tables

Have students make their own compare/contrast tables using two or more different sports or other activities, such as playing musical instruments. Emphasize that students should select characteristics that highlight the similarities and differences between the activities. *(Students' compare/contrast tables should include several appropriate characteristics and list information about each activity for every characteristic.)*

Organizing Information

As you read this textbook, how can you make sense of all the information it contains? Some useful tools to help you organize information are shown on this page. These tools are called *graphic organizers* because they give you a visual picture of a topic, showing at a glance how key concepts are related.

Concept Maps

Concept maps are useful tools for organizing information on broad topics. A concept map begins with a general concept and shows how it can be broken down into more specific concepts. In that way, relationships between concepts become easier to understand.

A concept map is constructed by placing concept words (usually nouns) in ovals and connecting them with linking words. Often, the most general concept word is placed at the top, and the words become more specific as you move downward. Often the linking words, which are written on a line extending between two ovals, describe the relationship between the two concepts they connect. If you follow any string of concepts and linking words down the map, it should read like a sentence.

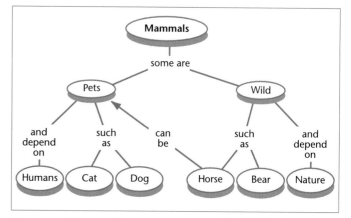

Some concept maps include linking words that connect a concept on one branch of the map to a concept on another branch. These linking words, called cross-linkages, show more complex interrelationships among concepts.

Compare/Contrast Tables

Compare/contrast tables are useful tools for sorting out the similarities and differences between two or more items. A table provides an organized framework in which to compare items based on specific characteristics that you identify.

To create a compare/contrast table, list the items to be compared across the top of a table. Then list the characteristics that will form the basis of your comparison in the left-hand

Characteristic	Baseball	Basketball
Number of Players	9	5
Playing Field	Baseball diamond	Basketball court
Equipment	Bat, baseball, mitts	Basket, basketball

column. Complete the table by filling in information about each characteristic, first for one item and then for the other.

Venn Diagrams

Another way to show similarities and differences between items is with a Venn diagram. A Venn diagram consists of two or more circles that partially overlap. Each circle represents a particular concept or idea. Common characteristics, or similarities, are written within the area of overlap between the two circles. Unique characteristics, or differences, are written in the parts of the circles outside the area of overlap.

To create a Venn diagram, draw two overlapping circles. Label the circles with the names of the items being compared. Write the

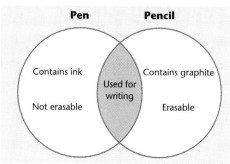

unique characteristics in each circle outside the area of overlap. Then write the shared characteristics within the area of overlap.

Flowcharts

A flowchart can help you understand the order in which certain events have occurred or should occur. Flowcharts are useful for outlining the stages in a process or the steps in a procedure.

To make a flowchart, write a brief description of each event in a box. Place the first event at the top of the page, followed by the second event, the third event, and so on. Then draw an arrow to connect each event to the one that occurs next.

Preparing Pasta

Boil water
↓
Cook pasta
↓
Drain water
↓
Add sauce

Cycle Diagrams

A cycle diagram can be used to show a sequence of events that is continuous, or cyclical. A continuous sequence does not have an end because, when the final event is over, the first event begins again. Like a flowchart, a cycle diagram can help you understand the order of events.

To create a cycle diagram, write a brief description of each event in a box. Place one event at the top of the page in the center. Then, moving in a clockwise direction around an imaginary circle, write each event in its proper sequence. Draw arrows that connect each event to the one that occurs next, forming a continuous circle.

Steps in a Science Experiment

Pose a question → Develop a hypothesis → Design an experiment → Interpret data → Draw conclusions → (back to Pose a question)

G ◆ 161

Venn Diagrams

Students can use the same information from their compare/contrast tables to create a Venn diagram. Make sure students understand that the overlapping area of the circles is used to list similarities and the parts of the circles outside the overlap area are used to show differences. If students want to list similarities and differences among three activities, show them how to add a third circle that overlaps each of the other two circles and has an area of overlap for all three circles. *(Students' Venn diagrams will vary. Make sure they have accurately listed similarities in the overlap area and differences in the parts of the circles that do not overlap.)*

Flowcharts

Encourage students to create a flowchart to show the things they did this morning as they got ready for school. Remind students that a flowchart should show the correct order in which events occurred or should occur. *(Students' flowcharts will vary somewhat. A typical flowchart might include: got up → ate breakfast → took a shower → brushed teeth → got dressed → gathered books and homework → put on jacket.)*

Cycle Diagrams

Review that a cycle diagram shows a sequence of events that is continuous. Then challenge students to create a cycle diagram that shows how the weather changes with the seasons where they live. *(Students' cycle diagrams may vary, though most will include four steps, one for each season.)*

Creating Data Tables and Graphs

Data Tables

Have students create a data table to show how much time they spend on different activities during one week. Suggest that students first list the main activities they do every week. Then they should determine the amount of time they spend on each activity each day. Remind students to give this data table a title. *(Students' data tables will vary. A sample data table is shown below.)*

Bar Graphs

Students can use the data from the data table they created to make a bar graph showing how much time they spend on different activities during a week. The vertical axis should be divided into units of time, such as hours. Remind students to label both axes and give their graph a title. *(Students' bar graphs will vary. A sample bar graph is shown below.)*

Creating Data Tables and Graphs

How can you make sense of the data in a science experiment? The first step is to organize the data to help you understand them. Data tables and graphs are helpful tools for organizing data.

Data Tables

You have gathered your materials and set up your experiment. But before you start, you need to plan a way to record what happens during the experiment. By creating a data table, you can record your observations and measurements in an orderly way.

Suppose, for example, that a scientist conducted an experiment to find out how many Calories people of different body masses burn while doing various activities. The data table shows the results.

Notice in this data table that the manipulated variable (body mass) is the heading of one column. The responding variable (for Experiment 1, the number of Calories burned while bicycling) is the heading of the next column. Additional columns were added for related experiments.

CALORIES BURNED IN 30 MINUTES OF ACTIVITY			
Body Mass	Experiment 1 Bicycling	Experiment 2 Playing Basketball	Experiment 3 Watching Television
30 kg	60 Calories	120 Calories	21 Calories
40 kg	77 Calories	164 Calories	27 Calories
50 kg	95 Calories	206 Calories	33 Calories
60 kg	114 Calories	248 Calories	38 Calories

Bar Graphs

To compare how many Calories a person burns doing various activities, you could create a bar graph. A bar graph is used to display data in a number of separate, or distinct, categories. In this example, bicycling, playing basketball, and watching television are three separate categories.

To create a bar graph, follow these steps.

1. On graph paper, draw a horizontal, or *x*-, axis and a vertical, or *y*-, axis.
2. Write the names of the categories to be graphed along the horizontal axis. Include an overall label for the axis as well.
3. Label the vertical axis with the name of the responding variable. Include units of measurement. Then create a scale along the axis by marking off equally spaced numbers that cover the range of the data collected.
4. For each category, draw a solid bar using the scale on the vertical axis to determine the

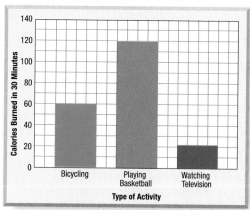

Calories Burned by a 30-kilogram Person in Various Activities

appropriate height. For example, for bicycling, draw the bar as high as the 60 mark on the vertical axis. Make all the bars the same width and leave equal spaces between them.
5. Add a title that describes the graph.

Time Spent on Different Activities in a Week				
	Going to Classes	Eating Meals	Playing Soccer	Watching Television
Monday	6	2	2	0.5
Tuesday	6	1.5	1.5	1.5
Wednesday	6	2	1	2
Thursday	6	2	2	1.5
Friday	6	2	2	0.5
Saturday	0	2.5	2.5	1
Sunday	0	3	1	2

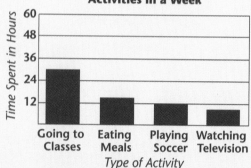

Time Spent on Different Activities in a Week

Line Graphs

To see whether a relationship exists between body mass and the number of Calories burned while bicycling, you could create a line graph. A line graph is used to display data that show how one variable (the responding variable) changes in response to another variable (the manipulated variable). You can use a line graph when your manipulated variable is *continuous*, that is, when there are other points between the ones that you tested. In this example, body mass is a continuous variable because there are other body masses between 30 and 40 kilograms (for example, 31 kilograms). Time is another example of a continuous variable.

Line graphs are powerful tools because they allow you to estimate values for conditions that you did not test in the experiment. For example, you can use the line graph to estimate that a 35-kilogram person would burn 68 Calories while bicycling.

To create a line graph, follow these steps.

1. On graph paper, draw a horizontal, or *x*-, axis and a vertical, or *y*-, axis.
2. Label the horizontal axis with the name of the manipulated variable. Label the vertical axis with the name of the responding variable. Include units of measurement.
3. Create a scale on each axis by marking off equally spaced numbers that cover the range of the data collected.
4. Plot a point on the graph for each piece of data. In the line graph above, the dotted lines show how to plot the first data point (30 kilograms and 60 Calories). Draw an imaginary vertical line extending up from the horizontal axis at the 30-kilogram mark. Then draw an imaginary horizontal line extending across from the vertical axis at the 60-Calorie mark. Plot the point where the two lines intersect.

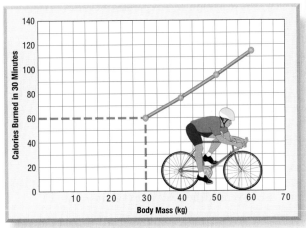

Effect of Body Mass on Calories Burned While Bicycling

5. Connect the plotted points with a solid line. (In some cases, it may be more appropriate to draw a line that shows the general trend of the plotted points. In those cases, some of the points may fall above or below the line. Also, not all graphs are linear. It may be more appropriate to draw a curve to connect the points.)
6. Add a title that identifies the variables or relationship in the graph.

> **ACTIVITY**
> Create line graphs to display the data from Experiment 2 and Experiment 3 in the data table.

> **ACTIVITY**
> You read in the newspaper that a total of 4 centimeters of rain fell in your area in June, 2.5 centimeters fell in July, and 1.5 centimeters fell in August. What type of graph would you use to display these data? Use graph paper to create the graph.

Line Graphs

Walk students through the steps involved in creating a line graph using the example illustrated on the page. For example, ask: **What is the label on the horizontal axis? On the vertical axis?** (*Body Mass (kg); Calories Burned in 30 Minutes*) **What scales are used on each axis?** (*3 squares per 10 kg on the x-axis and 2 squares per 20 calories on the y-axis*) **What does the second data point represent?** (*77 Calories burned for a body mass of 40 kg*) **What trend or pattern does the graph show?** (*The number of Calories burned in 30 minutes of cycling increases with body mass.*)

Have students follow the steps to carry out the first activity. (*Students should make a different graph for each experiment with different y-axis scales to practice making scales appropriate for data. See sample graphs below.*)

Have students carry out the second activity. (*Students should conclude that a bar graph would be best for displaying the data. A sample bar graph for these data is shown below.*)

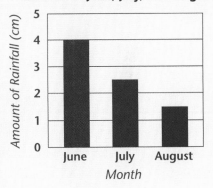

Rainfall in June, July, and August

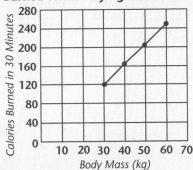

Effect of Body Mass on Calories Burned While Playing Basketball

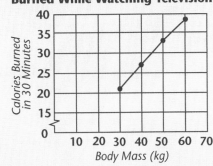

Effect of Body Mass on Calories Burned While Watching Television

Circle Graphs

Emphasize that a circle graph has to include 100 percent of the categories for the topic being graphed. For example, ask: **Could the data in the bar graph titled "Calories Burned by a 30-kilogram Person in Various Activities" (on the previous page) be shown in a circle graph? Why or why not?** (*No, because it does not include all the possible ways a 30-kilogram person can burn Calories.*) Then walk students through the steps for making a circle graph. Help students to use a compass and a protractor. Use the protractor to illustrate that a circle has 360 degrees. Make sure students understand the mathematical calculations involved in making a circle graph.

You might wish to have students work in pairs to complete the activity. (*Students' circle graphs should look like the graph below.*)

ACTIVITY

Circle Graphs

Like bar graphs, circle graphs can be used to display data in a number of separate categories. Unlike bar graphs, however, circle graphs can only be used when you have data for *all* the categories that make up a given topic. A circle graph is sometimes called a pie chart because it resembles a pie cut into slices. The pie represents the entire topic, while the slices represent the individual categories. The size of a slice indicates what percentage of the whole a particular category makes up.

The data table below shows the results of a survey in which 24 teenagers were asked to identify their favorite sport. The data were then used to create the circle graph at the right.

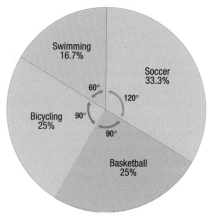

Sports That Teens Prefer

FAVORITE SPORTS	
Sport	Number of Students
Soccer	8
Basketball	6
Bicycling	6
Swimming	4

To create a circle graph, follow these steps.

1. Use a compass to draw a circle. Mark the center of the circle with a point. Then draw a line from the center point to the top of the circle.

2. Determine the size of each "slice" by setting up a proportion where *x* equals the number of degrees in a slice. (NOTE: A circle contains 360 degrees.) For example, to find the number of degrees in the "soccer" slice, set up the following proportion:

$$\frac{\text{students who prefer soccer}}{\text{total number of students}} = \frac{x}{\text{total number of degrees in a circle}}$$

$$\frac{8}{24} = \frac{x}{360}$$

Cross-multiply and solve for *x*.

$$24x = 8 \times 360$$
$$x = 120$$

The "soccer" slice should contain 120 degrees.

3. Use a protractor to measure the angle of the first slice, using the line you drew to the top of the circle as the 0° line. Draw a line from the center of the circle to the edge for the angle you measured.

4. Continue around the circle by measuring the size of each slice with the protractor. Start measuring from the edge of the previous slice so the wedges do not overlap. When you are done, the entire circle should be filled in.

5. Determine the percentage of the whole circle that each slice represents. To do this, divide the number of degrees in a slice by the total number of degrees in a circle (360), and multiply by 100%. For the "soccer" slice, you can find the percentage as follows:

$$\frac{120}{360} \times 100\% = 33.3\%$$

6. Use a different color to shade in each slice. Label each slice with the name of the category and with the percentage of the whole it represents.

7. Add a title to the circle graph.

ACTIVITY
In a class of 28 students, 12 students take the bus to school, 10 students walk, and 6 students ride their bicycles. Create a circle graph to display these data.

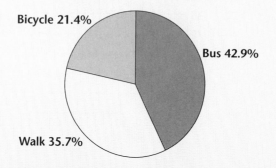

Ways Students Get to School

Bicycle 21.4%

Bus 42.9%

Walk 35.7%

Laboratory Safety

Safety Symbols

These symbols alert you to possible dangers in the laboratory and remind you to work carefully.

Safety Goggles Always wear safety goggles to protect your eyes in any activity involving chemicals, flames or heating, or the possibility of broken glassware.

Lab Apron Wear a laboratory apron to protect your skin and clothing from damage.

Breakage You are working with materials that may be breakable, such as glass containers, glass tubing, thermometers, or funnels. Handle breakable materials with care. Do not touch broken glassware.

Heat-resistant Gloves Use an oven mitt or other hand protection when handling hot materials. Hot plates, hot glassware, or hot water can cause burns. Do not touch hot objects with your bare hands.

Heating Use a clamp or tongs to pick up hot glassware. Do not touch hot objects with your bare hands.

Sharp Object Pointed-tip scissors, scalpels, knives, needles, pins, or tacks are sharp. They can cut or puncture your skin. Always direct a sharp edge or point away from yourself and others. Use sharp instruments only as instructed.

Electric Shock Avoid the possibility of electric shock. Never use electrical equipment around water, or when the equipment is wet or your hands are wet. Be sure cords are untangled and cannot trip anyone. Disconnect the equipment when it is not in use.

Corrosive Chemical You are working with an acid or another corrosive chemical. Avoid getting it on your skin or clothing, or in your eyes. Do not inhale the vapors. Wash your hands when you are finished with the activity.

Poison Do not let any poisonous chemical come in contact with your skin, and do not inhale its vapors. Wash your hands when you are finished with the activity.

Physical Safety When an experiment involves physical activity, take precautions to avoid injuring yourself or others. Follow instructions from your teacher. Alert your teacher if there is any reason you should not participate in the activity.

Animal Safety Treat live animals with care to avoid harming the animals or yourself. Working with animal parts or preserved animals also may require caution. Wash your hands when you are finished with the activity.

Plant Safety Handle plants in the laboratory or during field work only as directed by your teacher. If you are allergic to certain plants, tell your teacher before doing an activity in which those plants are used. Avoid touching harmful plants such as poison ivy, poison oak, or poison sumac, or plants with thorns. Wash your hands when you are finished with the activity.

Flames You may be working with flames from a lab burner, candle, or matches. Tie back loose hair and clothing. Follow instructions from your teacher about lighting and extinguishing flames.

No Flames Flammable materials may be present. Make sure there are no flames, sparks, or other exposed heat sources present.

Fumes When poisonous or unpleasant vapors may be involved, work in a ventilated area. Avoid inhaling vapors directly. Only test an odor when directed to do so by your teacher, and use a wafting motion to direct the vapor toward your nose.

Disposal Chemicals and other laboratory materials used in the activity must be disposed of safely. Follow the instructions from your teacher.

Hand Washing Wash your hands thoroughly when finished with the activity. Use antibacterial soap and warm water. Lather both sides of your hands and between your fingers. Rinse well.

General Safety Awareness You may see this symbol when none of the symbols described earlier appears. In this case, follow the specific instructions provided. You may also see this symbol when you are asked to develop your own procedure in a lab. Have your teacher approve your plan before you go further.

G ◆ 165

Laboratory Safety

Laboratory safety is an essential element of a successful science class. It is important for you to emphasize laboratory safety to students. Students need to understand exactly what is safe and unsafe behavior, and what the rationale is behind each safety rule.

Review with students the Safety Symbols and Science Safety Rules listed on this and the next two pages. Then follow the safety guidelines below to ensure that your classroom will be a safe place for students to learn science.

◆ Post safety rules in the classroom and review them regularly with students.

◆ Familiarize yourself with the safety procedures for each activity before introducing it to your students.

◆ Review specific safety precautions with students before beginning every science activity.

◆ Always act as an exemplary role model by displaying safe behavior.

◆ Know how to use safety equipment, such as fire extinguishers and fire blankets, and always have it accessible.

◆ Have students practice leaving the classroom quickly and orderly to prepare them for emergencies.

◆ Explain to students how to use the intercom or other available means of communication to get help during an emergency.

◆ Never leave students unattended while they are engaged in science activities.

◆ Provide enough space for students to safely carry out science activities.

◆ Keep your classroom and all science materials in proper condition. Replace worn or broken items.

◆ Instruct students to report all accidents and injuries to you immediately.

Laboratory Safety

Additional tips are listed below for the Science Safety Rules discussed on these two pages. Please keep these tips in mind when you carry out science activities in your classroom.

General Precautions

◆ For open-ended activities such as Chapter Projects, go over general safety guidelines with students. Have students submit their procedures or design plans in writing and check them for safety considerations.

◆ In an activity where students are directed to taste something, be sure to store the material in clean, *nonscience* containers. Distribute the material to students in *new* plastic or paper dispensables, which should be discarded after the tasting. Tasting or eating should never be done in a lab classroom.

◆ During physical activity, make sure students do not overexert themselves.

◆ Remind students to handle microscopes and telescopes with care to avoid breakage.

Heating and Fire Safety

◆ No flammable substances should be in use around hot plates, light bulbs, or open flames.

◆ Test tubes should be heated only in water baths.

◆ Students should be permitted to strike matches to light candles or burners *only* with strict supervision. When possible, you should light the flames, especially when working with younger students.

◆ Be sure to have proper ventilation when fumes are produced during a procedure.

◆ All electrical equipment used in the lab should have GFI switches.

Using Chemicals Safely

◆ When students use both chemicals and microscopes in one activity, microscopes should be in a separate part of the room from the chemicals so that when students remove their goggles to use the microscopes, their eyes are not at risk.

Science Safety Rules

To prepare yourself to work safely in the laboratory, read over the following safety rules. Then read them a second time. Make sure you understand and follow each rule. Ask your teacher to explain any rules you do not understand.

Dress Code

1. To protect yourself from injuring your eyes, wear safety goggles whenever you work with chemicals, burners, glassware, or any substance that might get into your eyes. If you wear contact lenses, notify your teacher.
2. Wear a lab apron or coat whenever you work with corrosive chemicals or substances that can stain.
3. Tie back long hair to keep it away from any chemicals, flames, or equipment.
4. Remove or tie back any article of clothing or jewelry that can hang down and touch chemicals, flames, or equipment. Roll up or secure long sleeves.
5. Never wear open shoes or sandals.

General Precautions

6. Read all directions for an experiment several times before beginning the activity. Carefully follow all written and oral instructions. If you are in doubt about any part of the experiment, ask your teacher for assistance.
7. Never perform activities that are not assigned or authorized by your teacher. Obtain permission before "experimenting" on your own. Never handle any equipment unless you have specific permission.
8. Never perform lab activities without direct supervision.
9. Never eat or drink in the laboratory.
10. Keep work areas clean and tidy at all times. Bring only notebooks and lab manuals or written lab procedures to the work area. All other items, such as purses and backpacks, should be left in a designated area.
11. Do not engage in horseplay.

First Aid

12. Always report all accidents or injuries to your teacher, no matter how minor. Notify your teacher immediately about any fires.
13. Learn what to do in case of specific accidents, such as getting acid in your eyes or on your skin. (Rinse acids from your body with lots of water.)
14. Be aware of the location of the first-aid kit, but do not use it unless instructed by your teacher. In case of injury, your teacher should administer first aid. Your teacher may also send you to the school nurse or call a physician.
15. Know the location of emergency equipment, such as the fire extinguisher and fire blanket, and know how to use it.
16. Know the location of the nearest telephone and whom to contact in an emergency.

Heating and Fire Safety

17. Never use a heat source, such as a candle, burner, or hot plate, without wearing safety goggles.
18. Never heat anything unless instructed to do so. A chemical that is harmless when cool may be dangerous when heated.
19. Keep all combustible materials away from flames. Never use a flame or spark near a combustible chemical.
20. Never reach across a flame.
21. Before using a laboratory burner, make sure you know proper procedures for lighting and adjusting the burner, as demonstrated by your teacher. Do not touch the burner. It may be hot. And never leave a lighted burner unattended!
22. Chemicals can splash or boil out of a heated test tube. When heating a substance in a test tube, make sure that the mouth of the tube is not pointed at you or anyone else.
23. Never heat a liquid in a closed container. The expanding gases produced may blow the container apart.
24. Before picking up a container that has been heated, hold the back of your hand near it. If you can feel heat on the back of your hand, the container is too hot to handle. Use an oven mitt to pick up a container that has been heated.

Using Glassware Safely

◆ Use plastic containers, graduated cylinders, and beakers whenever possible. If using glass, students should wear safety goggles.

◆ Use only nonmercury thermometers with anti-roll protectors.

◆ Check all glassware periodically for chips and scratches, which can cause cuts and breakage.

Using Chemicals Safely

25. Never mix chemicals "for the fun of it." You might produce a dangerous, possibly explosive substance.

26. Never put your face near the mouth of a container that holds chemicals. Many chemicals are poisonous. Never touch, taste, or smell a chemical unless you are instructed by your teacher to do so.

27. Use only those chemicals needed in the activity. Read and double-check labels on supply bottles before removing any chemicals. Take only as much as you need. Keep all containers closed when chemicals are not being used.

28. Dispose of all chemicals as instructed by your teacher. To avoid contamination, never return chemicals to their original containers. Never simply pour chemicals or other substances into the sink or trash containers.

29. Be extra careful when working with acids or bases. Pour all chemicals over the sink or a container, not over your work surface.

30. If you are instructed to test for odors, use a wafting motion to direct the odors to your nose. Do not inhale the fumes directly from the container.

31. When mixing an acid and water, always pour the water into the container first and then add the acid to the water. Never pour water into an acid.

32. Take extreme care not to spill any material in the laboratory. Wash chemical spills and splashes immediately with plenty of water. Immediately begin rinsing with water any acids that get on your skin or clothing, and notify your teacher of any acid spill at the same time.

Using Glassware Safely

33. Never force glass tubing or thermometers into a rubber stopper or rubber tubing. Have your teacher insert the glass tubing or thermometer if required for an activity.

34. If you are using a laboratory burner, use a wire screen to protect glassware from any flame. Never heat glassware that is not thoroughly dry on the outside.

35. Keep in mind that hot glassware looks cool. Never pick up glassware without first checking to see if it is hot. Use an oven mitt. See rule 24.

36. Never use broken or chipped glassware. If glassware breaks, notify your teacher and dispose of the glassware in the proper broken-glassware container. Never handle broken glass with your bare hands.

37. Never eat or drink from lab glassware.

38. Thoroughly clean glassware before putting it away.

Using Sharp Instruments

39. Handle scalpels or other sharp instruments with extreme care. Never cut material toward you; cut away from you.

40. Immediately notify your teacher if you cut your skin when working in the laboratory.

Animal and Plant Safety

41. Never perform experiments that cause pain, discomfort, or harm to animals. This rule applies at home as well as in the classroom.

42. Animals should be handled only if absolutely necessary. Your teacher will instruct you as to how to handle each animal species brought into the classroom.

43. If you know that you are allergic to certain plants, molds, or animals, tell your teacher before doing an activity in which these are used.

44. During field work, protect your skin by wearing long pants, long sleeves, socks, and closed shoes. Know how to recognize the poisonous plants and fungi in your area, as well as plants with thorns, and avoid contact with them. Never eat any part of a plant or fungus.

45. Wash your hands thoroughly after handling animals or a cage containing animals. Wash your hands when you are finished with any activity involving animal parts, plants, or soil.

End-of-Experiment Rules

46. After an experiment has been completed, turn off all burners or hot plates. If you used a gas burner, check that the gas-line valve to the burner is off. Unplug hot plates.

47. Turn off and unplug any other electrical equipment that you used.

48. Clean up your work area and return all equipment to its proper place.

49. Dispose of waste materials as instructed by your teacher.

50. Wash your hands after every experiment.

Using Sharp Instruments

◆ Always use blunt-tip safety scissors, except when pointed-tip scissors are required.

Animal and Plant Safety

◆ When working with live animals or plants, check ahead of time for students who may have allergies to the specimens.

◆ When growing bacteria cultures, use only disposable petri dishes. After streaking, the dishes should be sealed and not opened again by students. After the lab, students should return the unopened dishes to you. Students should wash their hands with antibacterial soap.

◆ Two methods are recommended for the safe disposal of bacteria cultures. *First method:* Autoclave the petri dishes and discard without opening. *Second method*: If no autoclave is available, carefully open the dishes (never have a student do this) and pour full-strength bleach into the dishes and let stand for a day. Then pour the bleach from the petri dishes down a drain and flush the drain with lots of water. Tape the petri dishes back together and place in a sealed plastic bag. Wrap the plastic bag with a brown paper bag or newspaper and tape securely. Throw the sealed package in the trash. Thoroughly disinfect the work area with bleach.

◆ To grow mold, use a new, sealable plastic bag that is two to three times larger than the material to be placed inside. Seal the bag and tape it shut. After the bag is sealed, students should not open it. To dispose of the bag and mold culture, make a small cut near an edge of the bag and cook in a microwave oven on high setting for at least 1 minute. Discard the bag according to local ordinance, usually in the trash.

◆ Students should wear disposable nitrile, latex, or food-handling gloves when handling live animals or nonliving specimens.

End-of-Experiment Rules

◆ Always have students use antibacterial soap for washing their hands.

Physical Map: United States

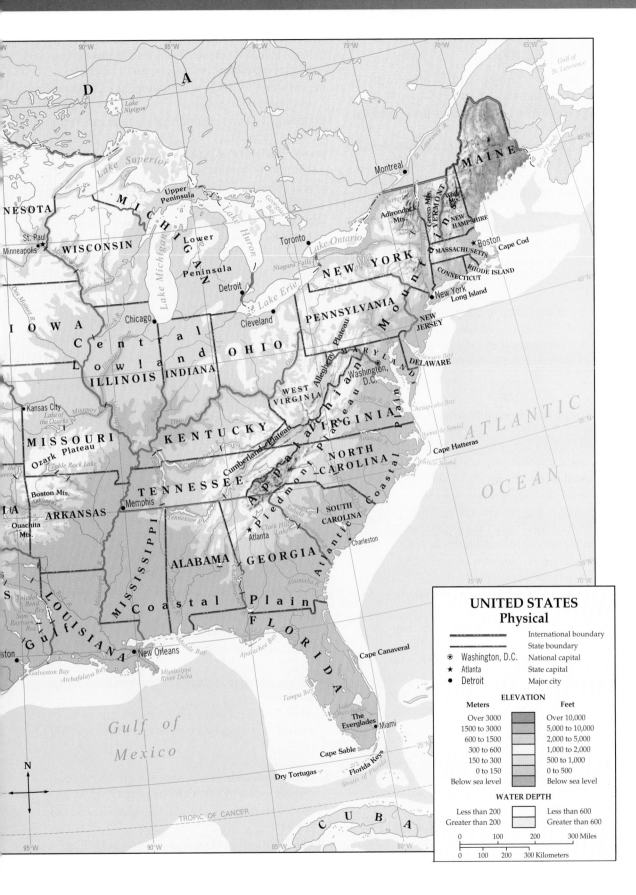

UNITED STATES
Physical

⊛ Washington, D.C.	International boundary
	State boundary
⊛ Washington, D.C.	National capital
★ Atlanta	State capital
● Detroit	Major city

ELEVATION

Meters	Feet
Over 3000	Over 10,000
1500 to 3000	5,000 to 10,000
600 to 1500	2,000 to 5,000
300 to 600	1,000 to 2,000
150 to 300	500 to 1,000
0 to 150	0 to 500
Below sea level	Below sea level

WATER DEPTH

Less than 200	Less than 600
Greater than 200	Greater than 600

0   100   200   300 Miles

0   100   200   300 Kilometers

G ◆ 169

A

abrasion The grinding away of rock by other rock particles carried in water, ice, or wind. (pp. 41, 86)

absolute age The age of a rock given as the number of years since the rock formed. (p. 113)

alluvial fan A wide, sloping deposit of sediment formed where a stream leaves a mountain range. (p. 77)

amphibian A vertebrate that lives part of its life on land and part of its life in water. (p. 130)

atmosphere The mixture of gases that surrounds Earth. The outermost of the four spheres into which scientists divide Earth. (p. 18)

atom The smallest particle of an element. (p. 119)

B

beach Wave-washed sediment along a coast. (p. 97)

bedrock The solid layer of rock beneath the soil. (p. 49)

biosphere All living things. One of the four spheres into which scientists divide Earth. (p. 18)

C

carbon film A type of fossil consisting of an extremely thin coating of carbon on rock. (p. 109)

cast A fossil that is a copy of an organism's shape, formed when minerals seep into a mold. (p. 108)

chemical weathering The process that breaks down rock through chemical changes. (p. 43)

conservation plowing Soil conservation method in which the dead stalks from the previous year's crop are left in the ground to hold the soil in place. (p. 60)

continental glacier A glacier that covers much of a continent or large island. (p. 89)

contour interval The difference in elevation from one contour line to the next. (p. 31)

contour line A line on a topographic map that connects points of equal elevation. (p. 31)

contour plowing Plowing fields along the curves of a slope to prevent soil loss. (p. 60)

controlled experiment An experiment in which all factors except one are kept constant. (p. 157)

D

decomposer Soil organism that breaks down the remains of organisms and digests them. (p. 53)

deflation Wind erosion that removes surface materials. (p. 99)

degree A unit used to measure distances around a circle. One degree equals $\frac{1}{360}$ of a full circle. (p. 22)

delta A landform made of sediment that is deposited where a river flows into an ocean or lake. (p. 77)

deposition Process in which sediment is laid down in new locations. (p. 67)

digitizing Converting information to numbers for use by a computer. (p. 28)

divide The ridge of land that separates one drainage basin from another. (p. 75)

drainage basin The land area from which a river and its tributaries collect their water. (p. 75)

Dust Bowl The area of the Great Plains where wind erosion caused soil loss during the 1930s. (p. 59)

E

element A type of matter in which all the atoms are the same. (p. 119)

elevation Height above sea level. (p. 15)

energy The ability to do work or cause change. (p. 85)

epochs Subdivisions of the periods of the geologic time scale. (p. 125)

equator An imaginary line that circles Earth halfway between the North and South poles. (p. 21)

era One of the three long units of geologic time between the Precambrian and the present. (p. 124)

erosion The process by which water, ice, wind, or gravity moves weathered rock and soil. (pp. 41, 67)

evolution The process by which all the different kinds of living things have changed over time. (p. 110)

extinct Describes a type of organism that no longer exists anywhere on Earth. (p. 110)

extrusion An igneous rock layer formed when lava flows onto Earth's surface and hardens. (p. 116)

F

fault A break or crack in Earth's lithosphere along which the rocks move. (p. 115)

flood plain Wide valley through which a river flows. (p. 76)

fossil The preserved remains or traces of living things. (p. 106)

friction The force that opposes the motion of one surface as it moves across another surface. (p. 87)

G

geologic time scale A record of the geologic events and life forms in Earth's history. (p. 123)

glacier A large mass of moving ice and snow on land. (p.89)

Global Positioning System A method of finding latitude and longitude using satellites. (p. 33)

globe A sphere that represents Earth's surface. (p. 19)

groundwater Water that fills the cracks and spaces in underground soil and rock layers. (p. 80)

gully A large channel in soil formed by erosion. (p. 73)

half-life The time it takes for half of the atoms of a radioactive element to decay. (p. 120)

hemisphere One half of the sphere that makes up Earth's surface. (p. 21)

humus Dark-colored organic material in soil. (p. 50)

hydrosphere Earth's water and ice. One of the four spheres into which scientists divide Earth. (p. 18)

hypothesis A possible explanation for a set of observations or answer to a scientific question; must be testable. (p. 156)

ice age One time in the past when continental glaciers covered large parts of Earth's surface. (p. 90)

ice wedging Process that splits rock when water seeps into cracks, then freezes and expands. (p. 42)

index fossils Fossils of widely distributed organisms that lived during only one short period. (p. 116)

intrusion An igneous rock layer formed when magma hardens beneath Earth's surface. (p. 116)

invertebrate An animal without a backbone. (p. 124)

karst topography A type of landscape in rainy regions where there is limestone near the surface, characterized by caverns, sinkholes, and valleys. (p. 81)

kettle A small depression that forms when a chunk of ice is left in glacial till. (p. 92)

key A list of the symbols used on a map. (p. 20)

kinetic energy The energy an object has due to its motion. (p. 85)

landform region A large area of land where the topography is similar. (p. 15)

landform A feature of topography formed by the processes that shape Earth's surface. (p. 15)

latitude The distance in degrees north or south of the equator. (p. 22)

law of superposition The geologic principle that states that in horizontal layers of sedimentary rock, each layer is older than the layer above it and younger than the layer below it. (p.114)

lithosphere Earth's solid rock outer layer. One of four spheres into which scientists divide Earth. (p. 18)

litter The loose layer of dead plant leaves and stems on the surface of the soil. (p. 52)

load The amount of sediment that a river or stream carries. (p. 86)

loam Rich, fertile soil that is made up of about equal parts of clay, sand, and silt. (p. 50)

loess A wind-formed deposit made of fine particles of clay and silt. (p.100)

longitude The distance in degrees east or west of the prime meridian. (p. 23)

longshore drift The movement of water and sediment down a beach caused by waves coming in to shore at an angle. (p. 97)

mammal A warm-blooded vertebrate that feeds its young milk. (p. 137)

manipulated variable The one factor that a scientist changes during an experiment. (p. 157)

map projection A framework of lines that helps to show landmasses on a flat surface. (p. 24)

map A model of all or part of Earth's surface as seen from above. (p. 19)

mass extinction When many types of living things become extinct at the same time. (p. 131)

mass movement Any one of several processes by which gravity moves sediment downhill. (p. 67)

meander A looplike bend in the course of a river. (p. 76)

mechanical weathering The type of weathering in which rock is physically broken into smaller pieces. (p. 41)

mold A fossil formed when an organism buried in sediment dissolves, leaving a hollow area. (p. 108)

moraine A ridge formed by the till deposited at the edge of a glacier. (p. 91)

mountain A landform with high elevation and high relief. (p. 16)

mountain range A series of mountains that have the same general shape and structure. (p. 16)

operational definition A statement that describes how to define or measure a particular variable. (p. 157)

oxbow lake A meander cut off from a river. (p. 76)

paleontologist A scientist who studies fossils to learn about organisms that lived long ago. (p. 106)

period One of the units of geologic time into which geologists divide eras. (p. 125)

permeable Characteristic of a material that is full of tiny, connected air spaces that water can seep through. (p. 45)

petrified fossil A fossil in which minerals replace all or part of an organism. (p. 107)

pixels The tiny dots in a satellite image. (p. 27)

plain A landform made up of flat or gently rolling land with low relief. (p. 16)

plateau A landform that has high elevation and a more or less level surface. (p. 17)

plucking The process by which a glacier picks up rocks as it flows over the land. (p. 90)

potential energy Energy that is stored and available to be used later. (p. 85)

prime meridian The line that makes a half circle from the North Pole to the South Pole and that passes through Greenwich, England. (p. 22)

radioactive decay The breakdown of a radioactive element, releasing particles and energy. (p. 120)

relative age The age of a rock compared to the ages of rock layers. (p. 113)

relief The difference in elevation between the highest and lowest parts of an area. (p. 15)

reptile A vertebrate with scaly skin that lays eggs with tough, leathery shells. (p. 131)

responding variable The factor that changes as a result of changes to the manipulated variable in an experiment. (p. 157)

rill A tiny groove in soil made by flowing water. (p. 73)

river A large stream. (p. 74)

runoff Water that flows over the ground surface rather than soaking into the ground. (p. 73)

sand dune A deposit of wind-blown sand. (p. 98)

satellite images Pictures of the land surface based on computer data collected from satellites. (p. 26)

scale Used to compare distance on a map or globe to distance on Earth's surface. (p. 19)

scientific theory A well-tested concept that explains a wide range of observations. (p. 110)

sedimentary rock The type of rock that is made of hardened sediment. (p. 107)

sediment Earth materials deposited by erosion. (p. 67)

sod A thick mass of grass roots and soil. (p. 57)

soil conservation The management of soil to prevent its destruction. (p. 60)

soil horizon A layer of soil that differs in color and texture from the layers above or below it. (p. 51)

soil The loose, weathered material on Earth's surface in which plants can grow. (p. 49)

spit A beach formed by longshore drift that projects like a finger out into the water. (p. 97)

stalactite A calcite deposit that hangs from the roof of a cave. (p. 81)

stalagmite A cone-shaped calcite deposit that builds up from the floor of a cave. (p. 81)

stream A channel through which water is continually flowing downhill. (p. 74)

subsoil The layer of soil beneath the topsoil that contains mostly clay and other minerals. (p. 51)

symbols On a map, pictures used by mapmakers to stand for features on Earth's surface. (p. 20)

till The sediments deposited directly by a glacier. (p. 91)

topographic map A map that shows the surface features of an area. (p. 29)

topography The shape of the land determined by elevation, relief, and landforms. (p. 14)

topsoil Mixture of humus, clay, and other minerals that forms the crumbly, topmost layer of soil. (p. 51)

trace fossils A type of fossil that provides evidence of the activities of ancient organisms. (p. 109)

tributary A stream that flows into a larger stream. (p. 74)

turbulence A type of movement of water in which, rather than moving downstream, the water moves every which way. (p. 88)

unconformity A place where an old, eroded rock surface is in contact with a newer rock layer. (p. 115)

valley glacier A long, narrow glacier that forms when snow and ice build up in a mountain valley. (p. 89)

variable Any factor that can change in an experiment. (p. 157)

vertebrate An animal with a backbone. (p. 130)

weathering The chemical and physical processes that break down rock at Earth's surface. (p. 40)

Acknowledgments

Staff Credits

The people who made up the **Science Explorer** team—representing design services, editorial, editorial services, electronic publishing technology, manufacturing & inventory planning, marketing, marketing services, market research, online services & multimedia development, production services, product planning, project office, and publishing processes—are listed below.

Carolyn Belanger, Barbara A. Bertell, Suzanne Biron, Peggy Bliss, Peter W. Brooks, Christopher R. Brown, Greg Cantone, Jonathan Cheney, Todd Christy, Lisa J. Clark, Patrick Finbarr Connolly, Edward Cordero, Robert Craton, Patricia Cully, Patricia M. Dambry, Kathleen J. Dempsey, Judy Elgin, Gayle Connolly Fedele, Frederick Fellows, Barbara Foster, Paula Foye, Loree Franz, Donald P. Gagnon Jr., Paul J. Gagnon, Joel Gendler, Elizabeth Good, Robert M. Graham, Kerri Hoar, Joanne Hudson, Linda D. Johnson, Anne Jones, Toby Klang, Carolyn Langley, Russ Lappa, Carolyn Lock, Cheryl Mahan, Dotti Marshall, Meredith Mascola, Jeanne Y. Maurand, Karen McHugh, Eve Melnechuk, Natania Mlawer, Paul W. Murphy, Cindy A. Noftle, Julia F. Osborne, Judi Pinkham, Caroline M. Power, Robin L. Santel, Suzanne J. Schineller, Emily Soltanoff, Kira Thaler-Marbit, Mark Tricca, Diane Walsh, Pearl Weinstein, Merce Wilczek, Helen Young.

Illustration

Kathleen Dempsey: 17, 25, 34, 46, 56, 82, 118T, 126
John Edwards & Associates: 22, 23T, 31, 44, 86, 87, 91, 95, 107
GeoSystems Global Corporation: 15, 23B, 24, 55, 58, 59, 75T, 77, 90, 98
Andrea Golden: 8T, 11B, 151
Martucci Design: 30, 50
Morgan Cain & Associates: 33, 50, 52–53, 66, 68, 69, 75B, 88, 99, 120, 122, 123, 124
Matt Myerchak: 35, 61, 141, 143
Ortelius Design Inc.: 20, 21, 136
Matthew Pippin: 51, 78–79, 92–93
Walter Stuart: 11T, 8–9
J/B Woolsey Associates: 37, 42, 63, 73, 111, 114, 117, 118B, 132–135

Photography

Photo Research Paula Wehde
Cover Image David Muench Photography

Nature of Science
Page 8, University of Wyoming Public Relations; **10 both**, Courtesy of Kelli Trujillo; **11**, University of Wyoming Public Relations.

Chapter 1
Pages 12–13, Tom Bean; **14**, The Granger Collection, NY; **16t**, Tom Bean; **16b**, David Muench Photography; **18**, ESA/PLI/The Stock Market; **19 both**, Russ Lappa; **20t**, Bodleian Library, Oxford, U.K.; **20b**, The Granger Collection, NY; **21t, br**, The Granger Collection, NY; **21bl**, British Library, London/Bridgeman Art Library, London/ Superstock; **26t**, Russ Lappa; **26b, 27 both**, Earth Satellite Corporation/Science Photo Library/Photo Researchers; **28tl**, Geographix; **28tr**, Bob Daemmrich/Stock Boston; **29t**, Richard Haynes; **29b**, Robert Rathe/Stock Boston; **31**, Paul Rezendes; **32**, U.S. Geological Survey; **33t**, Ken M. Johns/Photo Researchers; **34**, Richard Haynes; **37**, U.S. Geological Survey.

Chapter 2
Pages 38–39, Mike Mazzaschi/Stock Boston; **40**, Russ Lappa; **41l**, Ron Watts/Westlight; **41r**, Jerry D. Greer; **42l**, Breck P. Kent/Animals Animals/Earth Scenes; **42r**, Susan Rayfield/Photo Researchers; **43l**, John Sohlden/Visuals Unlimited; **43m**, E.R. Degginger/Photo Researchers; **43r**, Gerald & Buff Corsi/Visuals Unlimited; **45t**, Chromosohm/Sohm/Photo Researchers; **45b**, Breck P. Kent/Animals Animals/Earth Scenes; **47**, Richard Haynes; **48**, John G. Ross/Photo Researchers; **49t**, Richard Haynes; **49b**, Rod Planck/TSI; **54**, J. M. Labat/Jacana/Photo Researchers; **56**, Richard T. Nowitz/Photo Researchers; **57t**, Richard Haynes; **57b**, Jim Brandenburg/Minden Pictures; **58**, Corbis; **59**, AP/Wide World Photos; **60t**, Larry Lefever/Grant Heilman Photography; **60b**, Jim Strawser/Grant Heilman Photography; **61**, John G. Ross/Photo Researchers.

Chapter 3
Pages 64–65 & 66, Jim Steinberg/Photo Researchers; **67**, Paul Sequeira/Photo Researchers; **68t**, Eric Vandeville/Gamma-Liaison Network; **68b**, Thomas G. Rampton/Grant Heilman Photography; **69**, Steven Holt; **70–71**, Richard Haynes; **72**, Photo Disc; **72–73**, Walter Bibikow/The Viesti Collection; **73t**, Runk Schoenberger/ Grant Heilman Photography; **74**, Inga Spence/Tom Stack & Associates; **75**, David Ball/The Stock Market; **76l**, Glenn M. Oliver/Visuals Unlimited; **76r**, Index Stock Photography, Inc.; **77t**, E.R. Degginger; **77b**, NASA/SADO/Tom Stack & Associates; **80**, Chuck O'Rear/Westlight; **81**, *St. Petersburg Times*/Gamma-Liaison; **82**, Russ Lappa; **83**, Richard Haynes; **84**, Doug McKay/TSI; **85t**, Richard Haynes; **85b**, Eliot Cohen; **89t**, Richard Haynes; **89b**, Mark Kelley/Stock Boston; **91**, Grant Heilman Photography; **94**, Craig Tuttle/The Stock Market; **96**, Randy Wells/TSI; **97**, E.R.I.M./TSI; **98t**, Richard Haynes; **98b**, Jess Stock/TSI; **99**, Breck P. Kent; **100**, Connie Toops; **101**, Craig Tuttle/The Stock Market.

Chapter 4
Pages 104–105, Phil Degginger; **106t**, John Cancalosi/Stock Boston; **106b**, Flowers & Newman/Photo Researchers; **107**, Francois Gohier/Photo Researchers; **108 both**, Runk/Schoenberger/Grant Heilman Photography; **109t**, Breck P. Kent; **109b**, Tom Bean; **110**, Howard Grey/TSI; **111tl**, Khalid Ghani/Animals Animals; **111tr**, Frans Lanting/Minden Pictures; **111mr**, The Natural History Museum, London; **111bl**, John Sibbick; **112**, Sinclair Stammers/Science Photo Library/Photo Researchers; **113**, Richard Haynes; **114**, Jeff Greenberg/Photo Researchers; **116l**, G.R. Roberts/Photo Researchers; **116r**, Tom Bean; **116b**, Breck P. Kent; **119**, Mitsuaki Iwago/Minden Pictures; **121**, James King-Holmes/Science Photo Library/Photo Researchers; **125t**, Fletcher & Baylis/Photo Researchers; **125 inset**, John Cancalosi/Tom Stack & Associates; **127**, Richard Haynes; **128l**, Breck P. Kent; **128r**, Runk/Schoenberger/ Grant Heilman Photography; **129r**, The Natural History Museum, London; **129l, 130**, John Sibbick; **131t**, ©The Field Museum, Neg. # CSGEO 75400c.; **131b**, Natural History Museum/London; **137**, 1989 Mark Hallett; **138l**, Jane Burton/Bruce Coleman; **138r**, David M. Dennis/Tom Stack & Associates; **139t**, D. Van Ravenswaay/Photo Researchers; **139b**, C.M. Dixon; **140**, John Reader/Science Photo Library/Photo Researchers.

Interdisciplinary Exploration
Page 144t, Robert Caputo/Stock Boston; **144–145b**, David Sanger Photography; **145l**, Brian Braker/Photo Researchers; **146**, NASA; **147**, Groenendyk/Photo Researchers; **148–149b**, Thomas J. Abercrombie/National Geographic Society; **148 inset**, Robert Caputo/Stock Boston; **149t**, Robert Caputo/Stock Boston; **150**, David Ball/The Picture Cube; **151**, Richard Haynes.

Skills Handbook
Page 152, Mike Moreland/Photo Network; **153t**, Foodpix; **153m**, Richard Haynes; **153b**, Russ Lappa; **156**, Richard Haynes; **158**, Ron Kimball; **159**, Renee Lynn/Photo Researchers.